INTRODUCTION TO MICROWAVE THEORY

McGRAW-HILL ELECTRICAL AND ELECTRONIC ENGINEERING SERIES

FREDERICK EMMONS TERMAN, *Consulting Editor*
W. W. HARMAN AND J. G. TRUXAL,
Associate Consulting Editors

INTRODUCTION TO
MICROWAVE THEORY

H. A. ATWATER

Department of Electrical Engineering
Pennsylvania State University

McGRAW-HILL BOOK COMPANY, INC.   1962

New York   San Francisco   Toronto   London

INTRODUCTION TO MICROWAVE THEORY

Preface

The science and technology of ultrahigh frequency and microwave systems has undergone rapid development since the invention of radar established a requirement for electronic equipment operating at radio wavelengths small compared with the objects being detected. Systems of radiolocation continue to demand the development of new devices and methods in the microwave frequency range, but they by no means constitute the only motivation for the unabated expansion of research and design effort that continues in this field. Microwave techniques are being adopted increasingly in such diverse applications as radio astronomy, long-distance communication, navigation, and the study of the physical and chemical properties of matter. As a result of the accelerating rate of growth of microwave technology, the student entering this field is confronted with an increasingly large quantity of information to be assimilated and a rising level of advancement of the theoretical and experimental methods being employed in research in the field. Therefore it becomes necessary to select that which is significant for study and to emphasize the importance of the fundamentals of the science.

The present book is the outgrowth of course notes developed for use in a one-semester course in microwave theory given to upper division and first-year graduate students in electrical and aeronautical engineering and physics. A previous course in electricity and magnetism or electromagnetic theory is assumed. Knowledge of calculus is required, and some familiarity with vector analysis is desirable. Owing to the wide variety in background of students attending the course, a summary of those parts of electromagnetic theory and vector analysis which are essential for the reading of the book is included in the early chapters. It is the experience of the author that a review of these subjects is of value to the student, particularly since it serves to introduce the physical outlook and mathematical methods which are employed throughout the course. The inclusion of this material

vii

/ 2 5 / 5

should also add to the usefulness of the book for independent study.

The conventional two-conductor transmission line is discussed in the opening chapter, with emphasis being placed on those results which will be directly applied to the analysis of waveguide transmission. Following a review of the physical origins of the equations of the electromagnetic field, the propagation of fields in waveguides is treated as a boundary-value problem in the boundaries of rectangular and cylindrical waveguides. A chapter is devoted to the impedance and scattering formulation of the behavior of waveguide devices and discontinuities. The theory of the most frequently used microwave oscillators, the magnetron and klystron, is presented. More extensive treatment is given to the traveling-wave tube, since it demonstrates the propagation of waves in periodic systems and the interaction of an electron beam with the electromagnetic field.

A chapter is devoted to the study of the interaction of microwave radiation with magnetic materials and practical devices of importance which utilize the magnetic character of materials: the maser, magnetic parametric amplifier, and transmission devices such as the ferrite isolator. The physical theory of magnetic properties of electron spins is treated in sufficient detail to facilitate understanding of the operation of devices utilizing these properties. The concluding chapter summarizes the special problems encountered when microwave techniques and methods are extended to the millimeter-wavelength limit of the microwave domain.

The book endeavors to emphasize throughout the philosophy and methods of the analytical approach to the understanding of microwave systems, in terms of the electromagnetic fields in the systems. An effort is made to avoid obscuring the subject by an overly complicated analysis, while emphasizing the fundamental theory rather than the qualitative aspects of device behavior. To this end a selection of topics is treated in sufficient detail to illustrate modes of analysis. Problems are appended to each chapter to further the treatment of the subjects discussed in the text.

H. A. Atwater

Contents

CHAPTER 1

The Two-conductor Transmission Line

The microwave region of the electromagnetic spectrum may be broadly defined as that frequency range between approximately 10^9 and 10^{12} cps, corresponding to free-space wavelengths of the order of a few tens of centimeters to a few tenths of a millimeter. These wavelengths are of the same order of magnitude in size as the circuit components of conventional circuit electronics. The fact that these components tend to behave like individual antennas at microwave frequencies necessitates the introduction of a whole new set of circuit techniques for operation in the microwave range. It should not be unexpected, therefore, that a new set of techniques for the analysis of microwave circuits must be introduced to replace the conventional methods of electric circuit analysis. It is therefore desirable that the student who has had little previous experience with microwave systems should make early recognition of this shift of emphasis.

Microwave systems, involving hollow-pipe waveguides and empty-cavity resonators, differ conspicuously in appearance from the often more familiar lumped-element systems of circuit electronics. The connecting wires of the circuits provide obvious "conductors" for the electric currents, and the resistors, capacitors, and coils possess simple relationships between their currents and terminal voltage. Often overlooked is the fact that the wires and circuit components provide a framework over which charges move and disperse. The charges set up electric and magnetic fields which permeate the circuit, often having almost indescribably complicated field configurations. It would, in principle, be possible to treat the behavior of circuits entirely in terms of these fields, instead of in terms of the circuit voltages and currents, as usually is done.

As the operating frequency of the circuit goes higher, however, the effects of the "stray" capacitances and inductances alter the effective circuit radically from its low-frequency form. Radiation from the circuit increases rapidly with frequency also, and much power may be

1

lost from the system in this way.   This radiative power loss can be prevented by confining the fields to the interior of metallic enclosures, as is done in hollow waveguides.   The charges move exclusively on the interior surfaces of the conductors, and because of the simple geometry of the enclosures, the electric and magnetic fields which are set up have relatively simple analytical forms.   Since it is often not possible to uniquely define voltages and currents within the waveguides in any useful way, analysis of waveguides is usually conducted on the basis of the behavior of the electromagnetic fields within the guiding systems and of the observations we make upon them.

A fundamental component of a typical microwave system is a section of waveguide, the function of which is to transport energy from one point to another along its length.   An important part of the study of microwave systems is therefore the analysis of the behavior of uniform waveguides, or microwave transmission lines.   We find that configurations of electric and magnetic fields are propagated along the guide axis in the characteristic fashion of a wave motion.   By this we mean, as usual, that typical values of a field distribution all move along the guide at the same velocity, the phase velocity.   It turns out that the fields in a waveguide with arbitrary termination can be fully described in terms of pairs of such waves, traveling in opposite directions along the guide, everywhere adding to produce the observed fields in the terminated guide.   This oppositely traveling wave description is so useful that we shall base our entire analysis of transmission upon it.   There is, moreover, a fortunate analogy (not entirely coincidental) between the behavior of E and B field waves in waveguides and voltage and current waves on the classical two-conductor transmission line.   Since an extensive and useful mathematical machinery may be built up for the solution of transmission-line problems, we shall adopt this formulation essentially intact and employ it for our purposes in the waveguide problem.   The discussion will begin, therefore, with the derivation of the voltage and current wave solutions for the two-wire transmission line, followed by the expression of these solutions in terms of impedances.

The conventional two-conductor transmission line represents a typical example of the necessity for departure from the assumptions of lumped-element circuit analysis, wherein it is postulated that all points of an ideal connecting wire are instantaneously at the same potential. When a voltage source is connected to the input terminals of an indefinitely long transmission line, the voltage of all points of the line cannot rise simultaneously to the voltage of the source, since a finite time is required to transfer the energy corresponding to the potential difference between lines.† Similarly, when a harmonically time-varying voltage is connected to the line, the successive rises and falls of the potential are propagated along the line at a finite velocity, the phase velocity of the line. This wavelike propagation of fields along the line is typical of the transmission systems which will be studied in the present volume and constitutes an essential feature of their behavior. The steadily increasing phase delay of the voltages and currents in successive elements of length along a transmission line arises naturally from the geometrical configuration of the line. The linear configuration permits us to derive the wave expressions from an analysis based on an equivalent circuit representation of an element of length of the line.

1.1. The Transmission-line Equation

We consider a system of two conductors of constant cross-sectional form, extending indefinitely in the z direction, carrying equal and opposite currents $I(z)$, and having line-to-line voltage $V(z)$. It is assumed that an impedance Z per unit length of line can be defined such that the impedance of an infinitesimal length Δz of line is $Z\,\Delta z$. Hence the voltage drop along Δz is

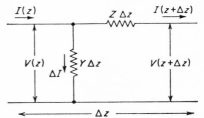

FIG. 1.1. Equivalent circuit of transmission-line element.

$$\Delta V = -IZ\,\Delta z \qquad (1.1)$$

where the minus sign indicates a decreasing voltage with increasing z. In a similar way, we assume that an admittance Y per unit length of line can be defined such that the increment of shunt current associated with length Δz is

$$\Delta I = -VY\,\Delta z \qquad (1.2)$$

where the minus sign indicates that the line current decreases with increasing z. The assumed situation is illustrated by the diagram of Fig. 1.1.

Passing to the limit in which $\Delta z \to dz$, these equations become

$$\frac{dV}{dz} = -IZ \qquad (1.3)$$

$$\frac{dI}{dz} = -VY \qquad (1.4)$$

---

† An instantaneous change of voltage along the entire line is forbidden also by the special theory of relativity, which postulates that no signal, such as a voltage pulse, can be transmitted at a speed greater than the speed of light.

Differentiating Eqs. (1.3) and (1.4) with respect to z and cross-substituting, we obtain

$$\frac{d^2V}{dz^2} = \gamma^2 V \tag{1.5}$$

$$\frac{d^2I}{dz^2} = \gamma^2 I \tag{1.6}$$

where γ^2 is defined as

$$\gamma^2 = ZY \tag{1.7}$$

The linear second-order differential equations (1.5) and (1.6) each have the two independent solutions $e^{-\gamma z}$ and $e^{+\gamma z}$. The general solution of Eq. (1.5) is obtained, therefore, by forming a linear combination of these two solutions, with arbitrary coefficients V_1 and V_2:

$$V = V_1 e^{-\gamma z} + V_2 e^{+\gamma z} \tag{1.8}$$

Using Eq. (1.3), the solution for line current is

$$I = \frac{\gamma}{Z}(V_1 e^{-\gamma z} - V_2 e^{+\gamma z}) \tag{1.9}$$

For normally constructed transmission lines, the series impedance is inductive in character, and the shunt admittance is capacitive. Hence

$$Z = R + jL\omega \tag{1.10}$$
$$Y = G + jC\omega \tag{1.11}$$

where R, L, G, and C are the resistance, inductance, shunt conductance, and capacitance per unit length of line, respectively. Here, $f = \omega/2\pi$ is the frequency of the line voltage.

Thus, the constant γ defined by Eq. (1.7) is

$$\gamma = \pm[(R + jL\omega)(G + jC\omega)]^{\frac{1}{2}} \tag{1.12}$$
$$\gamma = \pm[(RG - LC\omega^2) + j(LG + RC)\omega]^{\frac{1}{2}} \tag{1.13}$$

We define the complex propagation constant

$$\gamma = \alpha + j\beta \tag{1.14}$$

The above value of γ, used in Eq. (1.8), results in a complex expression for transmission-line voltage. The line voltage is, however, a real quantity that can be measured by a voltmeter and thus cannot have an imaginary part. This difficulty is resolved in the customary manner for alternating quantities by adopting the convention that all quantities of the form $e^{j\psi}$ shall be interpreted for practical application as "real part of $e^{j\psi}$," equal to cos ψ. Alternatively, the convention might, with equal validity, be established that $e^{j\psi}$ shall be interpreted to mean "$1/j$ times the imaginary part of $e^{j\psi}$," equal to $\sin \psi$. Either convention is valid as long as, once adopted, it is adhered to throughout. The exponential form of expression for alternating quantities will be frequently employed in the following text because of the economy of writing and analytical simplicity which is gained thereby. Identities involving the exponential function are noted below for reference:

$$e^{a \pm jb} = e^a \cos b \pm je^a \sin b$$
$$\cos b = \frac{e^{jb} + e^{-jb}}{2}$$
$$\sin b = \frac{e^{jb} - e^{-jb}}{2j}$$
$$j = e^{j\pi/2}$$

We recall that the complex algebra which has been used in deriving the line equations describes quantities which are harmonic functions of time. This requires that the factor $e^{j\omega t}$ be understood to be associated with each of the voltages and currents wherever they occur. Thus Eqs. (1.8) and (1.9) for line voltage and current are understood to be written

$$V = V_1 e^{(j\omega t - \gamma z)} + V_2 e^{(j\omega t + \gamma z)} \tag{1.15}$$

$$I = \frac{\gamma}{Z} \left(V_1 e^{(j\omega t - \gamma z)} - V_2 e^{(j\omega t + \gamma z)} \right) \tag{1.16}$$

1.2. Transmission Lines Having Low Loss

If the quantity $(-LC\omega^2)^{\frac{1}{2}}$ is factored from the radical in Eq. (1.13), the propagation constant becomes

$$\gamma = (-LC\omega^2)^{\frac{1}{2}} \left[1 - \frac{RG}{LC\omega^2} - j\left(\frac{G}{C\omega} + \frac{R}{L\omega}\right) \right]^{\frac{1}{2}} \tag{1.17}$$

Most practical transmission lines are constructed so as to minimize the series resistance and shunt-leakage conductance in order to reduce power losses in the line. Hence, for low-loss lines, $R/L\omega \ll 1$, and $G/C\omega \ll 1$. Consequently, $RG/LC\omega^2$ is negligible with respect to unity. Then,

$$\gamma \approx j\omega \sqrt{LC} \left[1 - j\left(\frac{G}{C\omega} + \frac{R}{L\omega}\right) \right]^{\frac{1}{2}} \tag{1.18}$$

Due to the smallness of the imaginary term in the square brackets, Eq. (1.18) may be expanded in a Taylor's expansion to first order in the small quantity

$$\gamma \approx j\omega \sqrt{LC}\left[1 - j\left(\frac{G}{2C\omega} + \frac{R}{2L\omega}\right)\right] \qquad (1.19)$$

In the construction of high-frequency transmission lines it is usually found possible to make $G/C\omega$ considerably less than $R/L\omega$. For lines of this type ("low-loss" lines) we may take

$$\gamma = j\omega \sqrt{LC}\left(1 - \frac{jR}{2L\omega}\right) \qquad (1.20)$$

Referring to the definition of Eq. (1.14), the real and imaginary parts of the propagation constant of the low-loss line are seen to be

$$\alpha = \frac{R}{2}\sqrt{\frac{C}{L}} \qquad (1.21a)$$

$$\beta = \omega \sqrt{LC} \qquad (1.21b)$$

When the complex form of the constant γ is used in Eq. (1.15) for line voltage, the result, including the harmonic time dependence, is

$$V = V_1 e^{j(\omega t - \beta z)}e^{-\alpha z} + V_2 e^{j(\omega t + \beta z)}e^{+\alpha z} \qquad (1.22)$$

Inspection of the first term of Eq. (1.22) shows that it represents a wave traveling in the positive z direction. The factor $e^{j(\omega t - \beta z)}$ is a phase function which remains unchanged when seen by an observer moving with the speed of the wave. Constancy of this phase function implies that $d(\omega t - \beta z) = 0$, or

$$\frac{dz}{dt} = \frac{\omega}{\beta} = v_p \qquad (1.23)$$

where $v_p = \omega/\beta$ is the phase velocity of the wave. Similarly, in the second term of Eq. (1.22), the factor $e^{j(\omega t + \beta z)}$ represents a traveling wave with negative phase velocity $v_p = -\omega/\beta$. For the two-conductor transmission lines of this chapter, v_p is equal to the velocity of light in the medium surrounding the line. Since the phase velocity of a propagating wave is equal to the product of its frequency by its wavelength λ, the propagation constant β is

$$\beta = \frac{\omega}{v_p} = \frac{2\pi f}{f\lambda} = \frac{2\pi}{\lambda} \qquad (1.23a)$$

The factor $e^{\pm \alpha z}$ in (1.22) is an attenuation factor which decreases the amplitude of each individual wave as it progresses.

1.3. Properties of the Lossless Transmission Line

For many practical transmission lines the over-all effect of the factor $e^{\pm \alpha z}$ is negligible when z is of laboratory dimensions. Hence it is useful to introduce the concept of the lossless line, for which it is assumed that α is zero. Thus, for the lossless transmission line, Eqs. (1.8) and (1.9) become

$$V = V_1 e^{-j\beta z} + V_2 e^{+j\beta z} \tag{1.24}$$

$$I = \frac{1}{Z_0}(V_1 e^{-j\beta z} - V_2 e^{+j\beta z}) \tag{1.25}$$

In Eqs. (1.24) and (1.25) the factor $e^{j\omega t}$ has been omitted since all voltages and currents on the line are assumed to be multiplied by this factor. V_1 and V_2 are in general complex constants which determine the magnitudes and phases of the respective waves. In addition, the quantity Z_0, the characteristic impedance of the line, has been introduced and is defined, for the lossless line, as

$$Z_0 = \frac{Z}{\gamma} = \sqrt{\frac{L}{C}} \tag{1.26}$$

and, as before, the propagation constant β is

$$\beta = \omega \sqrt{LC}$$

The characteristic impedance Z_0 is purely real for a lossless line. We may see the significance of its definition by means of the following example. Assume that a line of length A is terminated by an impedance equal to Z_0. Then, at $z = A$, $V/I = Z_0$. By the use of Eqs. (1.24) and (1.25), we have

$$\frac{V(A)}{I(A)} = Z_0 = Z_0 \frac{V_1 e^{-j\beta A} + V_2 e^{+j\beta A}}{V_1 e^{-j\beta A} - V_2 e^{+j\beta A}}$$

Upon solving for V_2/V_1, there appears the result

$$\frac{V_2}{V_1} = -\frac{V_2}{V_1}$$

from which we deduce that $V_2 = 0$. The conclusion from this result is that there is no reflected wave $V_2 e^{+j\beta z}$ on a line terminated in its characteristic impedance, Z_0. A line terminated in Z_0 is called a matched line. An infinitely long, uniform transmission line produces no reflected wave $V_2 e^{j\beta z}$, and hence the infinite line likewise presents an impedance equal to Z_0 at all points.

A line of length A terminated in an arbitrary impedance Z_r will, however, require in general the presence of both the forward- and backward-traveling-wave terms in the voltage and current expressions, in order that their quotient at $z = A$ shall correctly yield $V(A)/I(A) = Z_r$. Over the remaining length of the line, the two oppositely traveling waves add to produce a standing wave of stationary maxima and minima. The standing wave may be regarded as a one-dimensional interference pattern of voltage or current on the line, produced by the superposition of the oppositely traveling waves.

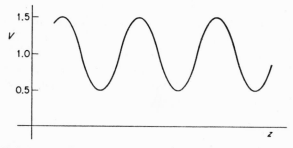

FIG. 1.2. Voltage standing wave on transmission line with $V_2/V_1 = 0.5e^{j\pi/4}$.

Equation (1.24) for line voltage, for example, may be placed in the form

$$V = V_1 e^{-j\beta z} \left(1 + 2\frac{|V_2|}{|V_1|}\cos\chi + \frac{|V_2|^2}{|V_1|^2} \right)^{\frac{1}{2}}$$

$$\times \exp\left(j\tan^{-1}\frac{\dfrac{|V_2|}{|V_1|}\sin\chi}{1 + \dfrac{|V_2|}{|V_1|}\cos\chi} \right) \quad (1.27)$$

where $\chi = 2\beta z + \theta_2 - \theta_1$, and θ_2 and θ_1 are the phase angles of V_2 and V_1, respectively. A typical plot of Eq. (1.27) is shown in Fig. 1.2. Since the exponential function of an imaginary quantity always has unit amplitude and the cosine function varies between $+1$ and -1 as z varies along the line, the amplitude of the alternating voltage changes along the line between the extrema

$$|V|_{\max} = |V_1|\left(1 + \frac{|V_2|}{|V_1|} \right) = |V_1| + |V_2| \quad (1.27a)$$

$$|V|_{\min} = |V_1|\left(1 - \frac{|V_2|}{|V_1|} \right) = |V_1| - |V_2| \quad (1.27b)$$

1.4. Terminal Conditions for the Lossless Transmission Line

The solutions for the transmission-line voltage and current given by Eqs. (1.24) and (1.25) could now be completed by the evaluation of constants V_1 and V_2 in terms of some pair of experimental values such as, for example, the voltage and current V_g and I_g at the sending end of the line ($z = 0$) or the voltage and current V_r and I_r at the receiving end ($z = A$). This will not be done here, however, since the line equations are being developed for eventual use at frequencies so high that voltmeter and ammeter readings are no longer practically available. The form into which we put the transmission-line equations will be governed, instead, by the nature of the experimental data which can be readily obtained in the laboratory, for use in the evaluation of the remaining unknown constants.

We now assume that the transmission line is terminated at the point $z = A$ by an arbitrary terminating impedance Z_r. It will be found convenient to change the position coordinate on the line to s, where s is distance measured from the receiving end of the line toward the generator at the sending end.

Hence, $z = A - s$, and (1.24) and (1.25) become

$$V = V_1 e^{-j\beta(A-s)} + V_2 e^{+j\beta(A-s)} \tag{1.28}$$

$$I = \frac{1}{Z_0}(V_1 e^{-j\beta(A-s)} - V_2 e^{+j\beta(A-s)}) \tag{1.29}$$

For convenience, the constant factors $e^{-j\beta A}$ and $e^{+j\beta A}$ may be absorbed into V_1 and V_2, respectively, to form two new factors V_{1s} and V_{2s}:

$$V = V_{1s}e^{j\beta s} + V_{2s}e^{-j\beta s} \tag{1.30}$$

$$I = \frac{1}{Z_0}(V_{1s}e^{j\beta s} - V_{2s}e^{-j\beta s}) \tag{1.31}$$

The voltage and current are again seen to be composed of two oppositely traveling waves. The amplitudes and phases of the waves traveling toward the load and away from the load are given by the complex constants V_{1s} and V_{2s}, respectively. Equations (1.30) and (1.31) may now be written

$$V = V_{1s}e^{j\beta s}(1 + \rho e^{-2j\beta s}) \tag{1.32}$$

$$I = \frac{V_{1s}e^{j\beta s}}{Z_0}(1 - \rho e^{-2j\beta s}) \tag{1.33}$$

In (1.32) and (1.33) the complex reflection coefficient ρ has been defined as

$$\rho = \frac{V_{2s}}{V_{1s}} \tag{1.34a}$$

The polar coordinates of ρ are

$$\rho = |\rho|e^{j\psi} = \frac{|V_{2s}|}{|V_{1s}|} e^{j(\theta_{2s}-\theta_{1s})} \tag{1.34b}$$

where θ_{2s} and θ_{1s} are the phase angles of V_{2s} and V_{1s}, respectively.

With this definition of reflection coefficient, the line voltage, Eq. (1.32), may be written

$$V = V_{1s}e^{j\beta s}(1 + |\rho|e^{j(\psi-2\beta s)}) \tag{1.35}$$

The quantity in parentheses in (1.35) will have its smallest absolute value when

$$e^{j(\psi-2\beta s)} = -1$$

or

$$\psi - 2\beta s = (2m + 1)\pi \tag{1.36}$$

where $m = 0, 1, 2, 3, \ldots$. Equation (1.36) determines the points on the transmission line where the minima of the voltage standing wave occur, since V_{1s} is constant, and the amplitude of exp $(j\beta s)$ is always unity. The distance between two adjacent minima, the mth and the $(m + 1)$st, will thus be given by

$$-2\beta(s_m - s_{m+1}) = 2(m - m - 1)\pi = -2\pi$$

or

$$s_m - s_{m+1} = \frac{\pi}{\beta}$$

Since $\beta = 2\pi/\lambda$, the distance between two adjacent minima thus is one half-wavelength of the traveling waves on the line

$$s_m - s_{m+1} = \frac{\lambda}{2} \tag{1.37}$$

Equation (1.37) provides a means for experimentally determining λ and hence the frequency of the traveling waves, since, in air or vacuum,

$$v_p = f\lambda = 3 \times 10^8 \ m/sec$$

We may now define two characteristic quantities of the standing-wave distribution set up by a given terminating impedance. The first of these, denoted by d_{min}, is the distance from the termination to the first voltage minimum, which corresponds to $m = 0$ in Eq. (1.36):

$$\psi - 2\beta d_{min} = \pi \tag{1.38}$$

By the use of Eq. (1.38), the phase angle ψ of the reflection coefficient ρ may be determined from a measurement of the distance between load and first voltage minimum.

In order to determine the magnitude of ρ, we define the standing-wave ratio S, of the voltage distribution on the line

$$S = \frac{|V|_{max}}{|V|_{min}} \tag{1.39}$$

We may see from Eq. (1.35) that the maximum voltage occurring on the line is equal to $|V_{1s}|(1 + |\rho|)$ at points where $\exp j(\psi - 2\beta s)] = +1$. In the same way, the minimum line voltage is $|V_{1s}|(1 - |\rho|)$, occurring when $\exp [j(\psi - 2\beta s)] = -1$. Using these values in Eq. (1.39), we obtain

$$S = \frac{1 + |\rho|}{1 - |\rho|} \tag{1.40}$$

from which we may evaluate the magnitude of ρ,

$$|\rho| = \frac{S - 1}{S + 1} \tag{1.41}$$

The quantities which we have just defined, namely, d_{min}, the distance from the load to the first minimum of the voltage standing wave, and the standing-wave ratio S, are convenient experimentally observable variables of high-frequency transmission lines, whereas line voltage and current values are not in all cases readily obtainable by measurement. For this reason our practical interest in numerical values of voltage and current on the line diminishes in favor of a characterization of line behavior in terms of the quantities d_{min} and S, which are established by the impedance terminating the line. A transmission line provides, in fact, a convenient means of measurement of the value of its terminating impedance and is frequently used in the laboratory for this purpose. The terminating impedance, in general complex, is specified by two scalar numbers, its real and imaginary parts, or by its magnitude and phase angle. For the purpose of determining these two numbers, we may use the two observed quantities d_{min} and S. To formulate the connection between these two pairs of numbers, we write the quotient of line voltage and line current at a point s on the line

$$Z(s) = \frac{V(s)}{I(s)} = Z_0 \frac{1 + \rho e^{-2j\beta s}}{1 - \rho e^{-2j\beta s}} \tag{1.42}$$

where Eqs. (1.32) and (1.33) have been used. At the termination of the line, the impedance is equal to the load impedance Z_r, and s equals zero:

$$Z_r = Z_0 \frac{1 + \rho}{1 - \rho} \tag{1.43}$$

Writing $z_r = Z_r/Z_0$ for the load impedance normalized to the Z_0 of the line and employing the polar coordinates $|\rho|$ and ψ of the reflection coefficient ρ, we obtain

$$z_r = \frac{Z_r}{Z_0} = \frac{1 + |\rho|e^{j\psi}}{1 - |\rho|e^{j\psi}} \tag{1.44}$$

Substituting for $|\rho|$ and ψ from Eqs. (1.41) and (1.38), we have

$$z_r = \frac{(S + 1) + (S - 1)e^{j(2\beta d_{min}+\pi)}}{(S + 1) - (S - 1)e^{j(2\beta d_{min}+\pi)}}$$

which may be put into the form, using $\exp(j\pi) = -1$,

$$z_r = \frac{1 - jS \tan \beta d_{min}}{S - j \tan \beta d_{min}} \tag{1.45}$$

With Eq. (1.45) the complex impedance terminating the transmission line may be calculated from measured values of the standing-wave ratio and distance to the first minimum of voltage from the load.

In carrying out the measurement of d_{min}, it is not necessary to directly observe the voltage minimum nearest the load. If a short circuit is substituted for the load, the standing-wave pattern then appearing on the line exhibits voltage minima at integral multiples of $\lambda/2$ from the load. When the load is then replaced, d_{min} can be measured on the line from any conveniently located one of the short-circuit minimum points to the nearest voltage minimum appearing with load connected, in the direction toward the generator.

In some instances the structure of the transmission system may make it difficult or impossible to determine the specific location of the load terminals. Then, any suitable transverse plane along the system may be defined to represent the load terminals. When the distance from this plane to the nearest voltage minimum is used as d_{min}, the value of impedance so calculated will represent the impedance of whatever lies beyond the plane.

1.5. The Transmission-line Chart

The necessity for making the calculations involved in Eqs. (1.43) to (1.45) may be obviated by the use of a graphical device, the Smith chart transmission-line diagram.† We may write Eq. (1.42) in the form

$$z(s) = \frac{1 + W}{1 - W} \tag{1.46}$$

where W is the complex number

$$W = |\rho|e^{j(\psi - 2\beta s)} \tag{1.47}$$

The bilinear transformation (1.46) maps rectangular coordinates of the normalized line-impedance plane, $z = r + jx = [R(s) + jX(s)]/Z_0$, into coordinate lines having the form indicated in Fig. 1.3. The center of

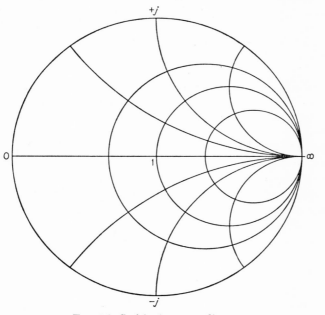

FIG. 1.3. Smith chart coordinates.

the Smith chart corresponds to the point for which $|W| = |\rho| = 0$. By the use of Eq. (1.43) it is readily shown that ρ is given by

$$\rho = \frac{z_r - 1}{z_r + 1} \tag{1.48}$$

Equating the absolute values of both sides of (1.48), we see that a given load impedance Z_r corresponds to a circle of constant $|\rho|$. Hence it is also associated with a given value of standing-wave ratio S, as implied by (1.40). Motion around the circle of constant S (or S circle)

† P. H. Smith, *Electronics*, vol. 12, p. 29, 1939.

with change of $\psi - 2\beta s$, the phase angle of W, corresponds to motion along the transmission line with changing s. Inspection of Eqs. (1.46) and (1.47) shows that changing $2\beta s$ by π radians corresponds to multiplication of W by $e^{j\pi} = -1$, with the result

$$z(2\beta s + \pi) = \frac{1 - W}{1 + W} = \frac{1}{z(2\beta s)} = y(2\beta s) \qquad (1.49)$$

wherein the argument of z has been written as $2\beta s$, the angle variable in the circle diagram. Equation (1.49) shows that reflection of an impedance point through the center of the transmission-line diagram yields its reciprocal y, the corresponding normalized admittance. The transmission-line chart may be used either as a chart of the normalized impedances or of the normalized admittances observed along the transmission line. The characteristic admittance of the line is $Y_0 = 1/Z_0$, equal to $\sqrt{C/L}$ for a lossless line.

Since motion around a complete S circle in the chart changes $2\beta s$ by 2π radians, the corresponding change in position along the line is $\Delta s = \pi/\beta = \lambda/2$. Therefore, a full cycle of values of transmission-line impedances (or admittances) is completed in every half-wavelength along the line. The horizontal radius to the left of chart center is the direction for which $\psi - 2\beta s = (2m + 1)\pi$, which corresponds to positions of voltage minima. Similarly, the horizontal radius to the right of the chart center corresponds to voltage maxima. From the properties of $z(s)$ as given by (1.42), these may be seen to be also points of minima and maxima of impedance on the line, respectively. The maxima of normalized impedance magnitudes are

$$|z|_{max} = r_{max} = \frac{(1 + |\rho|)}{(1 - |\rho|)} = S$$

wherein Eq. (1.40) has been used for S. Thus when the voltage standing-wave ratio is known, the S circle can be constructed with its center at the chart center and passing through the point $r = S$. This circle is then the locus of all impedances appearing along the transmission line, normalized to the Z_0 of the line. The circle therefore passes through the value z_r, at the point corresponding to the location of the load at $s = 0$. The angular distance measured clockwise† around

---

† Clockwise motion around the chart corresponds to motion "toward generator" on the line. This may be readily remembered by noting that if the line were terminated in a short circuit, the load impedance would correspond to the point $z = 0$ on the chart. Then, a small clockwise motion around the $S = \infty$ circle carries the impedance point into the region of small inductive reactances. This corresponds to the inductive reactance of the loop of wire created by the short circuit plus a short segment of transmission line.

the Smith chart from z_r to the first intersection with the real axis to the left of chart center is $2\beta d_{min}$, the angular distance from load to first voltage minimum.

The initial data in a typical transmission-line problem may take one of the forms: S and d_{min} given, with z_r the unknown, or z_r given, with the standing wave and line impedance characteristics the unknowns. From the foregoing discussion, we see that with either type of initial data given, the S circle can be readily constructed and the remainder of the problem is fully determined.

1.6. Transmission-line Impedance Matching

A familiar theorem of circuit analysis states that maximum power is transferred from a generator to a load when the internal resistance of the generator equals the resistance of the load and the reactive components of generator and load impedances are either zero or equal in magnitude and opposite in sign. This theorem holds true for power transfer when a part of the system consists of a transmission line. Consequently, impedance-matching techniques for transmission lines are frequently employed. In the interests of maximum signal transfer, a usual practice is to operate the line with matched impedances at source and load. It has been seen in Sec. 1.3 that when a line is terminated in its own characteristic impedance Z_0, there is no reflected wave on the line and the reflection coefficient is everywhere zero. In the transmission-line chart, the point $\rho = 0$ corresponds to the center of the chart, for which case the ratio $|V|_{max}/|V|_{min} = S$ is everywhere unity; i.e., the line is "flat."

Since it is sometimes necessary to drive a load having impedance other than Z_0, various means may be used for modifying a transmission system so that the impedance on the line and at its input terminals is corrected to Z_0. The correction is often accomplished by the parallel connection of nondissipative impedances of suitable value on the line. A length of transmission line terminated in a short circuit, called a shorted stub, is a convenient means of obtaining a reactive impedance of arbitrary value at high frequencies. The standing-wave circle of a lossless stub line is the outer perimeter of the transmission-line chart ($S = \infty$), passing through points of zero and infinite impedance. By the use of Eq. (1.48), we find that since $Z_r = 0$, $\rho = -1$ for a short-circuited termination. From Eq. (1.42) it then follows that the normalized input impedance of a shorted stub is

$$z = j \tan \beta d \qquad (1.50)$$

where d is the length of the stub.

Single-stub Impedance Matching. A load impedance of arbitrary finite value may be matched to a transmission line by the connection of a tuning stub of suitable length in parallel with the line at the proper distance from load to stub. The Smith chart may be used to determine the required length of stub and its distance from the load. It is here most convenient to use the Smith chart as an admittance diagram. The standing-wave circle of the load is plotted, passing through the load admittance at y_r, as shown in Fig. 1.4. It can now be seen that

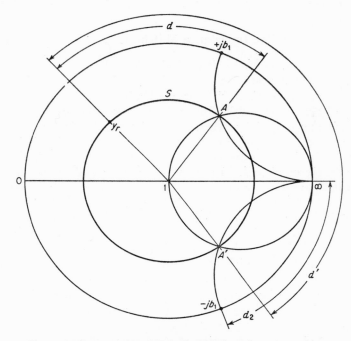

FIG. 1.4. Construction for single-stub impedance matching.

at the points on the line shown by A and A' in Fig. 1.4, where the S circle intersects the circle of $g = 1$, the addition of a pure susceptance in parallel with the line admittance can bring the resultant admittance to $y = 1 + j0$, and the line will be matched. The angular distances from load to A and A' can be read directly from the chart as d and d', respectively. If the stub is to be connected at point A, it must present an admittance equal to $-jb_1$. The necessary stub length may now be obtained by treating the stub as a transmission line with short-circuited termination. Measuring clockwise from $y = \infty$, the admittance of the short circuit, around the perimeter of the chart to the point $-jb_1$,

yields d_2, the necessary length of stub in line wavelengths.   If point
A' had been chosen for the connection of the stub, a stub admittance
of $+jb_1$ would be required.   The necessary length of stub can then be
found as before to be the clockwise distance around the circumference of the Smith chart from $y = \infty$ to the point $+b_1$.

Double-stub Impedance Matching.   In many cases the structure of
the transmission line may make it difficult or impossible to connect a
parallel stub at arbitrary positions along the line to satisfy various

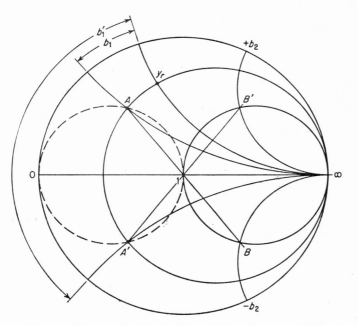

Fig. 1.5. Construction for double-stub impedance matching.

impedance-matching requirements.   In this event two or more stubs
of adjustable length may be built into the line at fixed positions.   A
typical arrangement is that of two tuning stubs, one placed at the load
and the other a quarter-wavelength away.   The Smith chart may be
used to determine the stub lengths as follows (refer to Fig. 1.5): In
order for matching to be accomplished by the connection of the stub
at $\lambda/4$ from the load, the line admittance at that point must lie on the
$g = 1$ circle.   The fact may now be used that the admittance transformation accomplished by moving a quarter-wavelength along the
line is equivalent to a half-circle rotation around the S circle or a
reflection of the starting admittance through the center of the chart.

Therefore the locus of all admittances one quarter-wavelength from the $g = 1$ circle is the dashed circle in Fig. 1.5. Hence the stub at the load must be chosen so as to bring the resultant load admittance to this circle, i.e., to either point A or A', in the example shown. The necessary stub length for the required susceptance b_1 or b_1' is found from the Smith chart by the procedure described above. The admittance at the quarter-wavelength-distant stub is therefore the admittance at point B or B' in Fig. 1.5, depending upon whether A or A' has been chosen. Then, if this stub is chosen to have admittance $+jb_2$ or $-jb_2$, respectively, the load will be matched to the line.

Impedance Transformation by Transmission-line Section. The foregoing discussion has shown that a section of transmission line may be regarded as a four-terminal device capable of effecting impedance transformations. Any impedance point lying on the S circle of a transmission line can be transformed into any other impedance point on the S circle, by the use of the requisite length of line between the terminal point and input point. We may express the impedance transformation effected by a length of line L between its terminating impedance z_r and its input impedance z_{in} (Fig. 1.6), by the use of Eq. (1.48) in Eq. (1.42):

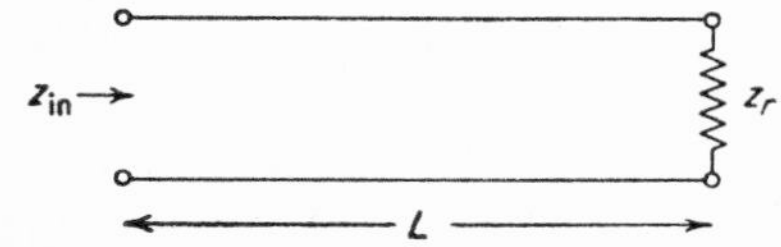

FIG. 1.6. Impedance transformation by transmission-line section.

$$z_{in} = \frac{1 + \dfrac{z_r - 1}{z_r + 1} e^{-j2\beta L}}{1 - \dfrac{z_r - 1}{z_r + 1} e^{-j2\beta L}}$$

which is readily put into the form

$$z_{in} = \frac{z_r + j \tan \beta L}{1 + jz_r \tan \beta L} \tag{1.51}$$

In Eq. (1.51) both z_r and z_{in} are normalized to the characteristic impedance Z_0 of the transmission line. The transformation of a terminating admittance y_r, which is effected by a length L of line, is readily found from (1.51) to be

$$y_{in} = \frac{y_r + j \tan \beta L}{1 + jy_r \tan \beta L} \tag{1.52}$$

If the transmission-line section is taken to be a quarter-wavelength long, then $\beta L = \pi/2$, and in Eq. (1.51), z_{in} becomes equal to $1/z_r$. This result confirms the observation that a motion of one-half revolution (one quarter-wavelength) around the Smith chart on an S circle yields the reciprocal of the starting impedance.

The quarter-wavelength line section may be used as a matching device between two unlike impedances. For example, a transmission line of impedance Z_{02} may be matched to a line of impedance Z_{01} by means of a quarter-wavelength section of line having impedance Z_{0m} (Fig. 1.7). Remembering that the connected impedances must be

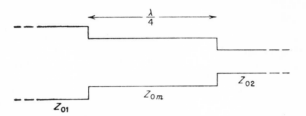

FIG. 1.7. Quarter-wavelength matching section.

normalized to the impedance Z_{0m}, the impedance at the input terminals of the quarter-wavelength section is

$$\frac{Z_{\text{in}}}{Z_{0m}} = \frac{1}{Z_{02}/Z_{0m}} = \frac{Z_{0m}}{Z_{02}}$$

Therefore, the necessary characteristic impedance for the matching section which makes Z_{in} equal to Z_{01} is

$$Z_{0m} = \sqrt{Z_{01}Z_{02}} \tag{1.53}$$

Thus, Z_{0m} must be equal to the geometric mean of the two impedances being matched.

1.7. Energy Transport on Lossless Lines

We have represented observed voltage and current on a lossless transmission line as the superposition of two oppositely traveling waves. A forward-traveling wave, for example, is represented by

$$V = V_{1s}e^{j\beta s} \tag{1.54}$$

$$I = \frac{V_{1s}}{Z_0}e^{j\beta s} \tag{1.55}$$

where s is the distance from the termination of the line. The ratio of voltage to current of this traveling wave is

$$\frac{V}{I} = Z_0 \tag{1.56}$$

Hence we see that an individual forward-traveling wave always effectively encounters an impedance equal to the Z_0 of the line. A similar result is found for the backward-traveling wave. Thus the impedance encountered by a traveling wave is characteristic of the transmission line rather than of the connected load. The properties of the load, or terminating impedance, govern only the relative magnitudes and phases of the two oppositely traveling waves.

Since the Z_0 of a lossless transmission line is real, an individual forward-traveling wave transports an amount of power given by

$$P_1 = \text{Re} \frac{V_1 I_1}{2} = \frac{V_1 I_1^*}{2} = \frac{V_1 V_1^*}{2Z_0} \tag{1.57}$$

where the subscripts $_s$ have been omitted for simplicity. The corresponding backward-traveling power is

$$P_2 = \text{Re} \frac{V_2 I_2}{2} = \frac{V_2 V_2^*}{2Z_0} \tag{1.58}$$

If the reflection coefficient of the load impedance is ρ,

$$P_2 = \frac{(\rho V_1)(\rho V_1)^*}{2Z_0} = \rho\rho^* \frac{V_1 V_1^*}{2Z_0} \tag{1.59}$$

Therefore the total power traveling forward on the line is

$$P = P_1 - P_2 = \frac{V_1 V_1^*}{2Z_0} (1 - \rho\rho^*) \tag{1.60}$$

The total power may also be calculated by means of the alternative expression

$$P = \text{Re} \frac{V I^*}{2}$$

which may be verified by substitution of V and I^*, the total voltage and the complex conjugate of the total current of the line, as given by Eqs. (1.24) and (1.25).

If an admittance Y_p is connected in parallel with an infinite or matched transmission line at $s = 0$ (Fig. 1.8), the resultant admittance presented at terminals aa to a voltage wave incident from the left is $Y_p + Y_0$, where $Y_0 = 1/Z_0$ is the

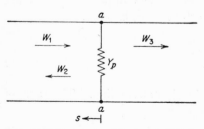

FIG. 1.8. Power transfer at parallel-connected admittance.

characteristic admittance of the transmission line.   Hence the reflection coefficient at aa is, from Eq. (1.48),

$$\rho_a = \frac{1 - y_a}{1 + y_a} = \frac{1 - (y_p + 1)}{1 + (y_p + 1)} = -\frac{Y_p}{2Y_0 + Y_p} \tag{1.61}$$

where y_a and y_p are the normalized values of Y_a and Y_p, respectively.

If a voltage wave $V_1 \exp (j\beta s)$ is incident upon aa from the left, the incident power is

$$W_1 = \frac{V_1 V_1^*}{2Z_0} \tag{1.62}$$

and the reflected power is

$$W_2 = \rho_a \rho_a^* \frac{V_1 V_1^*}{2Z_0} \tag{1.63}$$

Hence we may define a power-reflection coefficient at aa

$$R_{aa} = \rho_a \rho_a^* \tag{1.64}$$

The line voltage at aa, where $s = 0$, is

$$V_{aa} = V_1 + V_2 = V_1(1 + \rho_a) \tag{1.65}$$

from which the energy transferred by the wave traveling to the right beyond aa is

$$W_3 = \frac{V_1 V_1^*(1 + \rho_a)(1 + \rho_a)^*}{2Z_0} \tag{1.66}$$

Thus we may define a power-transfer coefficient at aa

$$T_{aa} = (1 + \rho_a)(1 + \rho_a)^* \tag{1.67}$$

Since R_{aa} and T_{aa} represent the fractions of the incident power which are reflected and transmitted from the admittance Y_p at aa, the fraction of the incident power absorbed by Y_p is

$$A_{aa} = 1 - R_{aa} - T_{aa} = -(\rho_a + \rho_a^* + 2\rho_a \rho_a^*) \tag{1.68}$$

PROBLEMS

1.1. A lossless transmission line is short-circuited at the points $z = 10$ and $z = 30$ m.

(a) Find an expression of the form of Eq. (1.24) for the pair of traveling waves of minimum frequency which add to satisfy the given terminating conditions.

(b) What are the frequency and wavelength of the waves of part a?

(c) Repeat (a) and (b) for the waves of next higher frequency which can exist on the line.

1.2. If the inductance and capacitance per unit length of a parallel-wire line in free space are given by

$$L = \frac{\mu_0}{\pi} \ln \frac{D}{r_0} \qquad \text{henrys/m}$$

$$C = \frac{\pi \epsilon_0}{\ln (D/r_0)} \qquad \text{farads/m}$$

where D and r_0 are the distance between centers and the radius of the wires, respectively,

(a) Show that the phase velocity of waves in the line is equal to the velocity of light (see Appendix I).

(b) Show that the characteristic impedance Z_0 of the line is equal to $120 \ln (D/r_0)$ ohms, if the line is considered to be lossless.

1.3. A parallel-wire line, as in Prob. 1.2, is constructed of two No. 18 wires, each having resistance of 0.021 ohm/m, radius of $r_0 = 0.5$ mm, and center-to-center distance of $D = 5$ cm. The conductance of the insulation is $(10^7 \text{ ohms})^{-1}$/m, and the operating frequency is 10^8 cps.

(a) Verify that $R/L\omega$ and $G/C\omega$ are both much smaller than unity.

(b) Calculate the distance along the line at which a single forward-traveling wave has decreased by 1 per cent of its starting value. (Note that $e^x \approx 1 + x$, if $x \ll 1$.)

(c) Calculate the phase delay in the length of line found in part b.

1.4. A lossless transmission line is terminated in an admittance $g + jb$ in which b is variable.

(a) Find the value of b which minimizes the standing-wave ratio on the line.

(b) Assume that b is varied until the standing-wave ratio reaches a minimum value $S_{\min}$. What are two values that g may have in this case?

1.5. A lossless line of $Z_0 = 100$ ohms is terminated by an unknown impedance. The termination is found to be at a maximum of the voltage standing wave, and the standing-wave ratio is $S = 5$. What is the value of the terminating impedance?

1.6. A lossless transmission line having $Z_0 = 50$ ohms is terminated by an impedance Z_r. The observed standing-wave ratio on the line is $S = 8$; the distance between successive minima is 0.1 m, and distance from termination to the first voltage minimum is 0.0812 m.

(a) Find Z_r.

(b) Find the distance from the termination and the length of a single tuning stub which will match Z_r to the line.

1.7. A lossless transmission line having $Z_0 = 200$ ohms is terminated by an impedance Z_r. The observed standing-wave ratio on the line is $S = 6.5$, and $d_{\min} = 0.168\lambda$.

(a) Find Z_r.

(b) Find the lengths of two shorted stubs, one at the load and one at $\lambda/4$ from the load, which are required to match Z_r to the line.

1.8. A section of line one quarter-wavelength long at 10^8 cps is to be used to match a 50-ohm resistive load to a transmission line having $Z_0 = 200$ ohms.

(a) Find the characteristic impedance of the matching section.

(b) What is the input impedance of the matching section at 1.2×10^8 cps? (Note that the only effect of the change in frequency is a change in the electrical length of the section.)

(c) Repeat part b for a frequency of 0.8×10^8 cps.

1.9. Show that, for a transmission line in which the losses are not negligible, the normalized impedance at distance s from the termination is

$$z(s) = \frac{z_r + \tanh \gamma s}{1 + z_r \tanh \gamma s}$$

where $\gamma = \alpha + j\beta$ and z_r is the normalized load impedance.

1.10. A 50-ohm resistive impedance is connected in parallel with a lossless transmission line having $Z_0 = 50$ ohms. Assuming that the line is matched, beyond the point of connection of the impedance,

(a) Find the standing-wave ratio on the line preceding the parallel-connected impedance.

(b) Assuming that the *total* power being supplied by the source preceding the 50-ohm parallel impedance is 1 watt, calculate the power effectively carried by the incident traveling wave and that carried by the reflected traveling wave.

(c) How much power is transferred to the line beyond the parallel-connected impedance?

CHAPTER 2

Electromagnetic Field Equations

The existence of electric charge is known by virtue of the interactions of charge with its environment. Electromagnetic theory has established a compact formalism for dealing with these interactions by means of the concept of electric and magnetic fields. The fields may be defined in terms of the forces they exert upon electric charge. The force upon a charge q moving with velocity vector $\mathbf{v}$ in an electric field $\mathbf{E}$ and magnetic field $\mathbf{B}$ may be written as the sum of electric and magnetic forces:

$$\mathfrak{F} = \mathfrak{F}_{\text{electric}} + \mathfrak{F}_{\text{magnetic}}$$
$$= q\mathbf{E} + q\mathbf{v} \times \mathbf{B} \tag{2.1}$$

The electric field $\mathbf{E}$ is defined as the force per unit amount of charge acted upon by the $\mathbf{E}$ field. The units of $\mathbf{E}$ are therefore newtons per coulomb in mks units, which are equal to volts per meter in electrical terms.† The definition of $\mathbf{E}$ is preferably made in terms of the limiting process:

$$\mathbf{E} = \lim_{q \to 0} \frac{\mathfrak{F}_q}{q} \tag{2.2}$$

where $\mathfrak{F}_q$ is the force acting on test charge q. The test charge is assumed to be vanishingly small so that it does not perturb the distribution of charges which produce the field being observed. The magnitude of the magnetic field $\mathbf{B}$ is similarly definable, from the second term of Eq. (2.1), as the force in newtons per coulomb meter per second which acts upon a charge moving at right angles to the direction of the $\mathbf{B}$ field. The latter units are defined in magnetic terms as webers per square meter.

Since they have the character of forces, the electric and magnetic

---

† The mks system of units is used throughout this book, except for cases in which practical data are cited in terms of other units of measure.

24

fields are vectors, and we find that the differential equations of the fields arise in the form of vector operators acting upon the field vectors. The properties of vectors which will be required for our purposes are summarized briefly in the next section.† These properties are given in rectangular coordinate form below. Corresponding expressions in other orthogonal coordinate systems are listed in Appendix II.

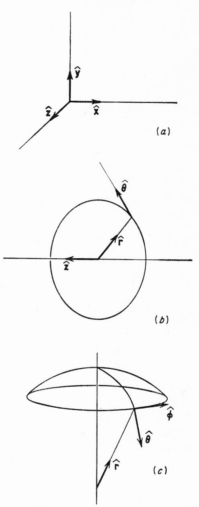

(a)

(b)

(c)

Fig. 2.1. Coordinate unit vectors. (a) Rectangular; (b) cylindrical; (c) spherical.

2.1. Properties of Vectors

A vector may be described as a quantity having magnitude and direction. In the orthogonal coordinate systems with which we shall be dealing, information concerning both of these attributes is contained in the set of three scalar numbers representing the projections of the vector in the directions of the three coordinate axes at the point in space where the vector is being described. With each component is associated the unit vector in the positive direction of the corresponding coordinate axis.

Notation. The unit vectors in the directions of the axes will be denoted by $\hat{x}$, $\hat{y}$, $\hat{z}$ in rectangular coordinates, by $\hat{r}$, $\hat{\theta}$, $\hat{z}$ in cylindrical, and by $\hat{r}$, $\hat{\theta}$, $\hat{\phi}$ in spherical coordinates (cf. Fig. 2.1a, b, c, respectively). Thus, for example, the vector **E** in rectangular coordinates will be written

$$\mathbf{E} = \hat{x}E_x + \hat{y}E_y + \hat{z}E_z \quad (2.3)$$

† For a more extensive treatment of vector analysis, see references such as H. B. Phillips, "Vector Analysis," John Wiley & Sons, Inc., New York, 1933; G. A. Korn and T. M. Korn, "Mathematical Handbook for Scientists and Engineers," McGraw-Hill Book Company, Inc., New York, 1961.

Equality. When two vectors **A** and **B** are equal, their components are separately equal; i.e., when we have

$$\mathbf{A} = \mathbf{B}$$
$$\hat{x}A_x + \hat{y}A_y + \hat{z}A_z = \hat{x}B_x + \hat{y}B_y + \hat{z}B_z \qquad (2.4)$$

we may conclude that

$$A_x = B_x$$
$$A_y = B_y$$
$$A_z = B_z$$

Thus, every vector equation represents the set of three scalar equations expressing the separate equality of each of the components.

Addition. The vector addition law requires addition of components:

$$\mathbf{A} + \mathbf{B} = \hat{x}(A_x + B_x) + \hat{y}(A_y + B_y) + \hat{z}(A_z + B_z) \qquad (2.5)$$

Scalar Multiplication. Two types of product may be formed between two vectors. The scalar product of vectors **A** and **B** is expressed by

$$\mathbf{A} \cdot \mathbf{B} = A_x B_x + A_y B_y + A_z B_z \qquad (2.6)$$
$$\mathbf{A} \cdot \mathbf{B} = |\mathbf{A}|\,|\mathbf{B}|\,\cos \theta_A{}^B \qquad (2.7)$$

where $\theta_A{}^B$ is the angle between the directions of vectors **A** and **B**. The scalar product of two vectors is a scalar.

Vector Multiplication. The vector product of vectors **A** and **B** is

$$\mathbf{A} \times \mathbf{B} = \hat{x}(A_y B_z - A_z B_y) + \hat{y}(A_z B_x - A_x B_z)$$
$$+ \hat{z}(A_x B_y - A_y B_x) \qquad (2.8)$$
$$\mathbf{A} \times \mathbf{B} = \hat{n}_{A \times B}|\mathbf{A}|\,|\mathbf{B}|\,\sin \theta_A{}^B \qquad (2.9)$$

where $\hat{n}_{A \times B}$ is the unit vector normal to the plane defined by vectors **A** and **B**. The direction of $\hat{n}_{A \times B}$ is the direction of advance of a right-handed screw when turned through the smaller angle between **A** and **B** so as to carry **A** into coincidence with **B**. Angle $\theta_A{}^B$ has the magnitude of the latter angle. The vector product of two vectors is itself a vector. Note that the determinantal form exists:

$$\mathbf{A} \times \mathbf{B} = \begin{vmatrix} \hat{x} & \hat{y} & \hat{z} \\ A_x & A_y & A_z \\ B_x & B_y & B_z \end{vmatrix} \qquad (2.10)$$

Line Integral and Surface Integral. We shall frequently need to perform the line integral of a vector **A** over a given path. The integrand of the line integral is defined as the product of an element of path length dl and the projection of **A** on the line parallel to the path element. Defining dl as a vector having magnitude dl and the direction of the tangent to the path, the line integral between points a and b takes the form

$$\int_a^b |\mathbf{A}| \, dl \cos \theta_{dl}{}^A = \int_a^b \mathbf{A} \cdot d\mathbf{l} \qquad (2.11)$$

A closed line integral travels a closed path, returning to the starting point. Note that over a closed path

$$\oint d\mathbf{l} = 0 \qquad (2.12)$$

Integral (2.12) provides a convenient check on the choice of elements of path, in the calculation of a closed line integral.

A surface integral of vector $\mathbf{A}$ is the integral of the product of an element of surface area da, by the projection of $\mathbf{A}$ on the direction of the surface normal at da. Vector da is defined as a vector of magnitude da and having the direction of the surface normal at da. The integrand of the surface integral then takes the form

$$d\phi = |\mathbf{A}| \, da \cos \theta_{da}{}^A = \mathbf{A} \cdot d\mathbf{a} \qquad (2.13)$$

where $d\phi$ is an element of flux of the vector $\mathbf{A}$ through da, and the surface integral is

$$\Phi = \iint \mathbf{A} \cdot d\mathbf{a} \qquad (2.14)$$

Ordinary Differentiation. The scalar derivative of a vector $\mathbf{A}$ has the form

$$\frac{\partial \mathbf{A}}{\partial t} = \hat{\mathbf{x}} \frac{\partial A_x}{\partial t} + \hat{\mathbf{y}} \frac{\partial A_y}{\partial t} + \hat{\mathbf{z}} \frac{\partial A_z}{\partial t} \qquad (2.15)$$

Operator $\boldsymbol{\nabla}$ (*"del"*)

$$\boldsymbol{\nabla} = \hat{\mathbf{x}} \frac{\partial}{\partial x} + \hat{\mathbf{y}} \frac{\partial}{\partial y} + \hat{\mathbf{z}} \frac{\partial}{\partial z} \qquad (2.16)$$

Applications of the vector differential operator $\boldsymbol{\nabla}$ appear in the vector operations defined below.

Gradient Operator. The operator $\boldsymbol{\nabla}$, when applied to a scalar function of coordinates, produces a vector which has the direction and magnitude of the maximum space rate of change of the scalar:

$$\boldsymbol{\nabla} f = \hat{\mathbf{x}} \frac{\partial f}{\partial x} + \hat{\mathbf{y}} \frac{\partial f}{\partial y} + \hat{\mathbf{z}} \frac{\partial f}{\partial z} \qquad (2.17)$$

Divergence of a Vector

$$\boldsymbol{\nabla} \cdot \mathbf{A} = \frac{\partial E_x}{\partial x} + \frac{\partial E_y}{\partial y} + \frac{\partial E_z}{\partial z} \qquad (2.18)$$

In rectangular coordinates the divergence operation formally resembles the scalar product of operator $\boldsymbol{\nabla}$ with the vector, but this resemblance does not hold in other coordinate systems (see Appendix II). The divergence of a vector is a scalar.

The divergence of a vector has an alternative definition which gives physical insight into the character of vector fields having divergence:

$$\boldsymbol{\nabla} \cdot \mathbf{A} = \lim_{\Delta\tau \to 0} \frac{\iint \mathbf{A} \cdot d\mathbf{a}}{\Delta\tau} \tag{2.19}$$

In (2.19) $d\mathbf{a}$ is an area element of the surface enclosing a volume $\Delta\tau$, as in Fig. 2.2. The integral of $\mathbf{A} \cdot d\mathbf{a}$ over the complete surface enclos-

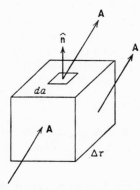

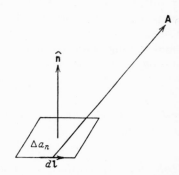

FIG. 2.2. Volume element for divergence calculation.

FIG. 2.3. Surface element for calculation of component of curl.

ing $\Delta\tau$ is the total flux of vector $\mathbf{A}$ emerging from the surface. In the limit as $\Delta\tau$ approaches zero, the divergence of $\mathbf{A}$ may be regarded as a measure of the density of sources of field at that point.

Curl of a Vector

$$\boldsymbol{\nabla} \times \mathbf{A} = \hat{\mathbf{x}} \left(\frac{\partial A_z}{\partial y} - \frac{\partial A_y}{\partial z} \right) + \hat{\mathbf{y}} \left(\frac{\partial A_x}{\partial z} - \frac{\partial A_z}{\partial x} \right) \\ + \hat{\mathbf{z}} \left(\frac{\partial A_y}{\partial x} - \frac{\partial A_x}{\partial y} \right) \tag{2.20}$$

The formal resemblance of the curl operation to the vector product of $\boldsymbol{\nabla}$ with a vector holds in rectangular coordinates only. (See Appendix II.) The curl of a vector is a vector.

An alternative definition of the component of the curl in a given space direction is

$$(\boldsymbol{\nabla} \times \mathbf{A})_n = \hat{\mathbf{n}} \lim_{\Delta a_n \to 0} \frac{\oint \mathbf{A} \cdot d\mathbf{l}}{\Delta a_n} \tag{2.21}$$

where n̂ is the unit vector in the direction for which the component of curl is being calculated and Δa_n is an element of area normal to the direction of n̂. The closed line integral in (2.21) is carried out by following the perimeter of Δa_n in the direction of travel that would carry a right-handed screw in the direction of n̂ (Fig. 2.3). Thus each component of the curl of a vector may be regarded as a measure of the strength of rotation or vorticity of the vector field $\mathbf{A}$ around the corresponding coordinate direction.

Scalar Laplacian

$$\nabla^2 f = \mathbf{\nabla} \cdot \mathbf{\nabla} f \tag{2.22}$$

The divergence of the gradient of a scalar is the Laplacian of the scalar. In rectangular coordinates this operator has the form

$$\nabla^2 f = \frac{\partial^2 f}{\partial x^2} + \frac{\partial^2 f}{\partial y^2} + \frac{\partial^2 f}{\partial z^2}$$

Gauss' Integral Theorem. A vector theorem of great practical utility takes the form

$$\iiint_V \mathbf{\nabla} \cdot \mathbf{A} \, d\tau = \iint_\Sigma \mathbf{A} \cdot d\mathbf{a} \tag{2.23}$$

wherein $d\tau$ is a volume element in volume V and $d\mathbf{a}$ is a surface element of the surface Σ which encloses V. There is a close relation apparent between Gauss' integral theorem (2.23) and the physical definition of divergence, Eq. (2.19).

Stokes' Integral Theorem. Stokes' theorem may be regarded as the integral expression corresponding to the definition of curl in Eq. (2.21) and has the form

$$\iint_\Sigma \mathbf{\nabla} \times \mathbf{A} \cdot d\mathbf{a} = \oint_C \mathbf{A} \cdot d\mathbf{l} \tag{2.24}$$

where $d\mathbf{a}$ is an element of area on the nonclosed, singly connected surface Σ and $d\mathbf{l}$ is a line element of the perimeter C of Σ.

2.2. Physical Bases of the Field Equations

Historically, the electromagnetic field equations were established by inductive reasoning from the observed results of experiments. We shall cite below some simple typical experiments and show how their results lead to the field equations.

In the region surrounding an electric point charge q, electric field $\mathbf{E}$

is established.   By Coulomb's law, this field is

$$\mathbf{E} = \hat{\mathbf{r}}\,\frac{q}{4\pi\epsilon r^2} \tag{2.25}$$

where r is the distance from q, $\hat{\mathbf{r}}$ is the unit vector parallel to r, and ϵ is a constant of the medium.

Consider a closed surface surrounding q.   An element of area on this surface which subtends solid angle $d\omega = \sin\theta\,d\theta\,d\phi$ from q is given by

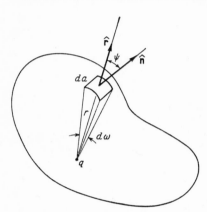

$$da = \frac{r^2\,d\omega}{\cos\psi} \tag{2.26}$$

where ψ is the angle between $\hat{\mathbf{r}}$ and the surface normal at da (see Fig. 2.4).

We now integrate the quantity $\mathbf{E} \cdot d\mathbf{a}$ over the closed surface surrounding q.   The result of this integral is

$$\iint \mathbf{E} \cdot d\mathbf{a} = \iint \frac{q}{4\pi\epsilon r^2}\,\frac{r^2\,d\omega}{\cos\psi}\cos\psi$$

$$= \frac{q}{4\pi\epsilon}\iint d\omega = \frac{q}{\epsilon} \tag{2.27}$$

FIG. 2.4. Calculation of electric flux through a closed surface due to charge q.

The result of the integration is independent of the location of q within the surface.   If, therefore, the above calculation of $\iint \mathbf{E} \cdot d\mathbf{a}$ is made for the case in which there is a continuous distribution of charges within the surface, described by a volume density of charge ρ, the result will be

$$\iint \mathbf{E} \cdot d\mathbf{a} = \frac{Q_{\text{enclosed}}}{\epsilon} = \frac{\iiint \rho\,d\tau}{\epsilon} \tag{2.28}$$

Now let Gauss' integral theorem [Eq. (2.23)] be applied to the left side of Eq. (2.28).   We thus obtain

$$\iiint \boldsymbol{\nabla} \cdot \mathbf{E}\,d\tau = \iiint \frac{\rho}{\epsilon}\,d\tau$$

or

$$\iiint \left(\boldsymbol{\nabla} \cdot \mathbf{E} - \frac{\rho}{\epsilon}\right)d\tau = 0 \tag{2.29}$$

Since the integral of Eq. (2.29) vanishes for all closed surfaces of integration, the integrand is equal to zero. Then,

$$\nabla \cdot \mathbf{E} = \frac{\rho}{\epsilon} \tag{2.30}$$

Equation (2.30) is the first of the electromagnetic field equations. The corresponding divergence equation for the magnetic field may also be obtained on the basis of experimental observation. It is the result of observation that the surface integral $\int\int \mathbf{B} \cdot d\mathbf{a}$ is always zero for every closed surface. Consequently, again applying Gauss' theorem,

$$\int\int\int \nabla \cdot \mathbf{B} \, d\tau = 0$$

and

$$\nabla \cdot \mathbf{B} = 0 \tag{2.31}$$

The field equation (2.31) may be regarded as an expression of the fact that there occur no magnetic point charges (monopoles) in nature. Most of the fundamental particles are, however, magnetic dipoles. The total integrated flux emanating from a dipole is zero, and Eq. (2.31) is preserved.

The next equation to be sought is the electric curl equation. This may be deduced from the observed law of electric induction in stationary media (Lenz's law):

$$\mathcal{E}_{\text{ind}} = -\frac{\partial \Phi}{\partial t} \tag{2.32}$$

in which $\mathcal{E}_{\text{ind}}$ is the electromotive force induced in a closed loop through which magnetic flux Φ is changing at the rate $\partial\Phi/\partial t$. Here, the loop electromotive force is defined as

$$\mathcal{E}_{\text{ind}} = \oint \mathbf{E} \cdot d\mathbf{l} \tag{2.33}$$

and the magnetic flux is

$$\Phi = \int\int \mathbf{B} \cdot d\mathbf{a} \tag{2.34}$$

When Stokes' theorem [Eq. (2.24)] is applied to Eq. (2.33) with (2.34), Lenz's law becomes

$$\int\int \nabla \times \mathbf{E} \cdot d\mathbf{a} = -\frac{\partial}{\partial t} \int\int \mathbf{B} \cdot d\mathbf{a}$$

or

$$\int\int \left(\nabla \times \mathbf{E} + \frac{\partial \mathbf{B}}{\partial t} \right) \cdot d\mathbf{a} = 0 \tag{2.35}$$

Since the integral of Eq. (2.35) is equal to zero for every surface of integration, the integrand is zero. Hence

$$\nabla \times \mathbf{E} = -\frac{\partial \mathbf{B}}{\partial t} \tag{2.36}$$

The final one of the set of four fundamental equations of the electromagnetic field may be developed, although in incomplete form, by a generalization of the law of Biot and Savart. The latter law may be written in the form

$$\Delta \mathbf{H} = \frac{I}{4\pi}\frac{\Delta \mathbf{l} \times \hat{\mathbf{r}}}{r^2} \tag{2.37}$$

in which $\Delta \mathbf{H}$ is the increment of the magnetic $\mathbf{H}$ field vector due to a directed line element $\Delta \mathbf{l}$ carrying constant current I, and r is the distance to the point at which the field is observed.[†] If $d\mathbf{l}$ is a segment of an indefinitely long straight wire coinciding with the z axis, the magnetic field at radial distance a from the wire is then

$$\mathbf{H} = \frac{I}{4\pi}\int_{\alpha=0}^{\pi}\frac{d\mathbf{z} \times \hat{\mathbf{r}}}{r^2} = \hat{\mathbf{\theta}}\frac{I}{4\pi}\int_{\alpha=0}^{\pi}\frac{dz \sin \alpha}{r^2} \tag{2.38}$$

where α is the angle between dz and $\hat{\mathbf{r}}$ (Fig. 2.5). The field is readily found to be

$$\mathbf{H} = \hat{\mathbf{\theta}}H_\theta = \hat{\mathbf{\theta}}\frac{I}{2\pi a} \tag{2.39}$$

In (2.39) the field is given as a vector in cylindrical coordinates and is seen to be tangent to circles centered upon the wire and lying in planes perpendicular to it.

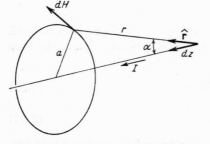

FIG. 2.5. Increment of field $d\mathbf{H}$ due to current element.

If the closed-path line integral $\oint \mathbf{H} \cdot d\mathbf{l}$ is obtained for the above field by measurement or by calculation, its value is found to be equal to I for every closed path which surrounds the wire and equal to zero for every closed path which does not surround the wire. This result is a particular case of a more general law which is true of every static magnetic field in nature: The closed line integral of magnetic $\mathbf{H}$ field is equal to the total current threading the closed path. Hence

$$\oint \mathbf{H} \cdot d\mathbf{l} = \iint \mathbf{J} \cdot d\mathbf{a} \tag{2.40}$$

[†] The magnetic fields $\mathbf{H}$ and $\mathbf{B}$ are connected by the linear relation $\mathbf{B} = \mu\mathbf{H}$, where the permeability μ is a constant in air, vacuum, and most simple media. Cases in which this linear relation must be modified are discussed in Sec. 2.3.

where **J** is the current density in amperes per square meter and the integral on the right is carried over any surface bounded by the path of the line integral.

Stokes' theorem may be applied to the left side of Eq. (2.40), with the result

$$\iint \nabla \times \mathbf{H} \cdot d\mathbf{a} = \iint \mathbf{J} \cdot d\mathbf{a} \tag{2.41}$$

or

$$\iint (\nabla \times \mathbf{H} - \mathbf{J}) \cdot d\mathbf{a} = 0 \tag{2.42}$$

Since the integral of Eq. (2.42) is equal to zero for every surface that may be chosen in a static field, the integrand is zero. Hence

$$\nabla \times \mathbf{H} = \mathbf{J} \tag{2.43}$$

Equation (2.43), resulting from (2.40), holds for all static fields and current distributions, but in situations where the fields and currents vary in time, it fails to hold true in general. A simple instance of this failure occurs in the case of a parallel-plate capacitor, with time-varying current flowing in the connecting leads (Fig. 2.6). If a measurement of the line integral $\oint \mathbf{H} \cdot d\mathbf{l}$ is performed experimentally over a closed path, such as that indicated between the plates (Fig. 2.6) where

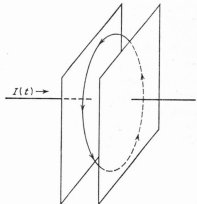

FIG. 2.6. Path of integration between capacitor plates for line integral of magnetic field **H**.

no current density **J** exists, the result is not found to be zero, in conflict with (2.40). This difficulty was resolved by Maxwell, who postulated that a displacement current density term $\epsilon\, \partial \mathbf{E}/\partial t$ should be added to **J** in Eqs. (2.40) to (2.43), to form the complete $\nabla \times \mathbf{H}$ equation

$$\nabla \times \mathbf{H} = \mathbf{J} + \epsilon \frac{\partial \mathbf{E}}{\partial t} \tag{2.44}$$

In Eq. (2.44), ϵ is a constant of the medium. In the present treatment, ϵ is assumed to be isotropic, i.e., independent of the direction of **E**, and constant over the region under consideration. (Exceptions for special media are discussed in Sec. 2.3.)

In summary, the completed set of equations describing the behavior of the electromagnetic field in uniform isotropic media is

$$\nabla \cdot \mathbf{E} = \frac{\rho}{\epsilon} \tag{2.45}$$

$$\nabla \cdot \mathbf{B} = 0 \tag{2.46}$$

$$\nabla \times \mathbf{E} = -\frac{\partial \mathbf{B}}{\partial t} \tag{2.47}$$

$$\nabla \times \mathbf{H} = \mathbf{J} + \epsilon \frac{\partial \mathbf{E}}{\partial t} \tag{2.48}$$

The above equations, usually identified as Maxwell's equations, are first-order partial differential equations describing the behavior of the components of field at coordinate points in space. Like differential equations in general, they are therefore local, or intensive expressions, although they may be converted to extensive expressions by the application of the integral theorems of Stokes and Gauss. Each of the two curl equations represents three scalar equations, since the separate vector components on the left and right may be equated individually. We shall be dealing in the present work with fields that depend harmonically on time, as exp $(j\omega t)$. With this time dependence, the partial differentiation $\partial/\partial t$ is equivalent to multiplication by $j\omega$. Employing this modification, the field equations become

$$\nabla \cdot \mathbf{E} = \frac{\rho}{\epsilon} \tag{2.49}$$

$$\nabla \cdot \mathbf{B} = 0 \tag{2.50}$$

$$\nabla \times \mathbf{E} = -j\omega \mathbf{B} \tag{2.51}$$

$$\nabla \times \mathbf{H} = \mathbf{J} + j\omega\epsilon \mathbf{E} \tag{2.52}$$

2.3. Auxiliary Field Vectors and Material Media

We are familiar with the point of view that the vectors of the electromagnetic field fall into the two physical classifications: vectors which are electrical in character and vectors which are magnetic in character. When the fields under consideration are static in time, an electric field is clearly distinguishable from a magnetic field by tests such as those implied by the two types of forces appearing in the force equation (2.1).† For the rapidly time-varying fields of a microwave transmis-

---

† The theory of special relativity shows that a field which appears to be purely electric in one coordinate system may appear to have both electric and magnetic character in a coordinate system which is in motion with respect to the first. (R. B. Leighton, "Principles of Modern Physics," p. 46, McGraw-Hill Book Company, Inc., New York, 1959, or W. W. Harman, "Fundamentals of Electronic

sion system, however, a purely electrical or a purely magnetic field cannot exist alone. Equations (2.51) and (2.52) show that the existence of electric field implies the simultaneous existence of magnetic field and vice versa. The two fields are complementary aspects of the electromagnetic field.

We have thus far dealt with the electric $\mathbf{E}$ field and the magnetic $\mathbf{B}$ and $\mathbf{H}$ field vectors. Considerable simplification can be effected, however, by the introduction of additional field vectors, particularly in describing the behavior of fields in material media. Thus there are defined the electric displacement $\mathbf{D}$ and polarization $\mathbf{P}$, and the magnetization vector $\mathbf{M}$. In most simple media, the electric vectors can be interrelated by scalar constants of proportionality:

$$\mathbf{D} = \epsilon\mathbf{E} \tag{2.53}$$
$$\mathbf{D} = \epsilon_0\mathbf{E} + \mathbf{P} \tag{2.54}$$
$$\mathbf{P} = \epsilon_0\chi_E\mathbf{E} \tag{2.55}$$
$$\mathbf{D} = \epsilon_r\epsilon_0\mathbf{E} \tag{2.56}$$

whence

$$\epsilon_r = \frac{\epsilon}{\epsilon_0} = 1 + \chi_E \tag{2.57}$$

where $\epsilon_0 \approx 1/(36\pi \times 10^9)$ is the dielectric constant of free space and χ_E is the electric susceptibility of the medium. The electric polarization $\mathbf{P}$ of a dielectric material results from the appearance of induced dipoles or the reorientation of permanent dipoles on the molecular scale in the material.

An additional material constant associated with the electric vector is the conductivity σ, appearing in the Ohm's law relation

$$\mathbf{J} = \sigma\mathbf{E} \tag{2.58}$$

Relations among the magnetic vectors which involve constants of the medium are

$$\mathbf{B} = \mu\mathbf{H} \tag{2.59}$$
$$\mathbf{B} = \mu_0(\mathbf{H} + \mathbf{M}) \tag{2.60}$$
$$\mathbf{M} = \chi_M\mathbf{H} \tag{2.61}$$
$$\mathbf{B} = \mu_r\mu_0\mathbf{H} \tag{2.62}$$

whence

$$\mu_r = \frac{\mu}{\mu_0} = 1 + \chi_M \tag{2.63}$$

Motion," p. 293, McGraw-Hill Book Company, Inc., New York, 1953.) Unless otherwise specified we shall consider currents and charges in a single stationary coordinate system only.

where $\mu_0 = 4\pi/10^7$ is the magnetic permeability of free space and χ_M is the magnetic susceptibility of the medium. The magnetization **M** is proportional to the effective density of magnetic dipoles in the material.

In the analysis of electromagnetic problems in microwave systems, it is frequently sufficient to employ only the four vectors **E, D, B, H** and the two connecting relations

$$\mathbf{D} = \epsilon\mathbf{E}$$
$$\mathbf{B} = \mu\mathbf{H}$$

Materials having finite conductivity σ may be included in the above formulation by the use of an "effective" dielectric constant ϵ_{eff}. The form of the magnetic curl equation (2.52) suggests that we write

$$\begin{aligned}
\nabla \times \mathbf{H} &= (\sigma + j\omega\epsilon)\mathbf{E} \\
&= j\omega\epsilon\left(1 + \frac{\sigma}{j\omega\epsilon}\right)\mathbf{E}
\end{aligned} \tag{2.64}$$

The dielectric behavior of poorly conducting materials is now fully described if the dielectric constant ϵ is replaced by

$$\epsilon_{\text{eff}} = \epsilon\left(1 + \frac{\sigma}{j\omega\epsilon}\right) \tag{2.65}$$

It has been stated that ϵ and μ may be regarded as scalar constants, for many practical materials. Departures from this simple situation may arise in a variety of ways, however. Such exceptions occur in the following situations:

1. Anisotropic media
2. Coordinate-dependent parameters
3. Nonlinear media
4. Complex material parameters

1. *Anisotropic Media.* Anisotropic materials are those in which **D** and **E**, or **B** and **H**, respectively, may be nonparallel. For example, the x component of **D** may have contributions from E_x, E_y, and E_z. Similar dependences may occur for D_y and D_z as well. The equation **D** = ϵ**E** then becomes

$$\begin{aligned}
D_x &= \epsilon_{xx}E_x + \epsilon_{xy}E_y + \epsilon_{xz}E_z \\
D_y &= \epsilon_{yx}E_x + \epsilon_{yy}E_y + \epsilon_{yz}E_z \\
D_z &= \epsilon_{zx}E_x + \epsilon_{zy}E_y + \epsilon_{zz}E_z
\end{aligned} \tag{2.66}$$

Here, the set of nine coefficients ϵ_{ij} forms the matrix of ϵ. The magnetic permeability μ in an anisotropic magnetic material may similarly require a matrix expression. In many cases, the crystalline symmetry of a material reduces the number of independent terms in the matrix of its magnetic or dielectric properties. The permeability matrix for ferrites such as are used in many microwave devices takes the form

$$\mathfrak{y} = \begin{bmatrix} \mu & -j\kappa & 0 \\ j\kappa & \mu & 0 \\ 0 & 0 & \mu_0 \end{bmatrix} \tag{2.67}$$

where the anisotropy expressed by (2.67) is induced in part by the application of a steady magnetic field to the material.

2. *Coordinate-dependent Parameters.* In materials in which the properties of the medium vary with coordinate location, this dependence must be taken into account when the material property is subject to a differential operation. This may occur in the equation $\nabla \cdot \mathbf{D} = \rho$, if the dielectric constant of the material, $\epsilon(x,y,z)$, is a function of coordinates. The divergence equation then takes the form (see Appendix II)

$$\begin{aligned} \nabla \cdot \mathbf{D} &= \nabla \cdot \epsilon \mathbf{E} \\ &= \nabla\epsilon \cdot \mathbf{E} + \epsilon\nabla \cdot \mathbf{E} \end{aligned}$$

Similarly, if the relationship between **B** and **H** is known as $\mathbf{H} = (1/\mu)\mathbf{B}$ and μ is a function of coordinates, we have

$$\nabla \times \mathbf{H} = \nabla \frac{1}{\mu} \times \mathbf{B} + \frac{1}{\mu}\nabla \times \mathbf{B}$$

3. *Nonlinear Media.* If the values of the material parameters μ and ϵ depend on the magnitude of the fields present, the linear relationships previously written no longer hold. A notable case is that of the ferromagnetic materials in which magnetic saturation can occur. The equation connecting **B** and **H** then requires terms in **H** of order higher than the first. Neglecting anisotropy, the relationship between **B** and **H** may be expressed as

$$|B| = \mu_1|H| + \mu_2|H|^2 + \mu_3|H|^3 + \cdots$$

where the coefficients μ_1, μ_2, μ_3, . . . are constants. For most materials, when the alternating components of field are of sufficiently small amplitude, $d\mathbf{B}/d\mathbf{H}$ (or $d\mathbf{D}/d\mathbf{E}$ in the electrical case) may be considered to be constant and equal to the μ (or ϵ) of the material. This is equivalent to the assumption that the saturation curve can be represented by a straight-line segment, in the region of operation. The departure from linearity of the magnetic response of certain magnetic materials at microwave frequencies is significant, under suitable conditions of d-c magnetic field bias, and can be utilized to achieve parametric amplification.†

The electrical conductivity of most homogeneous materials is independent of electric field strength at normal field levels. The current-voltage ratio of a semiconductor diode junction depends strongly, however, upon both the magnitude and sign of the electric field across the junction, as the result of the gradient of material properties which constitutes the junction. This property, essentially a characteristic of the device rather than of its bulk material, may also be used in the construction of microwave parametric amplifiers.‡

In addition to exhibiting a dependence upon field strength, the material parameters of many substances are to some degree functions of frequency. The atmospheric gases, for example, exhibit frequency-dependent absorption of energy at microwave frequencies. Water vapor absorbs energy selectively at a wavelength of 1.34 cm; and oxygen at 0.5 and 0.25 cm. The material parameters of many solids used at microwave frequencies can be considered for practical purposes to be independent of frequency over restricted bandwidths, however.

4. *Complex Material Parameters.* In addition to the foregoing conditions upon the electromagnetic properties of matter, the constants μ and ϵ may also be complex. Thus we may have

$$\epsilon = \epsilon' - j\epsilon'' \qquad (2.68a)$$
$$\mu = \mu' - j\mu'' \qquad (2.68b)$$

The imaginary parts ϵ'' and μ'' of ϵ and μ, respectively, signify the dissipation of energy in materials in the presence of time-varying electric and magnetic fields. These dissipation terms are distinct from the ohmic loss due to flow of free charges and are accompanied by the appearance of phase lags between **P** and **E**, or between **M** and **H**, respectively. These lags often arise from the interaction of atomic thermal vibrations with the dipole polarization in the substances in question.

2.4. Boundary Conditions for Electromagnetic Fields

Important applications of the effect of material media upon the field vectors occur in the set of relations connecting the components of

---

† Cf. Sec. 8.8.

‡ Small departures from Ohm's law may actually be observed in semiconductors germanium and silicon, however. The conductivity of the material may depend quadratically on E as $\sigma = \sigma_0(1 - \beta E^2)$, where $\beta \ll 1$. (See M. A. C. S. Brown, *J. Phys. Chem. Solids*, vol. 19, p. 218, May, 1961.)

field on two sides of an interface separating different media. These relations are of particular importance since they often designate the particular solutions of the field equations which are applicable within given boundary configurations.

The derivation of the boundary relations will be obtained here by the use of Maxwell's equations in the boundary region.

Normal Components of the Fields at an Interface between Two Media. Consider a small, flat volume element ΔV lying in the boundary separating medium 1 and medium 2, which have material constants ϵ_1 and ϵ_2, and μ_1 and μ_2, respectively. The volume ΔV extends into both media on the two sides of the boundary. It is assumed that δ, the dimension of ΔV normal to the boundary, is very much smaller than the length of the sides parallel to the boundary, as indicated in Fig. 2.7. Let the surface integral of the normal **D** field be calculated over the volume element, and then apply Gauss' theorem to the resulting integral

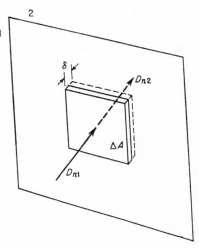

FIG. 2.7. Volume element for calculation of normal flux of **D** vector at an interface between two media.

$$\iint \mathbf{D} \cdot d\mathbf{a} = \iiint \boldsymbol{\nabla} \cdot \mathbf{D} \, d\tau \qquad (2.69)$$

By Maxwell's equations, $\boldsymbol{\nabla} \cdot \mathbf{D} = \rho$, and hence

$$\iint \mathbf{D} \cdot d\mathbf{a} = \iiint \rho \, d\tau \qquad (2.70)$$

If ΔA is sufficiently small, the normal **D** field and the surface charge density σ at the boundary are essentially constant over ΔA. Equation (2.70) then becomes

$$-D_{n1} \Delta A + D_{n2} \Delta A = \rho \, \Delta V = \sigma \, \Delta A \qquad (2.71)$$

where σ is defined as the surface density of free charge in ΔA. In Eq. (2.71), the contribution to the integral from the sides of ΔV having width δ has been neglected, since it is assumed that δ can be made vanishingly small. Consequently, for the normal **D** field at an interface,

$$D_{n2} - D_{n1} = \sigma \qquad (2.72)$$

The corresponding equation for the E field is

$$\epsilon_2 E_{n2} - \epsilon_1 E_{n1} = \sigma \qquad (2.73)$$

A similar calculation may be performed for the normal component of the magnetic B field, but since no magnetic charge exists, the equation corresponding to Eq. (2.71) is

$$B_{n2} \Delta A - B_{n1} \Delta A = 0$$

or

$$B_{n1} = B_{n2} \qquad (2.74)$$

and

$$\mu_1 H_{n1} = \mu_2 H_{n2}$$

Tangential Components of the Fields at an Interface between Two Media. The relation connecting the tangential components of field at an interface may also be obtained by the use of Maxwell's equations in integral form. For this purpose a loop path of integration is established, as indicated in Fig. 2.8. Two sides of length Δl of the loop lie on the two opposite sides of the interface. The connecting loop sides normal to the interface are of length δ. It is assumed that $\delta \ll \Delta l$. Now the line integral of electric **E** field is evaluated around the loop, and Stokes' theorem applied to the result:

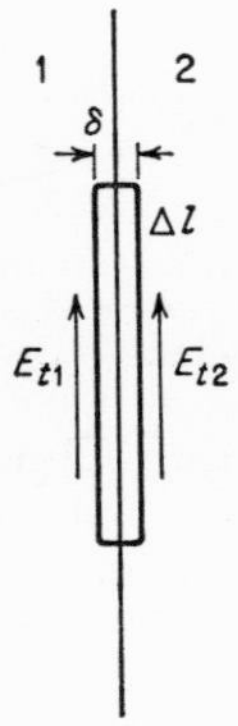

$$\oint \mathbf{E} \cdot d\mathbf{l} = \iint \mathbf{\nabla} \times \mathbf{E} \cdot d\mathbf{a} \qquad (2.75)$$

It is assumed that δ can be made small enough so that the contributions to the path integral from the sides of length δ are negligible, leaving

FIG. 2.8. Path of integration for tangential components of field at an interface.

$$E_{t1} \Delta l - E_{t2} \Delta l = - \frac{\partial B_\nu}{\partial t} \Delta l \delta \qquad (2.76)$$

In Eq. (2.76), $|\mathbf{\nabla} \times \mathbf{E}|$ has been replaced by $-(\partial B_\nu/\partial t)$, by the use of Eq. (2.36). B_ν is the component of B field normal to the surface surrounded by the loop. By choosing δ small, the term on the right of (2.76) can be made arbitrarily small, leaving

$$E_{t1} = E_{t2} \qquad (2.77)$$

The corresponding expression for the D field is

$$\frac{1}{\epsilon_1} D_{t1} = \frac{1}{\epsilon_2} D_{t2} \qquad (2.78)$$

Finally, the relations for the tangential components of magnetic field at an interface are found by the use of a loop path of integration similar to that used above. When Eq. (2.44) is used for $\nabla \times \mathbf{H}$, the $\mathbf{H}$ field equation corresponding to Eq. (2.76) is found to be

$$H_{t1}\, \Delta l - H_{t2}\, \Delta l = \left(J_\nu + \frac{\partial D_\nu}{\partial t}\right) \Delta l \delta \qquad (2.79)$$

In practice, the first term on the right side of Eq. (2.79) is different in character from the second. For some materials (specifically, for the good conductors), the current density in an extremely thin layer at the surface can reach such high values that the product $J_\nu \delta$ remains very large compared to $\delta\, \partial D_\nu / \partial t$ as δ is decreased, and $J_\nu \delta$ cannot be neglected.† The product is retained therefore, and defined as

$$K_\nu = J_\nu \delta$$

where K_ν is the surface-current component normal to the tangential H fields, in amperes per meter of linear width of surface. Equation (2.79) then becomes

$$H_{t1} - H_{t2} = K_\nu \qquad (2.80)$$

or, if we define $\Delta\mathbf{H}_t = \mathbf{H}_{t1} - \mathbf{H}_{t2}$, and defining also surface-current vector $\mathbf{K}$, we have

$$\hat{\mathbf{n}} \times \Delta\mathbf{H}_t = \mathbf{K} \qquad (2.80a)$$

where $\hat{\mathbf{n}}$ is the unit vector normal to the surface upon which $\mathbf{K}$ flows. The tangential $\mathbf{B}$ field expression corresponding to Eq. (2.80) is

$$\frac{1}{\mu_1} B_{t1} - \frac{1}{\mu_2} B_{t2} = K_\nu \qquad (2.81)$$

A summary of the relations connecting normal and tangential components of the electromagnetic fields on the two sides of an interface between medium 1 and medium 2 is given in Table 2.1.

Table 2.1. General Boundary Conditions on Fields at an Interface between Two Media

Normal components	Tangential components
$D_{n1} = D_{n2} - \sigma$	$\epsilon_2 D_{t1} = \epsilon_1 D_{t2}$
$\epsilon_1 E_{n1} = \epsilon_2 E_{n2} - \sigma$	$E_{t1} = E_{t2}$
$B_{n1} = B_{n2}$	$\dfrac{1}{\mu_1} B_{t1} = \dfrac{1}{\mu_2} B_{t2} + K_\nu$
$\mu_1 H_{n1} = \mu_2 H_{n2}$	$H_{t1} = H_{t2} + K_\nu$

† The quantity δ may be associated with the skin depth, or effective depth of penetration of fields and current into the conductor. The skin depth is shown in Sec. 3.9 to be equal to $(\pi f \mu \sigma)^{-\frac{1}{2}}$ and thus decreases with increasing frequency. For copper at a frequency of 10^{10} cps, it is approximately equal to 6×10^{-5} cm.

The general boundary relations assume useful special forms when one of the media at the interface is a good conductor and the other is air or vacuum. This may be the situation corresponding to the interior surface of a waveguide, for example. The boundary restrictions on the fields which may exist in the guide are determining factors in the selection of the permissible solutions of the field equations in waveguides.

An ideal conductor is defined as a material within which no electric field and no time-varying magnetic field can exist. Consequently, at the surface of an ideal conductor in a vacuum, the field components have the forms indicated in Table 2.2.

TABLE 2.2. BOUNDARY CONDITIONS ON TIME-VARYING FIELDS AT THE SURFACE OF AN IDEAL CONDUCTOR IN AIR OR VACUUM

Normal components	Tangential components
$D_n = \sigma$	$D_t = 0$
$\epsilon_0 E_n = \sigma$	$E_t = 0$
$B_n = 0$	$B_t = \mu_0 K_\nu$
$H_n = 0$	$H_t = K_\nu$

As may be seen in Table 2.2, there is a unique correspondence between the fields at the surface of a conductor in air or vacuum and the surface charges and currents on the conductor. When the fields at the surface are known, the charge densities and currents follow from them, or when the surface currents and charge densities are known, the fields at the surface are determined by them. These facts are of considerable practical value in the analysis of microwave-device behavior. For example, when the electromagnetic fields within a microwave device have been determined, the surface currents which correspond to the tangential magnetic fields at the walls are known and may be used for the calculation of power lost by dissipation on the enclosing surfaces.

2.5. Energy and the Poynting Vector

The concept of an energy function simplifies the analysis of many physical problems. The fact that energy is conserved in most practical processes, whether as heat, as electromagnetic energy, or in some other definable form, furnishes a useful constant of the problem for the calculation of the outcome of a given process. We shall therefore require an analytical expression for the energy of the electromagnetic fields existing in a microwave system. It turns out that the same field energy-density functions which are defined in static electricity and magnetism are suitable for application in the rapidly time-varying microwave case. We recall below the origin of these two energy-density expressions, both based upon the definition of energy in terms of equivalent mechanical work.

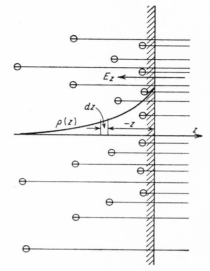

The force acting upon each element of area of a charged conductor can be found by the use of a model in which the surface charge at any point is assumed to be distributed in an extremely thin layer immediately under the surface, with a volume density distribution $\rho(z)$, where z is the coordinate normal to the surface (Fig. 2.9). Over any element of surface area ΔA, the electric field $E(z)$ is considered to be essentially uniform and normal to the surface. The charge contained in a layer between $-z$ and $-(z + dz)$ is equal to $\rho(z)\, dz\, \Delta A$, and the

FIG. 2.9. Charge density distribution at conducting surface.

force acting upon this charge is $d(\Delta F) = E(z)\rho(z)\, dz\, \Delta A$. Maxwell's divergence equation (2.30) in this one-dimensional problem becomes

$$\rho = \epsilon_0 \nabla \cdot \mathbf{E} = \epsilon_0 \frac{\partial E_z}{\partial z}$$

Hence

$$d(\Delta F) = \epsilon_0 E(z) \frac{\partial E_z}{\partial z} \, dz \, \Delta A$$

$$f = \int_0^f d\left(\frac{\Delta F}{\Delta A}\right) = \frac{\epsilon_0}{2} \int_0^{E_z(0)} d[E_z(z)]^2$$

where f is defined as the force per unit surface area and $E_z(0)$ is the normal field at the surface of the conductor. At large negative z within the conductor, $E_z = 0$, whence we obtain the lower limit on the right. Therefore, $f = \epsilon_0 E_z{}^2(0)/2$. If now we consider a charged parallel-plate capacitor, assumed to have a uniform field E_z between plates, the total force acting upon each plate is $A\epsilon_0 E_z{}^2/2$, where A is the area of the plates. If one plate is allowed to move an infinitesimal distance dz toward the other under this force, with the charge on the plates being held constant, the work done by the capacitor is

$$dW = F_z \, dz = A\epsilon_0 E_z{}^2 \frac{dz}{2}$$

The expenditure of this work is accompanied by the reduction of the volume occupied by the fields between plates by an amount $dv = A \, dz$.

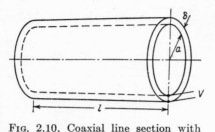

The interpretation placed upon the foregoing fact is that there is a volume density of electric energy associated with the field

$$W_E = \frac{dW}{dv} = \frac{\epsilon_0 E^2}{2} \quad (2.82)$$

FIG. 2.10. Coaxial line section with shorted termination.

For the magnetic energy density, we consider a section of coaxial line of length l, having inner and outer radii equal to a and $a + \delta$, where $\delta \ll a$ (Fig. 2.10). The coaxial section is terminated in a short circuit and carries current I.

If the current varies in time so as to cause a voltage V to appear at the terminals of the line, the work necessary to carry an element of charge $-dq$ through the line section is $-V \, dq$. The rate at which work is done to cause passage of a current $I = dq/dt$ is therefore

$$\frac{dW}{dt} = -VI \quad (2.83)$$

By Lenz's law, the voltage V is equal to the rate of change of flux through the closed loop of coaxial line

$$V = -\frac{d\Phi}{dt} = -\frac{d}{dt} \mu H A \quad (2.84)$$

where $A = l\delta$ is the area threaded by the flux in the line.

The magnetic field between conductors is essentially constant and equal to $H = I/2\pi a$. Using this relation and (2.84) in Eq. (2.83), the result is found to be

$$\frac{dW}{dt} = \mu A 2\pi a H \frac{dH}{dt}$$

$$= \upsilon \frac{\mu}{2} \frac{dH^2}{dt} \quad (2.85)$$

where $\upsilon = 2\pi a A$ is the volume between conductors which is occupied by the field. The form of (2.85) leads to the definition of a volume density of the energy of the magnetic field

$$W_M = \frac{\mu H^2}{2} \tag{2.86}$$

When the energy-density definitions of Eqs. (2.82) and (2.86) are applied to fields of arbitrarily high frequency, they furnish a consistent description of the disposition of energy for all cases of interest in microwave system analysis. They are also coherent with the definition of an energy-transport vector, the Poynting vector

$$\mathbf{S} = \mathbf{E} \times \mathbf{H} \tag{2.87}$$

In practice, the meaningful application of the Poynting vector is in the calculation of the total flux of $\mathbf{S}$ through a closed surface of integration

$$\iint_\Sigma \mathbf{S} \cdot d\mathbf{a} = \iiint_V \boldsymbol{\nabla} \cdot \mathbf{S}\, d\tau \tag{2.88}$$

where $d\mathbf{a}$ is an element of area on the surface Σ enclosing volume V and Gauss' theorem has been applied on the right. By the use of a vector identity for $\boldsymbol{\nabla} \cdot (\mathbf{E} \times \mathbf{H})$, Eq. (2.88) becomes

$$\iint \mathbf{S} \cdot d\mathbf{a} = -\iiint \mathbf{E} \cdot \boldsymbol{\nabla} \times \mathbf{H}\, d\tau + \iiint \mathbf{H} \cdot \boldsymbol{\nabla} \times \mathbf{E}\, d\tau \tag{2.89}$$

By the application of Maxwell's equations (2.47) and (2.48),

$$\iint \mathbf{S} \cdot d\mathbf{a} = -\iiint \sigma \mathbf{E} \cdot \mathbf{E}\, d\tau - \iiint \mathbf{E} \cdot \epsilon \frac{\partial \mathbf{E}}{\partial t}\, d\tau$$
$$- \iiint \mathbf{H} \cdot \mu \frac{\partial \mathbf{H}}{\partial t}\, d\tau \tag{2.90}$$

By the use of Eqs. (2.82) and (2.86), this becomes

$$\iint \mathbf{S} \cdot d\mathbf{a} = -\iiint P_d\, d\tau - \frac{\partial}{\partial t} \iiint (W_E + W_M)\, d\tau \tag{2.91}$$

where P_d is the volume rate of dissipation of energy as ohmic loss in the medium, and the entire right side of Eq. (2.91) may be interpreted as the rate of disappearance of electromagnetic field energy from volume V.

Although the Poynting vector is in a strict sense applicable only in an integration over a closed surface, the calculation of the flux of $\mathbf{S}$ through a nonclosed section of surface area is frequently used as a measure of the flux of electromagnetic energy through the surface.

Fortunately, in most microwave systems, a calculation of the integral

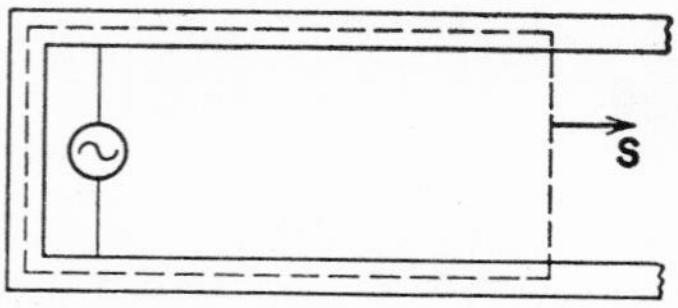

FIG. 2.11. Poynting surface for waveguide system.

of the Poynting-vector flux over the transverse cross section of a waveguide gives a valid measure of the power flowing in the waveguide. The remaining closed surface of integration may be completed, at least in principle, within the conducting material of the guiding system, where the fields are zero and no other contribution to the Poynting integral is obtained (see Fig. 2.11).

A useful form of the Poynting vector for calculation with time-varying fields is the complex Poynting vector

$$\mathbf{S} = \tfrac{1}{2}\mathbf{E} \times \mathbf{H}^* \tag{2.92}$$

By a procedure like that followed above, it may be shown that

$$\mathrm{Re}\,(\tfrac{1}{2}\iint \mathbf{E} \times \mathbf{H}^* \cdot d\mathbf{a}) = \iiint |P_d|\, d\tau \tag{2.93}$$

Thus, the real part of the surface integral of the complex Poynting vector is equal to the average rate of power flow through the surface.

PROBLEMS

2.1. A particle of charge q is projected with velocity v_0 in the z direction, in a region where the electric and magnetic fields are

$$\mathbf{E} = \hat{\mathbf{y}}E_1 e^{j(\omega t - \beta z)}$$
$$\mathbf{B} = \hat{\mathbf{x}}\frac{E_1}{c}\, e^{j(\omega t - \beta z)}$$

where c is the velocity of light.

Assuming that E_1 is small enough so that the particle departs by a negligible amount from its initial path, calculate the force on the particle. Can the velocity be chosen so as to reduce this force to zero? Explain.

2.2. The electric and magnetic fields about a long straight wire bearing a static line charge and carrying direct current are $\mathbf{E} = \hat{\mathbf{r}}(E_0/r)$ and $\mathbf{H} = \hat{\boldsymbol{\theta}}(H_0/r)$, respectively, where E_0 and H_0 are constants.

(a) Show that in the harmonically time-varying case, the field components $\hat{\mathbf{r}}(E_1/r) \exp{(j\omega t)}$ and $\hat{\boldsymbol{\theta}}(H_1/r) \exp{(j\omega t)}$ are not allowable solutions for the fields about the wire.

(b) Show that $\hat{\mathbf{r}}(E_1/r) \exp{[j(\omega t - \beta z)]}$ and $\hat{\boldsymbol{\theta}}(H_1/r) \exp{[j(\omega t - \beta z)]}$ are possible solutions for the fields. What value of the ratio E_1/H_1 is required for the solution?

2.3. In an electromagnetic field having the components

$$\mathbf{E} = \hat{\mathbf{y}}E_1 e^{j(\omega t - \beta z)}$$
$$\mathbf{B} = \hat{\mathbf{x}}\frac{E_1}{c}\, e^{j(\omega t - \beta z)}$$

where c is the velocity of light, prove that

(a) $\mathbf{E} \cdot \mathbf{B} = 0$

(b) $\rho = 0$, where ρ is the density of free charge

(c) $(\boldsymbol{\nabla} \times \mathbf{E})/(-\partial \mathbf{B}/\partial t) = 1$

(d) $\mathrm{Re} \displaystyle\iint_{\Sigma} (\mathbf{E} \times \mathbf{H}^*) \cdot d\mathbf{a} = 0$ where the integral is carried over the surface Σ

of a unit cube having its edges aligned parallel with the rectangular x, y, z axes

2.4. Show by direct differentiation that a vector derivable from a potential V has zero curl.

2.5. Transform the two-dimensional Laplacian

$$\nabla_t^2 f = \frac{\partial^2 f}{\partial x^2} + \frac{\partial^2 f}{\partial y^2}$$

to polar coordinates r and θ, using $\partial f/\partial x = (\partial f/\partial r)(\partial r/\partial x) + (\partial f/\partial \theta)(\partial \theta/\partial x);\ \ldots$ etc., where $r = (x^2 + y^2)^{\frac{1}{2}}$, and $\theta = \tan^{-1}(y/x)$.

2.6. (a) The magnetic field in a given region is $\mathbf{H} = (\hat{\mathbf{x}}ay - \hat{\mathbf{y}}ax) \exp(j\omega t)$. What is the current density in this region?

(b) The electric field in an electron accelerator is $\mathbf{E} = \hat{\theta}E_0 r^{-n} \exp(j\omega t)$, where r and θ are plane polar coordinates. What is the rate of change of the magnetic field in the region where this electric field exists?

2.7. The electric field between two parallel conducting planes of infinite extent which are normal to the z axis is $\mathbf{E} = \hat{\mathbf{z}} \exp[j(\omega t - k_x x - k_y y)]$. Find

(a) Surface-charge density on the conducting planes

(b) Direction and magnitude of the surface current on the planes

(c) Electric and magnetic energy densities in the region between plates

(d) Direction and magnitude of the Poynting vector between the planes

2.8. Find the tangential and normal components of the $\mathbf{E}$ and $\mathbf{D}$ fields on both sides of the interface between two materials having relative dielectric constants $\epsilon_{r1} = 2.0$ and $\epsilon_{r2} = 3.5$, when the electric $\mathbf{E}$ field in medium 1 is inclined at $45°$ with respect to the interface normal and has strength of 10^3 volts/m.

2.9. A closely wound helical coil, such as is used in traveling-wave-tube structures, can be represented electrically as a cylindrical surface having conductivity in one direction only, parallel to the windings. Consider the comparable two-dimensional case of a plane surface, perpendicular to the z axis, having ideal conductivity in the direction of the x axis and zero conductivity in the y direction. (This result might be accomplished by constructing a planar grid of parallel insulated wires.) Write the boundary conditions connecting E_x, E_y, H_x, and H_y at the surface, above and below the plane, if the surface may carry an effective sheet current K_x.

2.10. A long straight wire coinciding with the z axis carries current

$$I = I_0 \cos(\omega t - \beta z)$$

A long narrow rectangular loop of wire of length L lies in the xz plane, having its corners at coordinates (x,z) equal to $(1.0,0)$, $(1.0L)$, $(1.01,0)$, $(1.01,L)$. All dimensions are in meters, and $\omega = 10^6 \text{ sec}^{-1}$.

(a) Calculate the voltage induced in the loop.

(b) Show that if $L = 2\pi/\beta$ the induced voltage is zero.

CHAPTER 3

The Wave Equation and Its Solution
in Waveguides

Classical electromagnetic theory is unique among the sciences in having available a particularly compact and complete mathematical expression of the physical content of the science. Maxwell's equations provide a starting point for the solution of most problems concerning the behavior of electromagnetic fields. A typical requirement in the analysis of a microwave system is that of finding an analytic expression for one or all components of the electromagnetic fields in the system. Three key considerations will govern the procedure by which the desired solution is sought:

1. The coordinate system chosen should be appropriate to the form of the boundary structure.

2. The field components found must be simultaneously solutions of Maxwell's equations.

3. The solutions must satisfy boundary conditions at the surfaces of the boundary structure.

In the form in which they have been obtained, Maxwell's equations (2.49) to (2.52) are not suited to direct solution for the six unknown functions E_x, E_y, E_z, B_x, B_y, and B_z, since each equation contains three of the dependent variables and differentiation by two or more of the independent variables. We can eliminate this difficulty by combining Maxwell's equations to form equations in each of the dependent variables separately. We shall further find that by taking advantage of the systematic character of the solutions which represent propagating waves of particular types, it is not necessary to explicitly solve the equations for each of the six components, but that we need find only one component, and the remaining components are available from it by differential operation. This procedure is demonstrated first in rectangular coordinates for the hollow rectangular waveguide.

48

3.1. Wave Equation in Rectangular Coordinates

The two curl equations of the fields are

$$\nabla \times \mathbf{E} = -j\omega\mathbf{B} \qquad (3.1)$$
$$\nabla \times \mathbf{H} = j\omega\epsilon\mathbf{E} \qquad (3.2)$$

The conduction current term has been omitted from the $\nabla \times \mathbf{H}$ equation, since the fields being sought will usually be those within waveguides which are filled with dielectric media having negligible conductivity. After the solution has thus been found, the effects of finite conductivity can be reintroduced into the result by the replacement of ϵ with ϵ_{eff}, as given by Eq. (2.65).† Applying the curl operation to both sides of Eq. (3.1) and substituting into the result from Eq. (3.2), we obtain

$$\nabla \times \nabla \times \mathbf{E} = \mu\epsilon\omega^2\mathbf{E} \qquad (3.3)$$

By the use of the vector identity

$$\nabla \times \nabla \times \mathbf{E} = -\nabla^2\mathbf{E} + \nabla(\nabla \cdot \mathbf{E})$$

Eq. (3.3) becomes

$$\nabla^2\mathbf{E} = \nabla(\nabla \cdot \mathbf{E}) - \mu\epsilon\omega^2\mathbf{E} \qquad (3.4)$$

From Maxwell's equation (2.49), $\nabla \cdot \mathbf{E} = \rho/\epsilon$. We shall ordinarily be dealing with fields in regions where the density of free charge ρ is zero or negligible, and hence we take $\nabla \cdot \mathbf{E} = 0$ in Eq. (3.4)

$$\nabla^2\mathbf{E} = -\mu\epsilon\omega^2\mathbf{E} \qquad (3.5)$$

The vector Laplacian operator ∇^2 has the particularly simple form in rectangular coordinates

$$\nabla^2\mathbf{E} = \hat{\mathbf{x}}\nabla^2E_x + \hat{\mathbf{y}}\nabla^2E_y + \hat{\mathbf{z}}\nabla^2E_z$$

By using this identity in Eq. (3.5) and equating separate components on both sides of the resulting equation, we obtain

$$\nabla^2E_x = -\mu\epsilon\omega^2E_x \qquad (3.6)$$
$$\nabla^2E_y = -\mu\epsilon\omega^2E_y \qquad (3.7)$$
$$\nabla^2E_z = -\mu\epsilon\omega^2E_z \qquad (3.8)$$

We may show, by a procedure similar to that used above, starting with the application of the curl operation to Eq. (3.2) and using the

† In treating problems which specifically involve the interaction of electromagnetic waves with ionized gases, or with an electron beam of appreciable density, the current term cannot be neglected, and the problem must be formulated accordingly.

fact that $\nabla \cdot \mathbf{H} = 0$ at all times, a similar set of equations holds for the three components of the magnetic field:

$$\nabla^2 H_x = -\mu\epsilon\omega^2 H_x \tag{3.9}$$

$$\nabla^2 H_y = -\mu\epsilon\omega^2 H_y \tag{3.10}$$

$$\nabla^2 H_z = -\mu\epsilon\omega^2 H_z \tag{3.11}$$

By the use of the relation $\mathbf{D} = \epsilon\mathbf{E}$ in Eqs. (3.6) to (3.8) and $\mathbf{B} = \mu\mathbf{H}$ in Eqs. (3.9) to (3.11), where ϵ and μ are constants, we see that the three components of $\mathbf{D}$ and $\mathbf{B}$ each satisfy wave equations of the same form as $\mathbf{E}$ and $\mathbf{H}$. Consequently, there results a total of twelve equations identical in form, for the x, y, and z components of $\mathbf{E}$, $\mathbf{D}$, $\mathbf{B}$, and $\mathbf{H}$. Since the equations are identical, they will all have identical sets of solutions. We know, however, that the field vectors are physically different quantities, and we will therefore not expect them all to behave exactly alike. The distinction between their correct solutions arises when the various vectors are required to satisfy their respective boundary conditions. Application of the boundary conditions requires that, in general, different solutions be selected from among the complete set of solutions available for the wave equation in the given coordinate system, for the physically different vectors.

As an example of the procedure used in finding solutions for the wave equations of the field components, consider Eq. (3.7) for E_y. The component E_y will in general be a function of all three space coordinates. (Its time dependence, the factor $e^{j\omega t}$, has already been accounted for by the insertion of $j\omega$ for the operator $\partial/\partial t$.) Writing out the Laplacian in full, Eq. (3.7) becomes

$$\frac{\partial^2 E_y}{\partial x^2} + \frac{\partial^2 E_y}{\partial y^2} + \frac{\partial^2 E_y}{\partial z^2} = -\mu\epsilon\omega^2 E_y \tag{3.12}$$

We may now assume a product solution for $E_y(x,y,z)$ in the form of the product of a function of x alone, a function of y alone, and a function of z alone:

$$E_y(x,y,z) = X(x)Y(y)Z(z) \tag{3.13}$$

Substituting the assumed solution into (3.12) we find

$$X''YZ + XY''Z + XYZ'' = -\mu\epsilon\omega^2 XYZ \tag{3.14}$$

where each prime indicates differentiation of a function with respect to its own independent variable. Dividing (3.14) by XYZ, there results

$$\frac{X''}{X} + \frac{Y''}{Y} + \frac{Z''}{Z} = -\mu\epsilon\omega^2 \tag{3.15}$$

Inspection of the left side of (3.15) shows that it consists of the sum of a function of x alone, a function of y alone, and a function of z alone. These three functions add to the constant $-\mu\epsilon\omega^2$. Therefore, since x, y, and z are independent variables, the equation can be true only if each function is separately equal to a constant. Assigning the values $k_x{}^2$, $k_y{}^2$, and $k_z{}^2$ to these constants, we obtain

$$\frac{X''}{X} = k_x{}^2 \tag{3.16}$$

$$\frac{Y''}{Y} = k_y{}^2 \tag{3.17}$$

$$\frac{Z''}{Z} = k_z{}^2 \tag{3.18}$$

Therefore

$$k_x{}^2 + k_y{}^2 + k_z{}^2 = -k^2 \tag{3.19}$$

where we have defined

$$\mu\epsilon\omega^2 = k^2 \tag{3.20}$$

For convenience, let the constant $-k_c{}^2$ be defined as

$$-k_c{}^2 = k_x{}^2 + k_y{}^2 \tag{3.21}$$

Then, from (3.19),

$$k_z = \pm \sqrt{k_c{}^2 - k^2} \tag{3.22}$$

Here it may be noted that if $k^2 > k_c{}^2$, k_z is imaginary, and we have

$$k_z = \pm j \sqrt{k^2 - k_c{}^2} \tag{3.23}$$

We define the radical on the right in (3.23) to be the guide propagation constant β_g:

$$\beta_g = \sqrt{k^2 - k_c{}^2} \tag{3.24}$$

With $k_z = \pm j\beta_g$, the solution of Eq. (3.18) for the z-dependent factor of E_y is

$$Z(z) = e^{\pm j\beta_g z} \tag{3.25}$$

Using this result, and writing in the explicit time dependence, the solution for E_y becomes

$$E_y(x,y,z)e^{j\omega t} = X(x)Y(y)e^{j(\omega t \pm \beta_g z)} \tag{3.26}$$

The form of the result now resembles that of the traveling waves of voltage and current on a transmission line, where the z direction is parallel to the axis of the transmission line. The negative sign in (3.26) implies a forward-traveling wave, and the positive sign, a backward-traveling wave. The field solutions of interest to us in waveguide propagation have this wavelike character, and we see that they exist for frequencies high enough so that $\mu\epsilon\omega^2 > k_c{}^2$. For angular frequencies below $\omega = k_c/\sqrt{\mu\epsilon}$, the factor $e^{\pm k_z z}$ is a real attenuation factor, and waves do not propagate along the guide. For this reason we define the cutoff frequency

$$\omega_c = \frac{k_c}{\sqrt{\mu\epsilon}} \qquad (3.27)$$

separating domains of propagation and attenuation. Defining the cutoff wavelength λ_c to be equal to $2\pi/k_c$, Eq. (3.22) may be placed into the convenient form

$$\frac{1}{\lambda_c{}^2} + \frac{1}{\lambda_g{}^2} = \frac{1}{\lambda^2} \qquad (3.28)$$

where we have written $\lambda_g = 2\pi/\beta_g$, the wavelength of the waves traveling along the guide, and $\lambda = 2\pi/k$, the wavelength of free-space waves in the medium filling the guide. (The velocity of light in the medium is $c = 1/\sqrt{\mu\epsilon}$.)

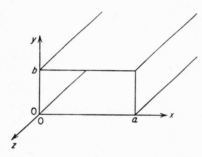

There remains the task of finding the function $X(x)Y(y)$ which delineates the cross-sectional distribution of E_y in the guide. We seek solutions in a rectangular waveguide of width a and height b, and choose coordinates as indicated in Fig. 3.1. The functions $X(x)$ and $Y(y)$ are separately solutions of Eqs. (3.16) and (3.17), respectively.

FIG. 3.1. Coordinates for rectangular waveguide.

These are second-order differential equations, and hence each must have two independent solutions for given values of the constants k. Suitable solutions are sine and cosine functions of x and y, which we may write in the form of the linear combinations

$$X = A \sin jk_x x + B \cos jk_x x \qquad (3.29)$$
$$Y = C \sin jk_y y + D \cos jk_y y \qquad (3.30)$$

The waveguide is assumed to be constructed of ideally conducting material, and hence no tangential electric field can exist at the waveguide walls. For this reason, E_y must vanish at $x = 0$ and $x = a$, where it is tangent to the boundary surface. This condition can be satisfied by taking $jk_x = n\pi/a$ and $B = 0$, in Eq. (3.29). The simplest assumption concerning the y dependence of E_y is that $Y(y)$ is a constant, so we set k_y equal to zero. With these conditions, Eq. (3.26) becomes

$$E_{yn}(x,y,z)e^{j\omega t} = E_{0n} \sin \frac{n\pi x}{a} e^{j(\omega t \pm \beta_g z)} \tag{3.31}$$

where E_{0n} is an amplitude factor. Using Eq. (3.21) we see that $k_c^2 = n^2\pi^2/a^2$, and consequently the propagation constant of the wave is

$$\beta_g = \sqrt{k^2 - \frac{n^2\pi^2}{a^2}} \tag{3.32}$$

There will be one solution of the form of (3.31) for each value of the integer n. The general solution of the wave equation for E_y will hence be a linear combination of all the available solutions:

$$E_y = \sum_{n=1}^{\infty} E_{yn} \tag{3.33}$$

Fortunately, it is usually not necessary to employ this solution in the form of an infinite series, since waveguides are normally operated in a single mode, corresponding, in this case, to the single pair of indices n and 0. The single-mode solution, Eq. (3.31), which we have just found, corresponds to the transverse electric TE_{n0} mode.

In finding solutions for the remaining components of the electromagnetic field in rectangular waveguides, we might proceed as we have just done for E_y: making a selection from the available solutions of the wave equation and evaluating constants so as to satisfy the requisite boundary conditions. We would find difficulty, however, in grouping the solutions for the various components of field into sets that are simultaneously solutions of Maxwell's equations. It is easy, for example, to find solutions for E_y, as we have done above, but we do not yet know which one of the many possible solutions for other components, such as E_z or H_z, corresponds to the same physical situation in the waveguide as does a given one of the functions E_{yn}.

We can eliminate this indeterminacy in selecting compatible sets of solutions for the field components and shorten the task of repeatedly solving the wave equation, by taking advantage of relations which exist among field components of waves belonging to various classifications, or modes. The modal classes are:

1. Transverse electric (TE) modes, in which $E_z = 0$ and the electric field lies in planes normal to the axis of the waveguide.

2. Transverse magnetic (TM) modes, in which $H_z = 0$ and the magnetic field is normal to the axis.

3. Transverse electromagnetic (TEM) mode, in which $E_z = 0 = H_z$. This mode cannot propagate in hollow waveguides, but is an important mode of propagation in two-conductor systems.

3.2. TE Modes in Rectangular Coordinates

The relations between TE-mode field components in rectangular coordinates may be readily derived from the field equations in the special form which they assume when describing waves propagating in the z direction, with E_z equal to zero. These fields have z and time dependence given by $\exp(j\omega t + k_z z)$, where k_z represents $\pm j\beta_g$. In this form, the differentiation $\partial/\partial z$ is equivalent to multiplication by k_z, and $\partial/\partial t$ equivalent to $j\omega$.

In rectangular coordinates, Maxwell's equations $\nabla \times \mathbf{E} = -j\omega\mathbf{B}$ and $\nabla \times \mathbf{H} = j\omega\epsilon\mathbf{E}$ are

$$\frac{\partial E_z}{\partial y} - \frac{\partial E_y}{\partial z} = -j\omega\mu H_x \qquad \frac{\partial H_z}{\partial y} - \frac{\partial H_y}{\partial z} = j\omega\epsilon E_x$$

$$\frac{\partial E_x}{\partial z} - \frac{\partial E_z}{\partial x} = -j\omega\mu H_y \qquad \frac{\partial H_x}{\partial z} - \frac{\partial H_z}{\partial x} = j\omega\epsilon E_y$$

$$\frac{\partial E_y}{\partial x} - \frac{\partial E_x}{\partial y} = -j\omega\mu H_z \qquad \frac{\partial H_y}{\partial x} - \frac{\partial H_x}{\partial y} = j\omega\epsilon E_z$$

With the substitutions $\partial/\partial z = k_z$ and $E_z = 0$, the equations take the form

$$-k_z E_y = -j\omega\mu H_x \qquad \frac{\partial H_z}{\partial y} - k_z H_y = j\omega\epsilon E_x$$

$$k_z E_x = -j\omega\mu H_y \qquad k_z H_x - \frac{\partial H_z}{\partial x} = j\omega\epsilon E_y$$

$$\frac{\partial E_y}{\partial x} - \frac{\partial E_x}{\partial y} = -j\omega\mu H_z \qquad \frac{\partial H_y}{\partial x} - \frac{\partial H_x}{\partial y} = 0$$

TABLE 3.1. TE-MODE FIELD EQUATIONS IN RECTANGULAR COORDINATES

$$E_x = -\frac{j\omega\mu}{k_c^2}\frac{\partial H_z}{\partial y} \tag{3.34}$$

$$E_y = \frac{j\omega\mu}{k_c^2}\frac{\partial H_z}{\partial x} \tag{3.35}$$

$$H_x = \frac{k_z}{k_c^2}\frac{\partial H_z}{\partial x} \tag{3.36}$$

$$H_y = \frac{k_z}{k_c^2}\frac{\partial H_z}{\partial y} \tag{3.37}$$

Summary:

$$\mathbf{H}_{tr} = \frac{k_z}{k_c^2}\nabla H_z \qquad\qquad \mathbf{E}_{tr} = \frac{j\omega\mu}{k_z}\hat{z} \times \mathbf{H}_{tr}$$

where

$$\mathbf{H}_{tr} = \hat{x}H_x + \hat{y}H_y \qquad\qquad \mathbf{E}_{tr} = \hat{x}E_x + \hat{y}E_y$$

When these equations are solved for E_x, E_y, H_x, and H_y, all four components are found to depend upon derivatives of H_z. These solutions are tabulated for reference in Table 3.1, in which we have used

$$k_c{}^2 = \mu\epsilon\omega^2 + k_z{}^2$$

From these results we see that when H_z is known, all the remaining field components of TE wave modes are available from it by differentiation. Consequently, we seek a solution of the wave equation for H_z:

$$\nabla^2 H_z = -k^2 H_z \qquad (3.38)$$

where $k^2 = \mu\epsilon\omega^2$.

We have seen in the preceding section that the wave equation has solutions of the form

$$H_z = \left(A_n \sin \frac{m\pi x}{a} + B_n \cos \frac{m\pi x}{a} \right)$$
$$\times \left(C_n \sin \frac{n\pi y}{b} + D_n \cos \frac{n\pi y}{b} \right) e^{j(\omega t \pm \beta_g z)} \qquad (3.39)$$

where m and n are integers designating the TE$_{mn}$ mode, and the dimensions of the waveguide are as in Fig. 3.1.

The constant coefficients in Eq. (3.39) may be evaluated on the basis of the boundary conditions for fields at the surface of the conducting boundaries. We recall that the normal **H** field vanishes at the surface of a conductor. The component H_x is normal to the guide walls at $x = 0$ and $x = a$. We deduce from Eq. (3.36) that this is equivalent to the condition

$$\frac{\partial H_z}{\partial x} = 0 \qquad \text{at } x = 0, a \qquad (3.40)$$

Similarly, H_y is required to vanish at $y = 0$ and $y = b$. Equation (3.37) shows that this implies

$$\frac{\partial H_z}{\partial y} = 0 \qquad \text{at } y = 0, b \qquad (3.41)$$

We may summarize Eqs. (3.40) and (3.41) by the condition

$$\frac{\partial H_z}{\partial n} = 0 \qquad \text{at guide walls} \qquad (3.42)$$

i.e., the boundary conditions on H_z require that its normal derivative must vanish at the conducting surfaces. Equations (3.34) and (3.35) show also that when the condition (3.42) is satisfied, the boundary conditions for the components of transverse electric field are simultaneously fulfilled.

Inspection of Eq. (3.39) shows that the normal derivative of H_z will vanish at the walls if $A_n = 0 = C_n$. The TE$_{mn}$ solution for H_z thus becomes

$$H_z = H_1 \cos \frac{m\pi x}{a} \cos \frac{n\pi y}{b} e^{j\beta_g z} \tag{3.43}$$

where H_1 is an amplitude constant and β_g has been arbitrarily chosen positive.

The solution for H_z [Eq. (3.43)], when used with the field relationships given in Table 3.1, completes the determination of the fields of the rectangular TE modes.

The results of these substitutions are

Rectangular TE$_{mn}$-mode fields:

$$E_x = \frac{j\omega\mu n\pi H_1}{bk_c^2} \cos \frac{m\pi x}{a} \sin \frac{n\pi y}{b} e^{j\beta_g z} \tag{3.44a}$$

$$E_y = -\frac{j\omega\mu m\pi H_1}{ak_c^2} \sin \frac{m\pi x}{a} \cos \frac{n\pi y}{b} e^{j\beta_g z} \tag{3.44b}$$

$$E_z = 0 \tag{3.44c}$$

$$H_x = -\frac{j\beta_g m\pi H_1}{ak_c^2} \sin \frac{m\pi x}{a} \cos \frac{n\pi y}{b} e^{j\beta_g z} \tag{3.44d}$$

$$H_y = -\frac{j\beta_g n\pi H_1}{bk_c^2} \cos \frac{m\pi x}{a} \sin \frac{n\pi y}{b} e^{j\beta_g z} \tag{3.44e}$$

In the case of a forward-traveling wave, the sign of β_g must be made negative in Eqs. (3.43) and (3.44). The cutoff constant k_c^2, as defined by Eq. (3.21), is seen for this mode to be given by

$$k_c^2 = \frac{m^2\pi^2}{a^2} + \frac{n^2\pi^2}{b^2} \tag{3.45}$$

The use of Eq. (3.45) in (3.24) shows that the propagation constant β_g has a value characteristic of each waveguide mode. For the TE$_{mn}$ mode it is

$$\beta_g = \sqrt{k^2 - \left(\frac{m^2\pi^2}{a^2} + \frac{n^2\pi^2}{b^2}\right)} \tag{3.46}$$

All the components appear in the form of traveling waves of transverse field distributions which move along the waveguide unchanged in form, with axial phase velocity

$$v_p = \frac{\omega}{\beta_g} = \frac{\omega}{\sqrt{k^2 - k_c^2}} \tag{3.47}$$

3.3. TM Modes in Rectangular Coordinates

The transverse magnetic mode solutions can be found by a procedure similar to that employed in finding the TE-mode waves. By substituting $H_z = 0$ and replacing $\partial/\partial t$ by $j\omega$ and $\partial/\partial z$ by k_z, the field curl equations are brought into the form

$$\frac{\partial E_z}{\partial y} - k_z E_y = -j\omega\mu H_x \qquad\qquad -k_z H_y = j\omega\epsilon E_x$$

$$k_z E_x - \frac{\partial E_z}{\partial x} = -j\omega\mu H_y \qquad\qquad k_z H_x = j\omega\epsilon E_y$$

$$\frac{\partial E_y}{\partial x} - \frac{\partial E_x}{\partial y} = 0 \qquad\qquad \frac{\partial H_y}{\partial x} - \frac{\partial H_x}{\partial y} = j\omega\epsilon E_z$$

These equations may be solved for E_x, E_y, H_x, and H_y, yielding the results listed in Table 3.2. Here the situation is comparable to that

Table 3.2. TM-mode Field Equations in Rectangular Coordinates

$$E_x = \frac{k_z}{k_c^2}\frac{\partial E_z}{\partial x} \tag{3.48}$$

$$E_y = \frac{k_z}{k_c^2}\frac{\partial E_z}{\partial y} \tag{3.49}$$

$$H_x = \frac{j\omega\epsilon}{k_c^2}\frac{\partial E_z}{\partial y} \tag{3.50}$$

$$H_y = -\frac{j\omega\epsilon}{k_c^2}\frac{\partial E_z}{\partial x} \tag{3.51}$$

Summary:

$$\mathbf{E}_{tr} = \frac{k_z}{k_c^2}\boldsymbol{\nabla}E_z \qquad\qquad \mathbf{H}_{tr} = -\frac{j\omega\epsilon}{k_z}\hat{z}\times\mathbf{E}_{tr}$$

where

$$\mathbf{E}_{tr} = \hat{x}E_x + \hat{y}E_y \qquad\qquad \mathbf{H}_{tr} = \hat{x}H_x + \hat{y}H_y$$

encountered in obtaining the TE-mode solutions, in that all of the remaining field components appear in terms of differentials of a single field component, in this case E_z. Thus we require solutions of the wave equation for E_z [Eq. (3.8)]. It has been seen that the wave equation has single-mode solutions of the form

$$E_z = \left(A_m \sin\frac{m\pi x}{a} + B_m \cos\frac{m\pi x}{a}\right)\left(C_n \sin\frac{n\pi y}{b} + D_n \cos\frac{n\pi y}{b}\right)e^{\pm j\beta_g z}$$

The boundary conditions on E_z require that it vanish at the waveguide walls, where it is tangent to the conducting surfaces. In the waveguide of Fig. 3.1, these conditions may be satisfied by choosing $B_m = 0 = D_n$. Thus there remains

$$E_z = E_1 \sin\frac{m\pi x}{a} \sin\frac{n\pi y}{b} e^{j\beta_g z} \tag{3.52}$$

Substituting the longitudinal electric field E_z of Eq. (3.52) into the TM relations (3.48) to (3.51) of Table 3.2, we find

Rectangular TM_{mn}-mode fields:

$$E_x = \frac{j\beta_g m\pi E_1}{ak_c^2} \cos \frac{m\pi x}{a} \sin \frac{n\pi y}{b} e^{j\beta_g z} \qquad (3.53a)$$

$$E_y = \frac{j\beta_g n\pi E_1}{bk_c^2} \sin \frac{m\pi x}{a} \cos \frac{n\pi y}{b} e^{j\beta_g z} \qquad (3.53b)$$

$$H_x = \frac{j\omega\epsilon n\pi E_1}{bk_c^2} \sin \frac{m\pi x}{a} \cos \frac{n\pi y}{b} e^{j\beta_g z} \qquad (3.53c)$$

$$H_y = -\frac{j\omega\epsilon m\pi E_1}{ak_c^2} \cos \frac{m\pi x}{a} \sin \frac{n\pi y}{b} e^{j\beta_g z} \qquad (3.53d)$$

$$H_z = 0 \qquad (3.53e)$$

where k_c^2 and β_g have values for the TM modes as given by Eqs. (3.45) and (3.46), respectively. Here, again, a positive β_g has been used.

3.4. Characteristics of Rectangular Waveguide Fields

Having established the analytical means for finding all of the components of the electromagnetic fields in rectangular waveguides, we are now in a position to investigate the physical characteristics of these fields. The fields in a waveguide, together with the associated surface charges and currents, enable the guide to perform its function of transporting energy along its length. We must know the character of the fields in order to be able to inject the high-frequency energy of an oscillator into the sending end and to extract it at the receiving end, as well as to accomplish the waveguide adjustments corresponding to transmission-line impedance matching.

We have seen one characteristic of the waveguide in which it differs from the conventional two-conductor transmission line. In Eq. (3.27) we have found the cutoff angular frequency ω_c. Below the cutoff frequency, the fields in the guide no longer have wavelike character but are attenuated in the axial direction. In this respect, the waveguide is unlike a conventional transmission line, which transmits energy at frequencies down to zero, or direct current. It is instructive to compare the ω-β diagrams, relating angular frequency and propagation constant, of the waveguide and the two-wire transmission line. For the waveguide, the ω-β relation is

$$\sqrt{\mu\epsilon}\,\omega = \sqrt{k_c^2 + \beta_g^2} \qquad (3.54)$$

and for the transmission line

$$\sqrt{\mu\epsilon}\ \omega = \beta_g \tag{3.55}$$

These two characteristics are shown in Fig. 3.2, in which the ordinate has been taken as $\sqrt{\mu\epsilon}\ \omega = k$ instead of frequency, so that the two axes have similar dimensions. At frequencies much greater than cut-off, the waveguide wavelength approaches that of the line, which is equal to the free-space wavelength of waves in the medium filling the

waveguide. At frequencies approaching cutoff, β_g diminishes, and vanishes at the cutoff frequency. Therefore the guide wavelength λ_g increases near cutoff, becoming infinite at ω_c. Below ω_c, β_g has no real value, but is imaginary. This denotes axial attenuation of the fields in the guide, as we have seen. The fields are attenuated rapidly when cutoff occurs, as may be illustrated by the following example: As the frequency of the signal falls

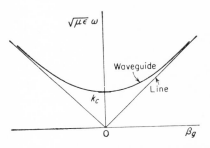

Fig. 3.2. k-β diagrams for waveguide and two-wire line.

below the cutoff angular frequency by a small amount $\Delta\omega$, the guide propagation constant may be placed into the form

$$\begin{aligned} k_z &= \sqrt{k_c{}^2 - k^2} = \sqrt{\mu\epsilon(\omega_c{}^2 - \omega^2)} \\ &= \sqrt{\mu\epsilon}\ \omega_c \sqrt{1 - \frac{\omega^2}{\omega_c{}^2}} \\ &= k_c \sqrt{1 - \frac{(\omega_c - \Delta\omega)^2}{\omega_c{}^2}} \\ &\approx k_c \sqrt{\frac{2\Delta\omega}{\omega_c}} \end{aligned}$$

where we have neglected $(\Delta\omega/\omega_c)^2$. If now $\Delta\omega$ is equal to $0.01\omega_c$, $k_z = 0.14k_c$. In the TE_{10} mode, $k_c = \dfrac{\pi}{a}$, where a is the width of the waveguide. Hence, in this example, the fields in the guide are attenuated by the factor $\exp(-k_z z) = \exp(-0.44z/a)$. Thus the fields will be decreased to $1/e$ of their value in a distance of 2.3 guide widths, measured along the guide axis, at a frequency only 1 per cent below cutoff. As frequency decreases toward zero, the attenuation factor of TE_{10}-mode fields approaches the limiting value $e^{-k_c z} = e^{-\pi z/a}$. Below cutoff, there is no wavelike progression of phase delay along the guide axis, the fields rising and falling in phase. Thus the waveguide does not transmit waves at frequency below ω_c. This cutoff attenuation characteristic occurs in wave-guiding systems of all structural forms, if there is a minimum allowed frequency of propagation, or cutoff frequency, associated with the system.

The rectangular mode having the lowest cutoff frequency in a waveguide of given width is the TE_{10} mode. For this reason the TE_{10} mode is called the dominant mode in rectangular waveguides, and it is the mode ordinarily employed for waveguide transmission. The field components of the dominant mode may be obtained by substituting $m = 1$, $n = 0$ into Eqs. (3.44):

$$E_x = 0 \tag{3.56}$$

$$E_y = E_1 \sin \frac{\pi x}{a} e^{j\beta_g z} \tag{3.57}$$

$$H_x = \frac{\beta_g}{\omega\mu} E_1 \sin \frac{\pi x}{a} e^{j\beta_g z} \tag{3.58}$$

$$H_y = 0 \tag{3.59}$$

A graphical representation of waveguide fields can be given by the use of the usual Faraday concept of "lines" of field, in which lines are drawn so that their tangents are everywhere parallel to the direction of the field, and the lateral density of lines indicates the intensity of field. By convention, electric field lines emerge from positive charges and terminate on negative charges. Magnetic lines must form closed loops, never terminating at any point. The familiar right-hand rule gives the direction of magnetic field due to a current of positive charges or a positive rate of increase of **D** vector. The electric and magnetic field lines of the TE_{10} mode at an instant of time are shown in Fig. 3.3a. The surface charges and currents on the inner surface of the waveguide which correspond to these fields are shown separately for clearness in Fig. 3.3b. The values of the surface distributions may be obtained by the application of the boundary conditions for normal electric and tangential magnetic fields at the surface of a conductor, applied in Eqs. (3.56) to (3.59). The field-line and current and charge distributions are repeated with reversed signs every half guide wavelength along the waveguide. The configurations depicted in Fig. 3.3a and b move along the guide axis at the phase velocity $v_p = \omega/\beta_g$ of the dominant mode. As the wave travels, the currents redistribute the charges so that at every instant they correctly terminate the **E** field lines. The cross-sectional field distributions of other rectangular waveguide modes are illustrated in Fig. 3.4.

The distinction as to which waveguide mode propagates in a given instance may be made by (1) the method of mode excitation and (2) mode filtering.   The field lines of the desired mode may be established in the waveguide by means of a probe or loop-coupling device.   A

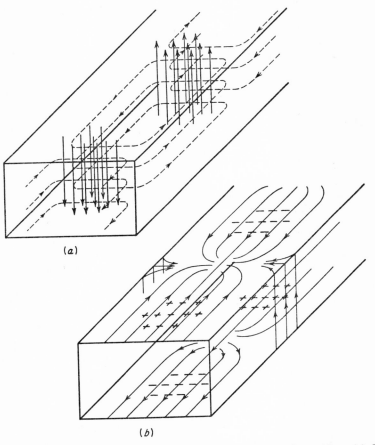

Fig. 3.3. Schematic representation of TE$_{10}$ mode in rectangular guide.   (a) Electric field represented by solid lines, magnetic field by broken lines; (b) currents and charges on waveguide walls.

probe should be located so as to establish the electric field lines of the mode, and a coupling loop to establish the magnetic fields.   Methods for excitation of various rectangular modes are shown in Fig. 3.5. A device which serves to excite a given waveguide mode can also serve reciprocally as a receiver or collector of energy in that mode.

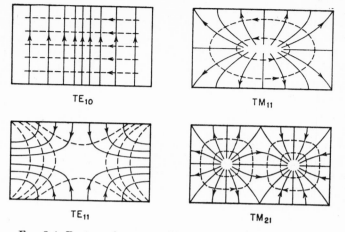

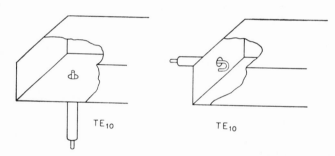

FIG. 3.4. Rectangular-waveguide mode field configurations.

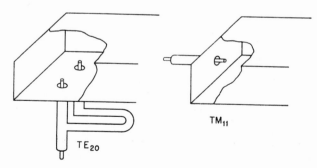

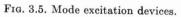

FIG. 3.5. Mode excitation devices.

It may in some instances be found necessary to prevent the conversion of a given waveguide mode to another. Mode conversion may result from irregularities in the guide or from impedance structures employed in the transmission system. Mode conversion can be suppressed by the proper selection of waveguide dimensions if the unwanted mode or modes have cutoff frequencies above that of the wanted mode. Otherwise, some form of mode filtration may be used. A mode filter may consist merely of a thin metallic plate or vane, placed in the waveguide where there exists at the metal surface no tangential component of electric field in the mode being retained, but where there are tangential electric field lines of the unwanted mode. For example, a horizontal metallic plate across the center of a waveguide and parallel to its axis, in the xz plane, would not disturb the propagation of the TE_{10} mode but would block the TE_{11} mode. Other mode filters of this type can be devised by inspection of the field lines of the various modes.

3.5. Wave Equation in Cylindrical Coordinates

The wave equation was derived as a direct consequence of Maxwell's equations, and in regions having no space charge, all components of field were found to obey an equation in the form

$$\nabla^2 F_i = -k^2 F_i \qquad (3.60)$$

where i is one of the space coordinates, F is E, B, H, or D, $k^2 = \mu\epsilon\omega^2$, and ∇^2 is the scalar Laplacian. The Laplacian is separable into transverse and longitudinal components:

$$\nabla^2 = \nabla_{tr}^2 + \frac{\partial^2}{\partial z^2}$$

We are interested in fields in the form of waves propagating along a waveguide axis in the z direction. The field components have therefore been assumed to have solutions of the form

$$F_i = P(p)Q(q)e^{j\omega t + k_z z}$$

where k_z is imaginary and $P(p)Q(q)$ is a product of functions of the transverse coordinates p and q. In the cylindrical coordinate case, the function of transverse coordinates will be $R(r)\Theta(\theta)$.

Thus, the wave equation for all of the components of field will have the form

$$\left(\nabla_{r,\theta}^2 + \frac{\partial^2}{\partial z^2} \right) R(r)\Theta(\theta)e^{k_z z} = -k^2 R(r)\Theta(\theta)e^{k_z z} \qquad (3.61)$$

where the time dependence $e^{j\omega t}$, always implicit, has been omitted. With the full form of the polar-coordinate Laplacian, (3.61) becomes

$$\frac{1}{r}\frac{\partial}{\partial r}r\frac{\partial}{\partial r}R\Theta + \frac{1}{r^2}\frac{\partial^2}{\partial\theta^2}R\Theta + (k_z^2 + k^2)R\Theta = 0$$

Carrying out the differentiations and dividing by $R\Theta$, we obtain

$$\frac{R'' + (1/r)R'}{R} + \frac{1}{r^2}\frac{\Theta''}{\Theta} + k_c^2 = 0 \tag{3.62}$$

where we have written $k_c^2 = k^2 + k_z^2$. Equation (3.62) may be rearranged to take the form

$$\frac{r^2R'' + rR'}{R} + r^2k_c^2 + \frac{\Theta''}{\Theta} = 0 \tag{3.63}$$

Examination of Eq. (3.63) shows that it consists of the sum of a function of r and a function of θ, which add to zero. Since r and θ are independent variables, Eq. (3.63) can be true only if each function is separately constant, for all values of r and θ. We assume a constant of magnitude n^2 and write

$$\frac{\Theta''}{\Theta} = -n^2 \tag{3.64}$$

$$\frac{r^2R'' + rR'}{R} + r^2k_c^2 = n^2 \tag{3.65}$$

Equation (3.64) has the solution

$$\Theta(\theta) = A_n \sin n\theta + B_n \cos n\theta \tag{3.66}$$

where $n = 0, 1, 2, 3, \ldots$.
Equation (3.65) is

$$R'' + \frac{1}{r}R' + \left(k_c^2 - \frac{n^2}{r^2}\right)R = 0 \tag{3.67}$$

which is Bessel's equation of nth order, and has the solution

$$R(r) = C_n J_n(k_c r) + D_n N_n(k_c r) \tag{3.68}$$

where $J_n(k_c r)$ and $N_n(k_c r)$ are nth-order Bessel functions of $k_c r$, of first and second kind, respectively. We therefore conclude from (3.68) and (3.66) that any existing axial components of the field vectors will have the solution

$$F_i = [C_n J_n(k_c r) + D_n N_n(k_c r)](A_n \sin n\theta + B_n \cos n\theta)e^{k_z z} \tag{3.69}$$

3.6. Cylindrical TE and TM Modes

Before proceeding to fit solutions of the type given by Eq. (3.69) to the boundary conditions required for the various components of field in cylindrical waveguides, we shall investigate the subdivision of cylindrical wave solutions into modal types. It turns out that, as in rectangular waveguides, we can simplify the problem considerably by grouping the solutions into classes having $E_z = 0$ and $H_z = 0$, which are the TE and TM modes, respectively. Proceeding in a manner analogous to that followed previously, we express the Maxwell equations $\nabla \times \mathbf{E} = -j\omega\mathbf{B}$ and $\nabla \times \mathbf{H} = j\omega\epsilon\mathbf{E}$ in cylindrical coordinates

$$\frac{1}{r}\frac{\partial E_z}{\partial \theta} - k_z E_\theta = -j\omega\mu H_r \qquad\qquad \frac{1}{r}\frac{\partial H_z}{\partial \theta} - k_z H_\theta = j\omega\epsilon E_r$$

$$k_z E_r - \frac{\partial E_z}{\partial r} = -j\omega\mu H_\theta \qquad\qquad k_z H_r - \frac{\partial H_z}{\partial r} = j\omega\epsilon E_\theta$$

$$\frac{1}{r}\frac{\partial}{\partial r}(rE_\theta) - \frac{1}{r}\frac{\partial E_r}{\partial \theta} = -j\omega\mu H_z \qquad \frac{1}{r}\frac{\partial}{\partial r}(rH_\theta) - \frac{1}{r}\frac{\partial H_r}{\partial \theta} = j\omega\epsilon E_z$$

where the differentiation $\partial/\partial z$ has been replaced by the factor k_z.

Circular TE Modes. Substituting $E_z = 0$ into the field equations, we find

$$k_z E_\theta = j\omega\mu H_r \qquad \frac{1}{r}\frac{\partial H_z}{\partial \theta} = k_z H_\theta + j\omega\epsilon E_r$$

$$k_z E_r = -j\omega\mu H_\theta \qquad \frac{\partial H_z}{\partial r} = k_z H_r - j\omega\epsilon E_\theta$$

The z-component equations, which are not needed for our purposes, have been omitted. The remaining four equations may be solved for the four components of transverse field, in terms of derivatives of H_z. The resulting solutions are tabulated for reference in Table 3.3.

Table 3.3. TE-mode Field Equations in Cylindrical Coordinates

$$E_r = -\frac{j\omega\mu}{k_c^2}\frac{1}{r}\frac{\partial H_z}{\partial \theta} \qquad\qquad (3.70)$$

$$E_\theta = \frac{j\omega\mu}{k_c^2}\frac{\partial H_z}{\partial r} \qquad\qquad (3.71)$$

$$H_r = \frac{k_z}{k_c^2}\frac{\partial H_z}{\partial r} \qquad\qquad (3.72)$$

$$H_\theta = \frac{k_z}{k_c^2}\frac{1}{r}\frac{\partial H_z}{\partial \theta} \qquad\qquad (3.73)$$

Summary:

$$\mathbf{H}_{tr} = \frac{k_z}{k_c^2}\nabla H_z \qquad\qquad \mathbf{E}_{tr} = \frac{j\omega\mu}{k_z}\hat{z} \times \mathbf{H}_t$$

where

$$\mathbf{H}_{tr} = \hat{r}H_r + \hat{\theta}H_\theta \qquad\qquad \mathbf{E}_{tr} = \hat{r}E_r + \hat{\theta}E_\theta$$

The solution for the cylindrical TE-mode fields can now be completed by finding the longitudinal component of magnetic field H_z. The general solution for all components of field is given by Eq. (3.69), and hence we may take

$$H_z = [C_n J_n(k_c r) + D_n N_n(k_c r)](A_n \sin n\theta + B_n \cos n\theta)e^{\pm j\beta_g z} \quad (3.74)$$

The Bessel functions of the first few integral orders are shown in Fig. 3.6.† The functions of second kind, $N_n(k_c r)$, are infinite at $r = 0$.

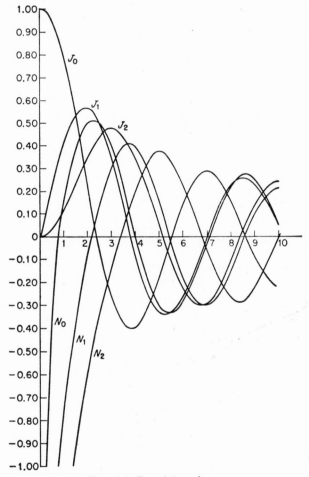

Fig. 3.6. Bessel functions.

† See Appendix III for a summary of the analytic properties of Bessel functions.

They therefore would represent inadmissible solutions for the field at the center of the waveguide, and hence we must set D_n equal to zero. The θ-dependent term is equivalent to $\sqrt{A_n{}^2 + B_n{}^2} \cos (n\theta + \phi)$, where $\phi = \tan^{-1} (A_n/B_n)$. Without loss of generality, we can rotate the angular reference axis to make ϕ equal to zero, and hence $A_n = 0$. With these conditions we now have

$$H_z = H_1 J_n(k_c r) \cos n\theta \, e^{\pm j\beta_g z} \qquad (3.75)$$

The undetermined constant k_c must now be chosen so as to cause H_z to satisfy the boundary conditions on the TE-mode fields. The θ component of electric field is tangent to the inner surface of the waveguide at $r = a$ and hence must vanish here. Equation (3.71) shows that this condition is equivalent to:

$$\left. \frac{\partial H_z}{\partial r} \right|_{r=a} = 0 \qquad (3.76)$$

which corresponds to the boundary condition on H_z found in the rectangular-coordinate case, which was that the normal derivative of H_z must vanish at the conducting boundary.

Thus we have the requirement

$$J'_n(k_c a) = 0 \qquad (3.77)$$

There is an infinite sequence of values of $k_c a$ which satisfy Eq. (3.77). These points, the roots of (3.77), correspond to the maxima and minima of the curve $J_n(k_c a)$. A tabulation of values of the first few roots of $J'_n(k_c a)$ for small integers n is given in Table 3.4.†

TABLE 3.4. mth ZERO OF $J'_n(p'_{nm})$

m	n			
	0	1	2	3
1	3.832	1.841	3.054	4.201
2	7.016	5.331	6.706	8.015
3	10.173	8.536	9.969	11.346
4	13.324	11.706	13.170	14.58

The selection of p'_{nm}, the mth root (not including $a = 0$) of $J'_n(k_c a)$, specifies the TE$_{nm}$ circular-waveguide mode. The first subscript of the modal designation conventionally refers to the number of cycles of field variation which occur in one rotation through 2π radians in angle

† See also E. L. Ginzton, "Microwave Measurements," p. 478, McGraw-Hill Book Company, Inc., New York, 1957; N. Marcuvitz (ed.), "Waveguide Handbook," p. 69, McGraw-Hill Book Company, Inc., New York, 1951.

θ. The second integral subscript is equal to the number of zeros of $J'_n(k_c r)$ [and hence of E_θ, as shown by Eq. (3.71)] which occur in the range $0 < r \le a$.

The complete transverse fields of the TE_{nm} circular-waveguide modes can now be written, by the use of Eq. (3.75) in Eqs. (3.70) to (3.73) of Table 3.3,† as

$$E_r = \frac{j\omega\mu n a^2 H_1}{(p'_{nm})^2} \frac{J_n(p'_{nm}r/a)}{r} \sin n\theta \, e^{j\beta_g z}$$

$$E_\theta = \frac{j\omega\mu a^2 H_1}{(p'_{nm})^2} \left[n\frac{J_n(p'_{nm}r/a)}{r} - \frac{p'_{nm}}{a} J_{n+1}\left(p'_{nm}\frac{r}{a}\right) \right] \cos n\theta \, e^{j\beta_g z}$$

$$H_r = \frac{j\beta_g a^2 H_1}{(p'_{nm})^2} \left[n\frac{J_n(p'_{nm}r/a)}{r} - \frac{p'_{nm}}{a} J_{n+1}\left(p'_{nm}\frac{r}{a}\right) \right] \cos n\theta \, e^{j\beta_g z}$$

$$H_\theta = -\frac{j\beta_g n a^2 H_1}{(p'_{nm})^2} \frac{J_n(p'_{nm}r/a)}{r} \sin n\theta \, e^{j\beta_g z}$$

The propagation constant β_g is equal to $\sqrt{\mu\epsilon\omega^2 - (p'_{nm}/a)^2}$, and has here been written positive.

Circular TM Modes. Derivation of the transverse magnetic mode fields in circular waveguide may be effected by substitution of the condition $H_z = 0$ into the field equations, and proceeding, as before, to satisfy boundary conditions for the axial field. The r and θ components of Maxwell's curl equations in cylindrical coordinates then are

$$\frac{1}{r}\frac{\partial E_z}{\partial \theta} - k_z E_\theta = -j\omega\mu H_r \qquad -k_z H_\theta = j\omega\epsilon E_r$$

$$k_z E_r - \frac{\partial E_z}{\partial r} = -j\omega\mu H_\theta \qquad k_z H_r = j\omega\epsilon E_\theta$$

These equations are readily solvable for the components of transverse field, with the results tabulated in Table 3.5. The only solution of

TABLE 3.5. TM-MODE FIELD EQUATIONS IN CYLINDRICAL COORDINATES

$$E_r = \frac{k_z}{k_c^2}\frac{\partial E_z}{\partial r} \tag{3.78}$$

$$E_\theta = \frac{k_z}{k_c^2}\frac{1}{r}\frac{\partial E_z}{\partial \theta} \tag{3.79}$$

$$H_r = \frac{j\omega\epsilon}{k_c^2}\frac{1}{r}\frac{\partial E_z}{\partial \theta} \tag{3.80}$$

$$H_\theta = -\frac{j\omega\epsilon}{k_c^2}\frac{\partial E_z}{\partial r} \tag{3.81}$$

Summary:

$$\mathbf{E}_{tr} = \frac{k_z}{k_c^2}\boldsymbol{\nabla} E_z \qquad \mathbf{H}_{tr} = -\frac{j\omega\epsilon}{k_z}\hat{z} \times \mathbf{E}_{tr}$$

where

$$\mathbf{E}_{tr} = \hat{r}E_r + \hat{\theta}E_\theta \qquad \mathbf{H}_{tr} = \hat{r}H_r + \hat{\theta}H_\theta$$

† See Appendix III for differential formulas involving Bessel functions.

the wave equation which is now required is E_z, from which the remaining circular TM field components may be obtained by the use of Eqs. (3.78) to (3.81) of Table 3.5. Using the solution from Eq. (3.69) which is finite at the origin, we have

$$E_z = E_1 J_n(k_c r) \cos n\theta \, e^{\pm j\beta_g z} \qquad (3.82)$$

E_z is tangential at $r = a$ and hence must vanish there. This condition leads to the requirement

$$J_n(k_c a) = 0 \qquad (3.83)$$

As indicated by Fig. 3.6, $J_n(k_c r)$ is an oscillating function of $(k_c r)$, and hence Eq. (3.83) has infinitely many roots. The first few roots for low-order J_n are given in Table 3.6.[†] Selection of the mth root of

TABLE 3.6. mth ZERO OF $J_n(p_{nm})$

m	n			
	0	1	2	3
1	2.405	3.832	5.136	6.380
2	5.520	7.016	8.417	9.761
3	8.654	10.173	11.620	13.015
4	11.792	13.323	14.796	16.20

$J_n(k_c a)$ specifies the TM$_{nm}$ circular-waveguide mode. The conventional assignment of modal index subscripts is analogous with that of the TE$_{nm}$ modes: the first subscript refers to the number of angular variations of field (and hence also to the order of the Bessel function representing the axial field), and the second integral subscript is equal to the number of zeros of axial electric field in the range $0 < r \leq a$.

Using E_z [Eq. (3.82)] in Eqs. (3.78) to (3.81), the remaining components of the TM circular-waveguide modes are found to be

$$E_r = \frac{j\beta_g a^2 E_1}{p_{nm}^2}\left[n\,\frac{J_n(p_{nm}r/a)}{r} - \frac{p_{nm}}{a} J_{n+1}\left(p_{nm}\frac{r}{a}\right)\right]\cos n\theta \, e^{j\beta_g z}$$

$$E_\theta = -\frac{j\beta_g a^2 n E_1}{p_{nm}^2}\frac{J_n(p_{nm}r/a)}{r}\sin n\theta \, e^{j\beta_g z}$$

$$H_r = -\frac{j\omega\epsilon a^2 n E_1}{p_{nm}^2}\frac{J_n(p_{nm}r/a)}{r}\sin n\theta \, e^{j\beta_g z}$$

$$H_\theta = -\frac{j\omega\epsilon a^2 E_1}{p_{nm}^2}\left[n\,\frac{J_n(p_{nm}r/a)}{r} - \frac{p_{nm}}{a} J_{n+1}\left(p_{nm}\frac{r}{a}\right)\right]\cos n\theta \, e^{j\beta_g z}$$

$$H_z = 0$$

where p_{nm} is the mth root of $J_n(k_c a)$.

[†] Ginzton, op. cit., p. 419.

The dominant mode, or mode of lowest cutoff frequency, in a circular waveguide of radius a will be that mode which has the smallest value of the product $k_c a$. Inspection of Tables 3.4 and 3.6 shows that the lowest cutoff frequency belongs to the TE_{11} mode, for which

$$k_c a = 1.841$$

The field configurations of circular-waveguide modes of low order are illustrated in Fig. 3.7.

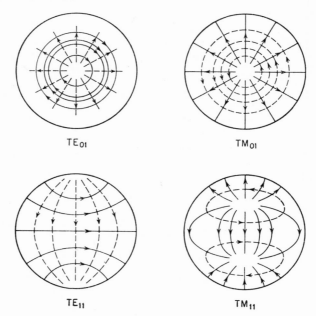

TE_{01} TM_{01}

TE_{11} TM_{11}

FIG. 3.7. Cylindrical-waveguide mode field configurations.

3.7. Two-conductor Systems and the TEM Mode

The familiar two-conductor transmission systems exemplified by the parallel-wire line and coaxial line are wave-guiding systems in the same sense as are the waveguides studied thus far. The electric and magnetic fields associated with transmission on these systems have wave-like solutions, which must satisfy boundary conditions at the conducting surfaces.† We can find solutions for the transmission modes

† In the case of open wire lines and other systems in which the regions at $r \rightarrow \infty$ are included in the domain of the fields, we also have the condition that the field intensities must vanish sufficiently rapidly as r becomes infinite. The fields must have a radial dependence such that they represent a finite total amount of field energy per unit length of line.

of two-conductor systems which fall into the TE and TM classifications. We find an additional transmission mode, however, the TEM, or transverse electromagnetic mode, which can be supported on two-conductor systems but which does not exist for hollow waveguides. The TEM mode is, in fact, the dominant mode for two-conductor systems.

In order to investigate the properties of the TEM mode, we consider the form of Maxwell's curl equations when subject to the condition $E_z = 0 = H_z$. In rectangular coordinates, for example, the two field curl equations

$$\nabla \times \mathbf{H} = \frac{\partial \mathbf{D}}{\partial t} \qquad \nabla \times \mathbf{E} = - \frac{\partial \mathbf{B}}{\partial t}$$

become, with $\partial/\partial z$ replaced by the propagation factor k_z,

$$-k_z E_y = -j\omega\mu H_x \tag{3.84}$$

$$k_z E_x = -j\omega\mu H_y \tag{3.85}$$

$$\frac{\partial E_y}{\partial x} - \frac{\partial E_x}{\partial y} = 0 \tag{3.86}$$

$$-k_z H_y = j\omega\epsilon E_x \tag{3.87}$$

$$k_z H_x = j\omega\epsilon E_y \tag{3.88}$$

$$\frac{\partial H_y}{\partial x} - \frac{\partial H_x}{\partial y} = 0 \tag{3.89}$$

Combining (3.84) and (3.88), we find

$$k_z{}^2 = -\mu\epsilon\omega^2$$

$$k_z = j \sqrt{\mu\epsilon}\, \omega \tag{3.90}$$

This is the propagation constant of a free plane wave in a medium like that filling the guide, having phase velocity equal to the velocity of light in the medium:

$$v_p = \frac{1}{\sqrt{\mu\epsilon}} \tag{3.91}$$

By the use of Eqs. (3.87) and (3.88) in (3.89), we obtain

$$\frac{\partial E_x}{\partial x} + \frac{\partial E_y}{\partial y} = 0 \tag{3.92}$$

By partial differentiation with respect to y, Eq. (3.92) becomes

$$\frac{\partial^2 E_x}{\partial x\, \partial y} + \frac{\partial^2 E_y}{\partial y^2} = 0 \tag{3.93}$$

Partial differentiation of Eq. (3.86) with respect to x yields

$$\frac{\partial^2 E_y}{\partial x^2} - \frac{\partial^2 E_x}{\partial x \, \partial y} = 0 \tag{3.94}$$

Combining Eqs. (3.93) and (3.94), we find

$$\frac{\partial^2 E_y}{\partial x^2} + \frac{\partial^2 E_y}{\partial y^2} = 0 \tag{3.95}$$

From the definition of $k_c{}^2$, Eqs. (3.12) to (3.21), the form of Eq. (3.95) implies that $k_c{}^2 E_y = 0$. We can similarly show that $k_c{}^2 E_x = 0$. These results indicate that, for TEM-mode fields, the cutoff frequency $\omega_c = (\mu\epsilon)^{-\frac{1}{2}} k_c$ is equal to zero. This conclusion is in agreement with our knowledge of two-conductor systems in that they transmit currents at all frequencies down to zero, or direct current.

The transverse field distributions of the TEM mode are readily determined since they are identical in form with the static fields associated with the given conductors. We may demonstrate this property of the TEM fields by noting that Eq. (3.86) shows

$$\frac{\partial E_y}{\partial x} - \frac{\partial E_x}{\partial y} = 0 \tag{3.96}$$

Due to Eq. (3.96), the transverse field $\mathbf{E}_t = \hat{x} E_x + \hat{y} E_y$ is derivable as the gradient of a scalar, $\phi(x,y)$, since, if $\mathbf{E} = \nabla\phi$, then, in (3.96), we obtain

$$\frac{\partial}{\partial x}\left(\frac{\partial \phi}{\partial y}\right) - \frac{\partial}{\partial y}\left(\frac{\partial \phi}{\partial x}\right) = 0 \tag{3.97}$$

which is identically equal to zero. Now, since $\nabla \cdot \mathbf{E} = 0$, using $\mathbf{E} = \nabla\phi$, we have

$$\nabla \cdot \nabla\phi = \nabla^2\phi = 0 \tag{3.98}$$

Consequently, the transverse electric field E_t of the TEM mode is derivable from a potential which is a solution of the two-dimensional Laplace's equation, as is true of the static $\mathbf{E}$ field associated with the same set of conductors. Since $\mathbf{E}_t$ must satisfy the same boundary conditions as the static $\mathbf{E}$ field, it will therefore have a solution identical with that of the static $\mathbf{E}$ field. When $\mathbf{E}_t$ is thus determined, the magnetic field $\mathbf{H}_t$ may be derived from it by the use of the curl equation $\nabla \times \mathbf{E} = -j\omega\mu\mathbf{H}$.

The TEM modes are restricted, however, to guiding systems having more than one conductor. We may demonstrate this fact by means of the example of the circular waveguide. The two field curl equations

for cylindrical TEM modes are

$$-k_z H_\theta = j\omega\epsilon E_r \tag{3.99}$$
$$k_z H_r = j\omega\epsilon E_\theta \tag{3.100}$$
$$\frac{\partial}{\partial r}(rH_\theta) - \frac{\partial H_r}{\partial \theta} = 0 \tag{3.101}$$
$$k_z E_\theta = j\omega\mu H_r \tag{3.102}$$
$$k_z E_r = -j\omega\mu H_\theta \tag{3.103}$$
$$\frac{\partial}{\partial r}(rE_\theta) - \frac{\partial E_r}{\partial \theta} = 0 \tag{3.104}$$

We evaluate the closed line integral $\oint \mathbf{H} \cdot d\mathbf{l}$ over a circular path of radius r_0 about the center of the guide (Fig. 3.8).

$$\oint \mathbf{H} \cdot d\mathbf{l} = \int H_\theta r_0 \, d\theta \tag{3.105}$$

The static field solutions within a continuous circular boundary are independent of θ. Using this fact for the TEM fields, we see that the operator $\partial/\partial\theta$ will yield a result of zero. Therefore, from (3.101), $\partial(rH_\theta)/\partial r = 0$ and $rH_\theta = C_H$ is a constant. Using this result in (3.105), together with an application of Stokes' theorem, we find

$$\iint \nabla \times \mathbf{H} \cdot d\mathbf{a} = C_H \oint d\theta$$
$$\iint (J_z + j\omega\epsilon E_z)\, da = 2\pi C_H$$

Therefore, if H_θ is not zero,

$$\iint J_z \, da = 2\pi C_H \tag{3.106}$$

Fig. 3.8. Path of integration in waveguide.

where we have used the fact that $E_z = 0$.

We conclude from Eq. (3.106) that there must be a current flow within the waveguide, for which the second conductor is required, in order to support the TEM mode. [We can easily prove that the above-mentioned condition, of nonvanishing H_θ, must hold if the H field does not vanish altogether. H_r can be shown to be zero by taking a circular path integral of E_θ in Eq. (3.102)

$$j\omega\mu \oint H_r r \, d\theta = k_z \oint E_\theta r \, d\theta = k_z \oint \frac{\partial \phi}{r \, \partial\theta} r \, \partial\theta = k_z \oint d\phi = 0$$

where ϕ is the potential from which $\mathbf{E}$ is derivable. Then, since H_r is independent of θ, it must vanish everywhere, and H_θ is the only component remaining.]

The requirement of a return current path is true of the TEM mode in general. In summary, the properties of TEM modes are:

1. Phase velocity equals the velocity of light in the medium.
2. Cutoff frequency is zero.
3. Transverse fields are of the same form as the static fields of the guiding system.
4. A two-conductor system is required.

The TEM-mode fields of the coaxial line are obtained by associating the propagation factor $e^{-j\beta z}$ with the static field functions

$$E_r = E_0 \frac{e^{-j\beta z}}{r} \qquad (3.107)$$

$$H_\theta = I_0 \frac{e^{-j\beta z}}{r} \qquad (3.108)$$

The relation between E_0 and I_0 may be obtained by deriving H_θ independently from $\nabla \times \mathbf{E} = -j\omega\mathbf{H}$. We find

$$-j\beta E_0 \frac{e^{-j\beta z}}{r} = -j\omega\mu I_0 \frac{e^{-j\beta z}}{r}$$

from which

$$I_0 = \frac{\beta}{\omega\mu} E_0 = \frac{1}{\mu c} E_0$$

where c is the velocity of light.

3.8. Coaxial TE and TM Modes

Transverse electric and transverse magnetic modes of propagation are possible in principle on any transmission system on which the boundary conditions of the modal field components can be satisfied. Thus, we can show that TE and TM modes may exist on the coaxial line of Fig. 3.9, in addition to the TEM principal mode which we have just discussed.

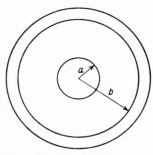

FIG. 3.9. Coaxial line cross section.

The complete single-mode solution of the wave equation in cylindrical coordinates was found to be

$$F_z = F_1[A_n J_n(k_c r) + B_n N_n(k_c r)] \cos n\theta \, e^{j\beta_g z} \qquad (3.109)$$

where F_z is E_z or H_z. In applying this solution to the hollow waveguide, the second term, containing $N_n(k_c r)$, was discarded since it is infinite at the origin, thus representing an impossible situation.   In the case of the coaxial line, the divergent term in $N_n(k_c r)$ is retained in the solution, since the origin of coordinates is excluded from the domain where the fields exist.

The boundary condition on the longitudinal magnetic field H_z of the coaxial TE modes is identical with that already found for hollow

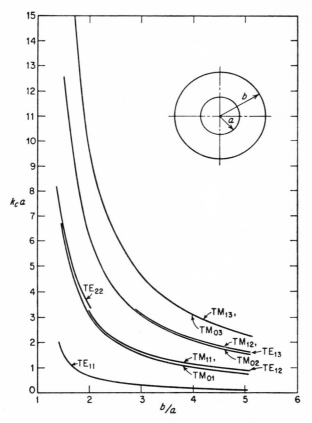

Fig. 3.10. Cutoff constants of higher modes in coaxial line.

waveguides, namely that $\partial H_z/\partial n = 0$ at conducting surfaces.   Applying this condition successively to the boundaries at $r = a$ and $r = b$, we obtain the relations

$$0 = A_n J'_n(k_c a) + B_n N'_n(k_c a) \tag{3.110}$$
$$0 = A_n J'_n(k_c b) + B_n N'_n(k_c b) \tag{3.111}$$

where the primes indicate differentiation with respect to r.   Combining Eqs. (3.110) and (3.111) yields the condition which determines allowable values of k_c on the given boundaries:

$$J'_n(k_ca)N'_n(k_cb) - J'_n(k_cb)N'_n(k_ca) = 0 \qquad (3.112)$$

Solutions of (3.112) for k_c with given values of b/a are shown graphically for several modes in Fig. 3.10† When k_c is determined, the complete expression for H_z is established, and from it all of the remaining components of field may be obtained by the use of Eqs. (3.70) to (3.73) in Table 3.3.

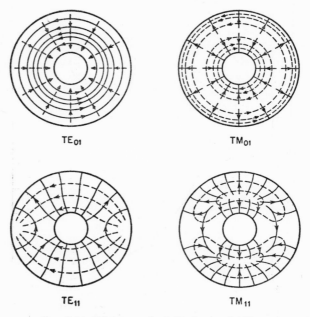

TE$_{01}$ TM$_{01}$

TE$_{11}$ TM$_{11}$

FIG. 3.11. Higher-mode fields in coaxial line.

The fields of the coaxial TM modes are obtained in a similar way, except that we now write (3.109) for the axial electric field and use the boundary condition $E_z = 0$ at $r = a$ and $r = b$. This leads to a transcendental equation for k_c in the form

$$J_n(k_ca)N_n(k_cb) - J_n(k_cb)N_n(k_ca) = 0 \qquad (3.113)$$

Values of k_c satisfying (3.113) are also given in Fig. 3.10, and the completed solution for E_z in the form of Eq. (3.109) can be found. The transverse components of field of the coaxial TM modes can then be

† See also T. Moreno, "Microwave Transmission Design Data," p. 71, Dover Publications, New York, 1958; N. Marcuvitz, *op. cit.*, pp. 77–78.

derived from E_z by the use of Eqs. (3.78) to (3.81) of Table 3.5, thus completing the solution for the coaxial TM modes. Field configurations of typical coaxial TE and TM modal fields are illustrated in Fig. 3.11. The constants $k_c a$ of TE_{01} coincide with those of TM_{11}.

3.9. Surface Current in a Nonideal Conductor

In our evaluation of boundary conditions for the fields in transmission systems, we have utilized the concept of the ideal conductor, assumed to have indefinitely great conductivity and within which no time-varying fields can exist. Real conducting materials approach this ideal but differ from it by amounts depending on their material properties.

In order to investigate the effects of departure from ideal conductivity, let us consider a wave in air or vacuum incident upon the surface of a material characterized by the constants σ, ϵ, and μ, for conductivity, dielectric constant, and permeability, respectively. The material surface is assumed to occupy the xy plane. The propagation factor of the wave outside the material may be taken in general to be

$$f_0 = e^{(j\omega t - k_x x - k_y y - k_z z)} \tag{3.114}$$

and the wave within the material is represented by the function

$$f_i = e^{(j\omega t - k_x' x - k_y' y - k_z' z)} \tag{3.115}$$

In order to match the two waves at the interface, we must have $k_x = k_x'$ and $k_y = k_y'$. The propagation in the direction normal to the boundary must be considered separately. To do so, we may consider a wave incident normally upon the boundary; $k_x = 0 = k_y$. Then, $k_z = j\omega/c = j \sqrt{\mu_0\epsilon_0}\,\omega$ outside the surface, where c is the velocity of light. However, within the material, we must use the effective dielectric constant ϵ_{eff} from Eq. (2.65).

$$k_z' = j \sqrt{\mu\epsilon_{\text{eff}}}\,\omega$$

$$= j \sqrt{\mu\epsilon \left(1 + \frac{\sigma}{j\omega\epsilon}\right)}\,\omega$$

$$= j^{\frac{1}{2}} \sqrt{\mu\sigma\omega \left(1 + \frac{j\omega\epsilon}{\sigma}\right)}$$

If the material is a moderately good conductor, $\omega\epsilon/\sigma \ll 1$, and we may write, to good approximation,

$$k_z' = \frac{1 + j}{\sqrt{2}} \sqrt{\mu\sigma\omega} \tag{3.116}$$

Thus the wave propagates in the material with the propagation factor

$$e^{-\sqrt{\mu\sigma\omega/2}\,z}e^{-j\sqrt{\mu\sigma\omega/2}\,z} \tag{3.117}$$

Therefore the field is attenuated in amplitude and will have fallen to a fraction $1/e$ of its surface value in a distance

$$\delta = \frac{1}{\sqrt{\pi f \mu \sigma}} \tag{3.118}$$

The distance δ is called the skin depth of the material and is a measure of the depth of penetration of the fields within a nonideal conductor. It may therefore for practical purposes be assumed that the surface current, which we have seen is related to tangential magnetic field $\mathbf{H}_t$ by

$$\mathbf{K} = \hat{n} \times \mathbf{H}_t \tag{3.119}$$

flows entirely in the skin layer of depth δ. This assumption enables us to define a surface resistance of the material

$$R_s = \frac{\rho}{\delta} = \frac{1}{\sigma\delta} = \sqrt{\frac{\pi f \mu}{\sigma}} \tag{3.120}$$

The surface resistance is measured in ohms per unit square of surface area. With this definition the energy dissipation due to surface current can be calculated:

$$W_s = \tfrac{1}{2} R_s K^2 \tag{3.121}$$

in watts per unit area.

3.10. Attenuation in Waveguide Transmission

In studying waveguide transmission, we are concerned with that special class of electromagnetic fields which we have regarded as waves traveling along the axis of a guiding system in the z direction. Each component of the electromagnetic field has therefore been described by an analytic expression of the general form

$$X(x)\,Y(y)e^{j\omega t - k_z z}$$

in rectangular coordinates, for example. When the guiding system is lossless, k_z is purely imaginary and equal to $j\beta_g$. In this event, the amplitude of the wave does not change during its travel, since the exponential function of imaginary argument always has unit amplitude. When the conductivity of the dielectric filling the guide is not zero, however, or the conductivity of the material composing the guide walls is noninfinite, there will occur power losses in these materials during the travel of the wave.

Attenuation due to lossy dielectric filling the guide is readily taken into account by replacing the dielectric constant ϵ with the effective dielectric constant: $\epsilon_{\text{eff}} = \epsilon(1 + \sigma/j\omega\epsilon)$. The propagation constant then becomes

$$
\begin{aligned}
k_z &= \pm \sqrt{k_c{}^2 - \mu\epsilon_{\text{eff}}\omega^2} \\
&\approx \pm \sqrt{\mu\epsilon_{\text{eff}}(\omega_c{}^2 - \omega^2)} \\
&= \pm \sqrt{\mu\epsilon(\omega_c{}^2 - \omega^2)} \sqrt{1 + \frac{\sigma}{j\omega\epsilon}}
\end{aligned}
\tag{3.122}
$$

In materials normally used as dielectrics, the displacement current is much greater than the conduction current, in the frequency range we are considering. Therefore, $\sigma/\omega\epsilon \ll 1$, and we may use the approximation

$$
k_z \approx \pm \sqrt{\mu\epsilon(\omega_c{}^2 - \omega^2)} \left(1 + \frac{\sigma}{2j\omega\epsilon}\right)
$$

At frequencies above cutoff

$$
k_z \approx \pm \left(\beta_g \frac{\sigma}{2\omega\epsilon} + j\beta_g\right)
\tag{3.123}
$$

$$
k_z = \pm(\alpha_d + j\beta_g)
\tag{3.124}
$$

where $\beta_g = \sqrt{\mu\epsilon(\omega^2 - \omega_c{}^2)}$ is the propagation constant which the guide would have if the dielectric were lossless. The real part α_d of Eq. (3.124) is the attenuation constant for lossy dielectric, and all the field components will be multiplied by the decrement factor $\exp(\pm\beta_g\sigma/2\omega\epsilon)z$, when dielectric loss occurs, if $\omega \gg \omega_c$.

The attenuation of waveguide waves which is caused by the dissipation of energy as ohmic loss in the guide walls may be calculated on the basis of the effect which this energy loss has upon the field amplitudes. The energy W_z being transported by the waveguide is given by the Poynting vector calculation

$$
W_z = \tfrac{1}{2}\iint \mathbf{E} \times \mathbf{H}^* \cdot da
\tag{3.125}
$$

Since all the components of the fields are interrelated by constant factors, the result of this calculation is proportional to the square of the peak value of any one of the field components, represented by E_1:

$$
W_z = CE_1{}^2
\tag{3.126}
$$

where C is a constant. Then, differentiating with respect to z,

$$
\frac{dW_z}{dz} = 2CE_1 \frac{dE_1}{dz}
\tag{3.127}
$$

Dividing Eq. (3.127) by (3.126), we have

$$\frac{d(\ln E_1)}{dz} = \frac{1}{2} \frac{dW_z/dz}{W_z} \tag{3.128}$$

When the variation of W_z with z is due to dissipation of energy in the walls, we can calculate

$$\frac{dW_z}{dz} = \lim_{\Delta z \to 0} \frac{\Delta W_z}{\Delta z} \tag{3.129}$$

where ΔW_z is the average ohmic loss in a length Δz of waveguide walls,

$$\begin{aligned} \Delta W_z &= \tfrac{1}{2} R_s \iint K^2 \, da \\ &= \tfrac{1}{2} R_s \iint H_t^2 \, da \end{aligned} \tag{3.130}$$

where H_t is the component of magnetic field tangential to the waveguide walls. The integral is performed at the conducting surfaces over a strip of axial length Δz, around the circumference of the waveguide cross section.

Using Eqs. (3.130) and (3.125) in Eq. (3.128), we have

$$\frac{d(\ln E_1)}{dz} = \frac{1}{2} \frac{R_s}{\Delta z} \frac{\iint H_t^2 \, da}{\iint \mathbf{E} \times \mathbf{H}^* \cdot da} \tag{3.131}$$

We define the right side of Eq. (3.131) as α_w. Then

$$E_1 = E_{10} e^{-\alpha_w z}$$

where α_w is the attenuation constant for wall losses:

$$\alpha_w = \frac{R_s}{2} \frac{\oint H_t^2 \, dl}{\iint \mathbf{E} \times \mathbf{H} \cdot da} \tag{3.132}$$

The integral in the numerator of (3.132) is carried over the guide perimeter, and in the denominator over its cross section. The total attenuation in the guide is then due to the combined effects:

$$E_1 = E_{10} e^{-(\alpha_d + \alpha_w) z} \tag{3.133}$$

Both α_d and α_w are frequency dependent, and both have a different value in general for each mode of propagation, as may be shown by calculation of Eqs. (3.123) and (3.132).† The frequency dependence of R_s, as established in Eq. (3.120), contributes to the influence of frequency variation upon the attenuation constant α_w.

3.11. Wave Velocities

It has been noted that in our study of wave-guiding systems, we have been dealing with a special class of electromagnetic fields

† Cf. also Fig. 9.2.

These are the fields of which the dependence upon coordinates z and t is expressed by the function exp $[j\phi(z,t)]$, where

$$\phi = \omega t + \beta_g z \tag{3.134}$$

Our reason for this choice, is, of course, that we have adopted the z axis as the direction parallel to the axis of the waveguide, and we attach a special significance to those variations of field which occur so as to keep ϕ constant. Constancy of ϕ implies that $d\phi$ is zero:

$$d\phi = \omega\, dt + \beta_g\, dz = 0 \tag{3.135}$$

from which we define the phase velocity of the traveling wave,

$$v_p = \frac{dz}{dt} = -\frac{\omega}{\beta_g} \tag{3.136}$$

The phase velocity is in fact just that velocity with which it would be necessary to move along the waveguide in order to always remain adjacent to points where the fields were instantaneously going through a specific phase of their cyclic variations. This would be comparable with following the peak of a ripple as it moves across the surface of a fluid. In waveguides, the phase velocity has been found to be equal to

$$v_p = \frac{\omega}{\sqrt{\mu\epsilon\omega^2 - k_c^2}} \tag{3.137}$$

We have encountered another velocity, however, in connection with our calculations. This is the velocity of plane electromagnetic waves in free space, far from any boundaries. A plane polarized electric wave in space distant from its source can be represented by an expression of the form

$$\hat{y}E_y = \hat{y}E_0 e^{j(\omega t - \beta z)} \tag{3.138}$$

where the direction of polarization has been taken parallel to the y axis. In the wave equation $\nabla^2 E_y = -\mu_0\epsilon_0\omega^2 E_y$, Eq. (3.138) is a solution if $\beta = \sqrt{\mu_0\epsilon_0}\,\omega$. Hence, the phase velocity of these waves is

$$v_p = c = \frac{1}{\sqrt{\mu_0\epsilon_0}} = 3 \times 10^8 \quad \text{m/sec} \tag{3.139}$$

This velocity is constant and independent of frequency. A similar wave traveling in a material medium, having constants $\mu = \mu_r\mu_0$ and $\epsilon = \epsilon_r\epsilon_0$, would have phase velocity

$$v_p' = \frac{c}{\sqrt{\mu_r\epsilon_r}} \tag{3.140}$$

In some material media, μ_r or ϵ_r may be functions of frequency. Consequently the phase velocity depends on frequency; i.e., these materials are dispersive.

Equation (3.137) shows that a waveguide is a dispersive medium for the propagation of waves of field along the guide axis. This is not due to the nature of the material filling the guide but is a consequence of the guide configuration as it influences the behavior of fields within it. It may be noted that the phase velocity of the waveguide is always greater than the velocity of light, increasing toward infinity as the frequency approaches the cutoff frequency of the guide. This fact is not in violation of the principle of relativity, however, which states that no signal can be transmitted at a velocity greater than the velocity of light. It will be seen below that the dispersion of the waveguide results in the disintegration of the signal, if an attempt is made to transmit at frequencies for which v_p approaches infinity.

The phase velocities which we have derived above are the velocities of continuous, steady-state waves of a single frequency. In order to transmit any intelligence electrically, it is necessary to interrupt or otherwise modulate the transmitted wave. The simplest form of signal conveyed by a wave may be considered to be a "dash," or wave train of constant amplitude, transmitted for a finite time. The methods of Fourier analysis show that this signal consists, not of the single frequency of the oscillator, but rather of a band of frequencies, distributed about the oscillator frequency. The shorter the wave train is made, the wider is the band of frequencies composing it. The significance of this fact for a dispersive medium of transmission, such as a waveguide, is apparent in that the high-frequency components of the pulse will travel more slowly than the low-frequency components [cf. Eq. (3.137)], with the result that the shape of the pulse is distorted during travel. The rate at which the pulse travels cannot be uniquely characterized by a single value of velocity, since all its wave components travel at different velocities. It is possible, however, to obtain a useful measure of the speed of a pulse. This measure is the group velocity of the pulse.

Consider a wave pulse centered on a wave of angular frequency ω_0 and also containing component waves each of amplitude a_n and separated by small frequency intervals $\Delta\omega_n$ from the center frequency. Thus, the center-frequency wave representing the steady-state oscillator signal is

$$f_0 = a_0 e^{j(\omega_0 t - \beta z)} \tag{3.141}$$

and the nth component wave, at frequency $(\omega_0 + \Delta\omega_n)$, may be expressed by a first-order expansion about ω_0:

$$
\begin{aligned}
f_n &= a_n \left(f_0 + \frac{df_0}{d\omega} \Delta\omega_n \right) \\
&= a_n \left[f_0 + \left(\frac{\partial f_0}{\partial \beta} \frac{d\beta}{d\omega} + \frac{\partial f_0}{\partial \omega} \right) \Delta\omega_n \right]
\end{aligned}
\tag{3.142}
$$

Then the total pulse composed by summing all of the component waves is

$$
\begin{aligned}
F &= f_0 + \sum_n f_n \\
&= f_0 + \sum_n a_n \left[f_0 + \left(\frac{\partial f_0}{\partial \omega} + \frac{\partial f_0}{\partial \beta} \frac{d\beta}{d\omega} \right) \Delta\omega_n \right] \\
&= f_0 \left\{ 1 + \sum_n a_n \left[1 + j \left(t - z \frac{\partial \beta}{\partial \omega} \right) \Delta\omega_n \right] \right\}
\end{aligned}
\tag{3.143}
$$

We now see that this expression for the pulse may be regarded as the wave $f_0 = a_0 e^{j(\omega_0 t - \beta z)}$, multiplied by an average amplitude term (in braces). Examination of this amplitude term shows that it will be kept constant if the coordinate z is changed at the rate

$$
\frac{dz}{dt} = v_g = \frac{d\omega}{d\beta} \bigg|_{\omega_0}
\tag{3.144}
$$

This rate is the group velocity, and it is the average speed at which the wave envelope (the pulse) travels along the waveguide.

In Sec. 3.4, we have discussed the $\omega - \beta$ diagram of a waveguide in comparison with that of a TEM mode system, the two-conductor line. Referring to this diagram, plotted in Fig. 3.2 as a k-β diagram, where $= \sqrt{\mu\epsilon}\,\omega = \omega/c$, we see that the slope of a straight line extending from the origin to the k-β curve is equal to v_p/c at angular frequency ω. Likewise, the slope of the k-β curve, equal to $dk/d\beta$, is v_g/c, the ratio of the group velocity of the transmission system to the velocity of light in the medium. The form of the k-β curve of the waveguide shows that ω_c, the slope v_g/c equals zero. Hence, no signal will travel along the guide at ω_c. At this frequency v_p is infinite, as we have found. In the TEM-mode line, $v_p = v_g = c$ at all frequencies. As frequency increases, the propagation constant of the waveguide approaches that of the line and hence that of free space.

PROBLEMS

3.1. Show that the TM_{01} wave is the transverse magnetic wave of lowest cutoff frequency traveling in the z direction with $H_z = 0 \neq E_z$, which satisfies the boundary conditions between two horizontal conducting planes of infinite extent, parallel to the xz plane.   Give, for this wave,

(a) All components of field

(b) Phase velocity and cutoff frequency

(c) Sketch of the electric and magnetic field lines of the wave

3.2. Obtain Eqs. (3.34) to (3.37) from Maxwell's equations in rectangular coordinates with $E_z = 0$ and $\partial/\partial z = k_z$.

3.3. Obtain Eqs. (3.78) to (3.81) from Maxwell's equations in cylindrical coordinates with $H_z = 0$ and $\partial/\partial z = k_z$.

3.4. Show that the maxima of the transverse H field of a traveling wave of the TE_{10} mode in rectangular waveguide coincide in axial position with the traveling maxima of the E field of this mode.

3.5. (a) Show that the superposition of the two rectangular TE_{10}-mode waves of equal amplitude and opposite directions of travel in a shorted guide produces standing-wave maxima and minima of field along the guide axis.

(b) Show that the standing-wave maxima of the E field of part a are displaced by $\lambda_g/4$ along the guide axis from the standing-wave maxima of transverse H field.

3.6. (a) Show that, for the transmission of a given amount of power in the TE_{10} mode in rectangular waveguide, increasing the frequency of transmission reduces the peak electric field in the guide.

(b) Show that operation in the TE_{10} mode requires lower electric field in the guide than operation in the TE_{n0} mode $(n > 1)$ for transmission of a given amount of power.

3.7. Determine the coordinate points in the cross section of a rectangular waveguide operating in the TE_{22} mode at which the peak absolute value of magnetic field occurs.

3.8. Prove that if the TE_{mn} and $TE_{m'n'}$ modes have the same guide wavelength at a given frequency in air-filled rectangular waveguide of inside dimensions 0. by 0.4 in., the condition $(m^2 - m'^2)/(n^2 - n'^2) = -(\frac{9}{4})^2$ must hold.   Find two mode pairs which satisfy this condition

3.9. Find the three rectangular-waveguide modes of lowest cutoff frequency which can propagate in a waveguide having conducting fins extending into the cross section of the guide as shown in Fig. 3.12.   All dimensions are in centimeters

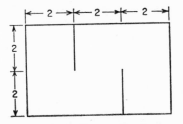

FIG. 3.12. Waveguide fins.

3.10. An air-filled waveguide of square cross section, 1 cm on a side, transports energy in the TE_{10} mode at the rate of 1 hp (746 joules/sec). If the frequency is 2×10^{10} cps, what is the peak value of electric field occurring in the guide?

3.11. A circular air-filled waveguide of 1 cm inside radius is operated in the TE_{21} mode.

(a) Find the cutoff frequency.

(b) If the guide is to be filled with a dielectric material having $\sigma = 0$, $\epsilon_r = 2$, and $\mu_r = 1$, to what value must its radius be changed in order to maintain the cutoff frequency at its initial value?

3.12. Derive the expression for the surface current flowing on the inner surface of a circular waveguide of radius a which is operating in the TE_{01} mode. From the result, explain what would be the effect on the transmission of the mode if the waveguide is cut completely through with a thin transverse saw cut.

3.13. Find the frequency at which the attenuation due to wall losses is at a minimum in air-filled circular waveguide of radius a, operating in the TM_{01} mode.

3.14. Consider the integral

$$W_{12} = \iint |\mathbf{E}_{t1} \times \mathbf{H}_{t2}^*| \, dx \, dy$$

where $\mathbf{E}_{t1}$ is the transverse electric field of the TE_{mn} mode and $\mathbf{H}_{t2}$ is the transverse magnetic field of the $TE_{m'n'}$ mode in rectangular waveguide. Show that this integral has zero value unless $m = m'$ and $n = n'$. Interpret this result in terms of the energy transported in multimode transmission.

3.15. What is the transverse magnetic mode of lowest cutoff frequency that will propagate in the half-coaxial guide shown in Fig. 3.13? (Dimensions are in centimeters.) Find the value of f_c for this mode.

FIG. 3.13. Half-coaxial guide.

CHAPTER 4

Discontinuities and Impedances in Waveguides

In the preceding chapter the complete single-mode solutions of the electromagnetic field equation in waveguide boundaries were obtained. A natural subdivision of the solutions was found, separating them into classes in which the axial component of field is electric or magnetic. In each of these classes, the vectors of transverse field are derivable from the axial component, the z component of field thus acting as a generating function for the transverse fields:†

$$\mathbf{E}_n = \mathbf{E}_{tn} + \hat{z}E_{zn} \tag{4.1}$$
$$\mathbf{H}_n = \mathbf{H}_{tn} + \hat{z}H_{zn} \tag{4.2}$$

where, in rectangular components, $\mathbf{E}_{tn} = \hat{x}E_{xn} + \hat{y}E_{yn}$ and

$$\mathbf{H}_{tn} = \hat{x}H_{xn} + \hat{y}H_{yn}$$

TE:

$$\mathbf{H}_{tn} = \frac{j\beta_g}{k_c^2}\,\boldsymbol{\nabla}_t H_{zn} \tag{4.3}$$

$$\mathbf{E}_{tn} = \frac{j\omega\mu}{k_c^2}\,\hat{z} \times \boldsymbol{\nabla}_t H_{zn} \tag{4.4}$$

TM:

$$\mathbf{E}_{tn} = \frac{j\beta_g}{k_c^2}\,\boldsymbol{\nabla}_t E_{zn} \tag{4.5}$$

$$\mathbf{H}_{tn} = -\frac{j\omega\epsilon}{k_c^2}\,\hat{z} \times \boldsymbol{\nabla}_t E_{zn} \tag{4.6}$$

TE:

$$H_z = \begin{cases} \cos\dfrac{m\pi x}{a}\cos\dfrac{n\pi y}{b}\,e^{j\beta_g z} & \text{rectangular guide} \\[2ex] J_n\!\left(p'_{nm}\dfrac{r}{a}\right)\cos n\theta\,e^{j\beta_g z} & \text{circular guide} \end{cases} \tag{4.}$$

† In Eqs. (4.1) to (4.6) and in Sec. 4.1, each individual waveguide mode assigned a single index letter such as n. Thus, n represents one of the TE_{mn} TM_{mn} modes. In addition, the subscript t refers to transverse-field quantit

TM:

$$E_z = \begin{cases} \sin \dfrac{m\pi x}{a} \sin \dfrac{n\pi y}{b}\, e^{j\beta_g z} & \text{rectangular guide} \\[2ex] J_n \left(p_{nm} \dfrac{r}{a} \right) \cos n\theta\, e^{j\beta_g z} & \text{circular guide} \end{cases} \qquad (4.8)$$

The traveling waves of field thus found correctly represent the electromagnetic field situation in lossless uniform waveguide. The field-component expressions received their form through having been required to satisfy the boundary conditions imposed by the smooth uninterrupted walls of the waveguide. By the superposition of two such waves having arbitrary complex amplitudes and opposite directions of travel, corresponding to positive and negative β_g, a resultant field expression having periodic variation in the z direction can be produced. The formation of a standing wave of field in this way does not affect the form of the transverse distribution.

4.1. The Analysis of Discontinuity Fields

In general, waveguides first become useful when they are terminated or interrupted by a discontinuity structure of some form. It is by means of the use of suitably selected discontinuities and obstacles that the conventional circuit functions of coupling, change of impedance level, frequency selection, and subdivision of energy are achieved in microwave systems. It is obvious, however, that our single-mode field solutions, having fixed transverse distributions and limited variability in the axial direction, will be incapable of satisfying boundary conditions for the fields over the surface of a conducting or dielectric obstacle of arbitrary shape extending in three dimensions in the waveguide. In the case of an obstacle of sufficiently irregular shape, it may, in fact, be a practical impossibility to obtain an exact solution for the electromagnetic fields in the neighborhood of the obstacle.

We are able, nonetheless, to retain our propagating-mode terminology for the description of waveguide fields in the neighborhood of arbitrary discontinuities, at least in principle, by reason of the fact that the collection of higher-mode solutions that we possess is a complete set of functions. The significance of this fact for our purposes is that we can represent an arbitrary function of the three space coordinates by a linear combination of waveguide modal functions with suitably selected coefficients, much in the same way that a general periodic function can be expressed as a Fourier series of sine and cosine functions. In actual cases, most or all of the higher-mode terms above the dominant mode will have cutoff frequencies greater than the operating frequency of the waveguide and thus will not propagate away from the vicinity of the discontinuity which causes them to arise.   The higher modes merely exist locally to serve the function of satisfying boundary conditions.   Out of the infinite series of modal terms, only the fundamental-mode wave survives at distances from the discontinuity, preserving the magnitude and phase required of it in the boundary series at the obstacle.   Thus it is that we customarily carry out our analysis of a waveguide discontinuity or impedance in terms of its effect upon the fundamental-mode wave in the guide.

By the use of Eqs. (4.3) to (4.6), we can prove the orthogonality of the expressions for the components of field of the various waveguide modes.   These orthogonalities are of importance to us in that they implement the hypothesis that we may expand an arbitrary field in a waveguide as an infinite series of higher-mode waveguide transmission fields.   We require for the proof an integral theorem related to Green's theorem which is derivable as follows.

Consider the function $V\nabla U$, where V and U are scalar functions of coordinates, and form the integral of $\nabla \cdot V\nabla U$ over the spatial domain of interest

$$\iiint \nabla \cdot V \nabla U \, d\tau = \iint V\nabla U \cdot d\mathbf{a} \tag{4.9}$$

where Gauss' theorem has been used to form the equality (4.9).   The integral on the left may be transformed by the use of a vector identity

$$\iiint (\nabla V \cdot \nabla U + V\nabla^2 U) \, d\tau = \iint V\nabla U \cdot d\mathbf{a} \tag{4.10}$$

Equation (4.10) is now converted to the form appropriate to the two-dimensional coordinate space of a waveguide cross section, so that $\iiint d\tau$ becomes $\iint da$; ∇^2 becomes $\nabla_t{}^2$, the transverse Laplacian; ∇ becomes ∇_t; and $V\nabla U \cdot d\mathbf{a}$ becomes $V(\partial U/\partial\nu) \, dl$, where $\partial/\partial\nu$ is the normal derivative on the boundary of the cross-sectional area.

$$\iint (\nabla_t V \cdot \nabla_t U + V\nabla_t{}^2 U) \, da = \oint V \frac{\partial U}{\partial \nu} \, dl \tag{4.11}$$

The equation corresponding to (4.11) which is obtained by starting with the function $U\nabla V$ is

$$\iint (\nabla_t U \cdot \nabla_t V + U\nabla_t{}^2 V) \, da = \oint U \frac{\partial V}{\partial \nu} \, dl \tag{4.12}$$

Subtraction of (4.12) from (4.11) yields

$$\iint (V\nabla_t{}^2 U - U\nabla_t{}^2 V) \, da = \oint \left(V \frac{\partial U}{\partial \nu} - U \frac{\partial V}{\partial \nu} \right) dl \tag{4.13}$$

Equation (4.13) is now employed by making the substitutions $V = H_{zn}$ and $U = H_{zm}$, and with the use of the definition of k_c^2, which is $\nabla_t^2 H_z = -k_c^2 H_z$, we obtain

$$(k_{cn}^2 - k_{cm}^2) \iint H_{zn} H_{zm} \, da = \oint \left(H_{zn} \frac{\partial H_{zm}}{\partial \nu} - H_{zm} \frac{\partial H_{zn}}{\partial \nu} \right) dl \qquad (4.14)$$

where $\partial H_z / \partial \nu$ is the normal derivative of H_z at the surface of the waveguide. Using the fact that $\partial H_z / \partial \nu = 0$ for the TE modes, the right side of Eq. (4.14) vanishes. Then, if $k_{cn}^2 - k_{cm}^2$ is not equal to zero, we obtain the expression of the orthogonality of the longitudinal magnetic field components

$$\iint H_{zn} H_{zm} \, da = 0 \qquad (4.15)$$

In the event that $k_{cn}^2 - k_{cm}^2 = 0$ for a pair of unlike modes H_{zn} and H_{zm} (i.e., the modes are degenerate), it is always possible to replace the two degenerate modes with the alternate pair of modes

$$H_{zn}, \qquad H_{zm} - H_{zn} \frac{\iint H_{zm} H_{zn} \, da}{\iint H_{zn}^2 \, da} \qquad (4.16)$$

The functions (4.16) are easily shown to be mutually orthogonal, and by their use, the orthogonality of the infinite set of functions H_{zn} is established.

With the orthogonality conditions (4.15) demonstrated, it is now possible to return to Eq. (4.11) and prove the orthogonality of the transverse components of magnetic field of the TE modes. Using the same substitutions for V and U as before, and employing Eq. (4.3) for $\nabla_t H_z$, we obtain from (4.11)

$$\frac{k_{cn}^2}{j\beta_{gn}} \frac{k_{cm}^2}{j\beta_{gm}} \iint \mathbf{H}_{tn} \cdot \mathbf{H}_{tm} \, da - k_{cm}^2 \iint H_{zn} H_{zm} \, da = \oint H_{zn} \frac{\partial H_{zm}}{\partial \nu} \, dl$$

$$(4.17)$$

The right side of (4.17) vanishes as before, and the orthogonality of the H_{zn} causes the second term on the left to vanish, leaving

$$\iint \mathbf{H}_{tn} \cdot \mathbf{H}_{tm} \, da = 0$$

By following procedures similar to those we have used above for the TE-mode magnetic fields, the H field components of the TM modes may also be shown to be mutually orthogonal, and orthogonal moreover to the TE component functions.† The orthogonality of the

† J. C. Slater, "Microwave Electronics," D. Van Nostrand Company, Inc., Princeton, N.J., 1950.

modal functions of the electric **E** field components can likewise be proved in similar fashion.

The orthogonality of the complete set of modal functions enables us to find an infinite series of modal functions which will represent the electromagnetic field disturbances in the neighborhood of an arbitrary discontinuity inserted into continuous waveguide. The form of the series expansions which will be used for this purpose is

$$\mathbf{E} = \sum_n \mathbf{E}_{tn}(A_n e^{-j\beta_g z} + B_n e^{+j\beta_g z}) + \hat{z} \sum_n E_{zn}(A_n e^{-j\beta_g z} - B_n e^{-j\beta_g z}) \quad (4.18)$$

$$\mathbf{H} = \sum_n \mathbf{H}_{tn}(A_n e^{-j\beta_g z} - B_n e^{+j\beta_g z}) + \hat{z} \sum_n H_{zn}(A_n e^{-j\beta_g z} + B_n e^{-j\beta_g z}) \quad (4.19)$$

In Eqs. (4.18) and (4.19), the wave numbers β_g of each term have values characteristic of the individual modes. The complex amplitudes A_n and B_n of the forward- and backward-traveling waves have been preceded by signs which are chosen consistently with respect to the respective phases of the various components. The forward and returning waves of $\mathbf{E}_{tn}$ have been added positively, by convention. When this assignment of signs is made, the returning wave of $\mathbf{H}_t$ necessarily receives a negative sign, so that the Poynting energy vector of the returning wave is opposite in sign from that of the forward wave. Since the transverse fields are derivable from the corresponding z-component fields, the assignment of signs to the former predetermines the signs of the latter, and hence they appear as in (4.18) and (4.19).

Having written the modal expansions (4.18) and (4.19) for the **E** and **H** fields in a waveguide region, there remains the task of evaluating the coefficients A_n and B_n of the general term, in the series appropriate to a given boundary situation. In order to find these two constants, we require two algebraic equations relating them. Two such equations are available if we know the distributions of any two components of the **E** or **H** fields over a suitable surface, such as a cross section of the waveguide. Alternatively, it is sufficient to know the distribution of one of the components over two cross sections bounding the region where the fields exist. For example, if we know that the distribution of E_y at the plane $z = 0$ is the function F_{y0}, we may then write the y-component equation of (4.18) as

$$F_{y0} = \sum_l E_{yn}(A_n + B_n) \quad (4.20)$$

Then, multiplying both sides of (4.20) by the mth modal function E_{ym} and integrating over the cross section at $z = 0$, we obtain

$$\frac{\iint F_{y0} E_{ym} \, dx \, dy}{\iint E_{ym}^2 \, dx \, dy} = A_m + B_m \quad (4.21)$$

All the terms of the summation in (4.20) except the mth term have vanished, owing to the orthogonality of the E_{yn}'s. Obviously, we shall require a second condition such as (4.21) to enable us to find both A_m and B_m, although Eq. (4.21) permits us to determine the ratio B_m/A_m, for a given incident-wave amplitude A_m.

The problem of finding the local field distributions set up by general waveguide structures is laborious and beyond the scope of our present work, but methods of solution are available, and distributions have been found for a number of cases.† We shall cite the results of such work at a later point, in our discussion of the effective impedances represented by typical structures. We can, however, consider here an elementary application of the field expansions (4.18) and (4.19). Consider the example of a section of waveguide with conducting plates placed transversely across the cross sections at $z = 0$ and $z = L$. Then, we know that $\mathbf{E}_t$ is tangent to the conductor at the plates and hence must vanish there. Likewise, H_z is normal to the planes at $z = 0$ and $z = L$ and must also vanish there. We may work with either of these conditions. Thus, using (4.18), the conditions on $\mathbf{E}_t$ lead to

At $z = 0$:

$$0 = \sum_n \mathbf{E}_{tn}(A_n + B_n) \tag{4.22}$$

At $z = L$:

$$0 = \sum_n \mathbf{E}_{tn}(A_n e^{-j\beta_g L} + B_n e^{+j\beta_g L}) \tag{4.23}$$

Formation of the scalar product of a modal function $\mathbf{E}_{tm}$ with both sides of (4.22) and integration over a cross section yield the result that $B_m = -A_m$ for all modes. Using this fact in (4.23), we obtain

$$0 = \sum_n \mathbf{E}_{tn} A_n \sin \beta_g L \tag{4.24}$$

Multiplication, as before, by any modal function $\mathbf{E}_{tm}$ and integration over a cross section show that

$$\sin \beta_g L = 0 \tag{4.25}$$

or

$$\beta_g L = p\pi \tag{4.26}$$

where $p = 0, 1, 2, 3, \ldots$.

A similar result is obtained for every mode, but the significance of this result appears when we recall that the value of β_g is typical of each

† N. Marcuvitz (ed.), "Waveguide Handbook," McGraw-Hill Book Company, Inc., New York, 1951; J. C. Slater, op. cit.; R. Collin, "Field Theory of Guided Waves," McGraw-Hill Book Company, Inc., New York, 1960.

mode, since we have $\beta_g = (\mu\epsilon\omega^2 - k_{cm}^2)^{\frac{1}{2}}$. We can use this fact to determine the frequencies at which Eq. (4.26) is valid, and hence the frequencies of operation which are allowed for the existence of the mth waveguide mode in the specified boundaries:

$$\omega_{mp} = \left(\frac{p^2\pi^2/L^2 + k_{cm}^2}{\mu\epsilon} \right)^{\frac{1}{2}} \tag{4.27}$$

The structure we have thus considered is a type of cavity resonator, with resonant frequencies given by Eq. (4.27). We shall return to further consideration of resonators in Chap. 5.

4.2. Waveguide Voltage and Current

It has been previously noted that, in many practical cases, the propagation constants β_g of all terms except that of the dominant mode in the field expansions are imaginary, corresponding to attenuation of the higher-mode fields. Therefore only the dominant-mode term will be observable at appreciable distances from the discontinuity. The dominant-mode waves of most waveguides are more stable, are more easily excited, and have lower loss than higher-mode waves. The usual practice is therefore to operate waveguides in the dominant mode. For this reason much of our study of microwave systems will be understood to be made in terms of the effects of the structural components of the system upon the propagation of dominant-mode waves in the connected waveguides.

A given piece of microwave equipment will give rise to relative values of A_1 and B_1, the magnitude and phase coefficients of the dominant-mode incident and reflected waves, which are characteristic of the piece of equipment. The two waves will add, in general, to produce a standing wave of the modal fields in the waveguide. This behavior is reminiscent of the effect of the connection of an impedance to a conventional transmission line, in that an impedance produces a specific reflection, for a given incident voltage wave in the line. Since the transverse distribution functions of all dominant-mode E fields in a waveguide are alike, we might inquire whether we cannot select as a voltage function the value of a field at some convenient point in the cross section of the waveguide, such as, for example, the peak value of E field at the center of the guide. This value of field would then be the counterpart of transmission-line voltage, having interference maxima and minima along the guide axis. From the standing waves of this field value, we could evaluate a standing-wave ratio S and a distance $d_{\min}$, from the input plane of the component to the first minimum of field.   Then by direct analogy with the transmission line, an effective impedance of the microwave component could be calculated by the use of Eq. (1.45).

$$z_r = \frac{1 - jS \tan \beta d_{\min}}{S - j \tan \beta d_{\min}}$$

The answer to this conjecture is that such a procedure is indeed possible and is often employed for measurement.   The impedance in its usual application, however, relates a cause with an effect.   In conventional circuit terms, an impedance relates the current with the voltage at a given pair of terminals.   If we can define, in the waveguides connecting microwave components, a voltagelike and a currentlike pair of variables, the ratio of which has the character of an impedance, we shall then be able to employ the great power of existing techniques of circuit analysis for the calculation of the behavior of microwave systems.

The conventionally defined waveguide voltage and current functions are chosen to be waves proportional in magnitude and phase to the transverse electric and magnetic field waves, respectively, of the dominant mode of the waveguide.   The fields E_t and H_t can be seen to be suitable choices for this definition, because in setting up a voltage and current terminology for waveguides, we require two functions which are related by a constant of proportionality.   Equations (4.3) and (4.4) show this to be true of E_t and H_t.

Consider for example the dominant-mode fields of a traveling wave in a rectangular waveguide:

$$E_y = E_0 \sin \frac{\pi x}{a} e^{-j\beta_g z} \tag{4.28}$$

$$H_x = \frac{\beta_g}{\omega\mu} E_0 \sin \frac{\pi x}{a} e^{-j\beta_g z} \tag{4.29}$$

We define voltage and current functions V and I, from which the transverse-coordinate dependence is abstracted, in the following way:

$$E_y = V \frac{1}{K} \sin \frac{\pi x}{a} \tag{4.30}$$

$$H_x = I \frac{1}{K} \sin \frac{\pi x}{a} \tag{4.31}$$

where K is a normalizing constant to be determined.   Equations (4.30) and (4.31) therefore define the voltage and current functions

$$V = KE_0 e^{-j\beta_g z} \tag{4.32}$$

$$I = K \frac{\beta_g}{\omega\mu} E_0 e^{-j\beta_g z} \tag{4.33}$$

The power carried by the traveling waves E_y and H_x is

$$W = \tfrac{1}{2} \iint E_y H_x^* \, dx \, dy = \frac{1}{2} \frac{\beta_g}{\omega\mu} E_0{}^2 \iint \sin^2 \frac{\pi x}{a} \, dx \, dy$$

$$= \frac{\beta_g E_0{}^2}{2\omega\mu} \frac{ab}{2} \tag{4.34}$$

Let us now compare this expression for the power carried by the wave-guide with the results of the following calculations, made by analogy with conventional transmission-line formulas, for the power carried by a single traveling wave. We calculate power in the following forms, using the V and I of Eqs. (4.32) and (4.33):

$$\frac{1}{2} \frac{VV^*}{Z_{0V}} = \frac{1}{2} \frac{K^2 E_0{}^2}{Z_{0V}} \tag{4.35}$$

$$\tfrac{1}{2} I I^* Z_{0I} = \tfrac{1}{2} K^2 \frac{\beta_g{}^2}{\omega^2 \mu^2} E_0{}^2 Z_{0I} \tag{4.36}$$

$$\tfrac{1}{2} V I^* = \tfrac{1}{2} K^2 \frac{\beta_g}{\omega\mu} E_0{}^2 \tag{4.37}$$

Inspection of Eqs. (4.35) to (4.37) shows that each of these correctly yields the power carried by the guide, when the constants Z_{0V}, Z_{0I}, and K^2 are defined by

$$Z_{0V} = Z_{0I} = Z_0 = \frac{\omega\mu}{\beta_g} \tag{4.38}$$

$$K^2 = \frac{ab}{2} \tag{4.39}$$

The quantity Z_0 is customarily called the wave impedance of the waveguide, and K^2 is the normalizing constant for the transverse distribution,

$$K^2 = \int_0^a \int_0^b \sin^2 \frac{\pi x}{a} \, dx \, dy = \frac{ab}{2} \tag{4.40}$$

The normalizing condition for the functions of transverse coordinates may be stated in a more general way, applicable to transmission modes in which the transverse fields are two-component vectors $\mathbf{E}_t$ and $\mathbf{H}_t$. Normalization is then carried out so that the following condition holds:

$$1 = \iint \frac{\mathbf{E}_t}{V} \times \frac{\mathbf{H}_t^*}{I} \cdot d\mathbf{a} \tag{4.41}$$

It is apparent that this condition ensures that the transmitted power is correctly given by $\frac{1}{2}VI^*$. We have

$$W = \frac{1}{2} \iint \mathbf{E}_t \times \mathbf{H}_t^* \cdot da = \frac{1}{2} \iint V \frac{\mathbf{E}_t}{V} \times I^* \left(\frac{\mathbf{H}_t}{I}\right)^* \cdot da$$

$$= \frac{1}{2}VI^* \tag{4.42}$$

since V and I^* do not depend upon the variables of integration.

The waveguide voltage and current, which we have defined in Eqs. (4.32) and (4.33), may now be written, using a normalized amplitude $V_a = KE_0$,

$$V = V_a e^{-j\beta_g z} \tag{4.43}$$

$$I = \frac{V_a}{Z_0} e^{-j\beta_g z} \tag{4.44}$$

The expressions (4.43) and (4.44) are identical in form with the traveling waves of voltage and current on a transmission line. It is readily seen that each satisfies a wave equation of the form $d^2V/dz^2 = -\beta_g^2 V$.

In the case of a waveguide interrupted by a general discontinuity, we have found that both incident and reflected waves of field may be present. Writing V_a and V_b as the respective amplitudes of the corresponding voltage waves, the total waveguide voltage and current will then be

$$V = V_a e^{-j\beta_g z} + V_b e^{+j\beta_g z} \tag{4.45}$$

$$I = \frac{1}{Z_0} (V_a e^{-j\beta_g z} - V_b e^{+j\beta_g z}) \tag{4.46}$$

In Eq. (4.46), a negative sign is associated with the reflected wave of current, owing to the appearance of β_g in the definition [Eq. (4.38)], of the Z_0 of a traveling wave, or, more properly, because of the relative reversal in phase of $\mathbf{H}_t$, as the direction of wave travel is reversed. If the transverse plane marking the input to a given waveguide discontinuity structure† is the plane $z = 0$, then at the input to the discontinuity,

$$V = V_a + V_b = V_a(1 + \rho)$$

$$I = \frac{1}{Z_0} (V_a - V_b) = \frac{V_a}{Z_0} (1 - \rho)$$

where $\rho = V_b/V_a$ is the reflection coefficient of the discontinuity.‡

† The input plane of a discontinuity or obstacle is usually chosen to be sufficiently far from the physical discontinuity so that all higher-mode waves have been attenuated, and only the dominant-mode wave appears.

‡ The reflection coefficient ρ sometimes appears as Γ or R in technical literature. The symbol ρ is that adopted by the IRE Standards on Letter Symbols and Mathematical Signs (57 IRE 21.S1), *Proc. IRE*, vol. 45, p. 1140, August, 1957.

The impedance at the input plane of the discontinuity then has the natural definition

$$Z = \frac{V}{I} = Z_0 \frac{1 + \rho}{1 - \rho} \tag{4.47}$$

It is apparent from the foregoing work that a system of microwave components interconnected by lengths of waveguide can be treated formally as an equivalent system of lumped impedances, interconnected by transmission lines.   In this way, the complete set of tech-

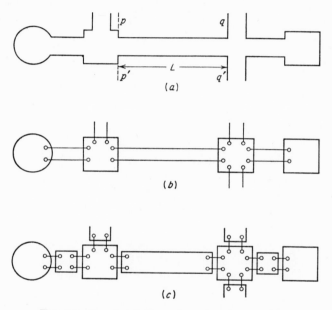

FIG. 4.1. Representations of a microwave system.

niques of transmission-line analysis developed in Chap. 1 can be applied to the connecting waveguides.   Figure 4.1a indicates schematically a portion of a microwave network.   The section of waveguide between the transverse planes pp' and qq' is equivalent to a transmission line of length L, terminated by an impedance $Z_{qq'}$ representing the effect of whatever lies beyond the plane qq' and presenting, therefore, at the input plane pp', an impedance $Z_{pp'}$ equal to [see Eq. (1.51)]

$$Z_{pp'} = Z_0 \frac{Z_{qq'}/Z_0 + j \tan \beta_g L}{1 + j(Z_{qq'}/Z_0) \tan \beta_g L} \tag{4.48}$$

In Eq. (4.48), β_g is the propagation constant of the waveguide. $Z_{pp'}/Z_0$ and $Z_{qq'}/Z_0$ are the input and terminating impedances, respectively, as normalized to the effective characteristic impedance of the section of waveguide. The normalized impedances of given microwave components will ordinarily be used in system calculations, since impedance parameters for the components are definable only in terms of their behavior when connected to specific waveguides.

The procedure we have outlined above consists therefore in treating a microwave system analytically by replacing the system with a set of multi-terminal-pair impedances and junction elements, interconnected by lengths of transmission line, as indicated in Fig. 4.1b. In analyzing the system by means of this representation, the transmission-line formulas are applied successively to the various lengths of waveguide between junction points. Some means must be available for determining the impedances presented at each terminal pair of the junctions or circuit elements to which transmission lines connect. This problem may be solved in simple cases by operating with matched impedances throughout. A matched waveguide component is one which produces no reflected wave in the connected guide. In more general cases, equivalent circuit methods may be used to replace a multiterminal component with an equivalent impedance, or impedance network.

From the equivalent impedance point of view, a section of transmission line or waveguide is, at a single frequency, a four-terminal network element. In this representation we can replace the microwave system by a second equivalent system in which all of the connecting guides are replaced by their corresponding networks, as indicated schematically in Fig. 4.1c. The microwave system is then completely replaced by a network of equivalent impedances. We shall see in the following sections how specific equivalent circuits may be assigned to microwave components. With the entire microwave system replaced by an equivalent circuit, the methods of conventional circuit analysis may be utilized to solve for the relations between waveguide currents and voltages in the various parts of the system.

4.3. Equivalent Impedances and Impedance Networks

In order to be able to proceed with the analysis of a microwave system as an equivalent impedance network, the impedance equivalents of representative waveguide devices and discontinuities will be required. From the point of view in which the microwave system is regarded as a set of discontinuity regions interconnected by lengths of waveguide, or microwave transmission line, the discontinuities will therefore be represented in general by n-terminal-pair devices. Because of the structure of waveguide connections, these may be called, more briefly, n-port devices.

One-terminal-pair Impedances. One-port waveguide components, corresponding to one-terminal-pair equivalent impedances, are, necessarily, terminating impedances. Of this class, the device with the simplest electrical behavior is a load impedance which absorbs all of the energy incident upon it. Since no reflected wave returns from this device, the voltage and current in the connected waveguide are given by Eqs. (4.45) and (4.46) with $V_b = 0$:

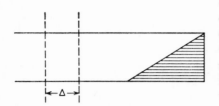

FIG. 4.2. Matched load input planes.

$$V = V_a e^{-j\beta_g z}$$

$$I = \frac{V_a}{Z_0} e^{-j\beta_g z}$$

and its normalized impedance is

$$z_r = \frac{Z}{Z_0} = \frac{V}{Z_0 I} = 1$$

The impedance of a matched load is invariant with respect to the location of its input terminals. We may see this by shifting the input plane by a distance $-\Delta$ along the waveguide, as in Fig. 4.2. This shift changes both the voltage and current by the same phase factor $e^{j\beta_g \Delta}$, and the impedance at the new input plane is therefore unchanged.

A different impedance behavior is presented by a second simple type of one-port impedance consisting of a movable shorting plunger in the waveguide, indicated in Fig. 4.3. Since the transverse electric

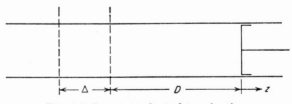

FIG. 4.3. Inputs to shorted termination.

field $\mathbf{E}_t$ must vanish at $z = 0$, the plane of the short, the waveguide voltage must also vanish there. Then from Eq. (4.45),

$$0 = V_a + V_b$$

and hence
$$V = -2jV_a \sin \beta_g z \qquad (4.49)$$

Similarly, in (4.46),

$$I = \frac{2V_a}{Z_0} \cos \beta_g z \qquad (4.50)$$

If the plane $z = -D$ is taken as the input plane of this device, its normalized impedance is

$$z(D) = \frac{V(-D)}{Z_0 I(-D)} = j \tan \beta_g D \qquad (4.51)$$

Obviously, a shift of the input terminals by a distance $-\Delta$ (Fig. 4.3) will change the input impedance to a new value

$$z(D + \Delta) = \frac{V(-D - \Delta)}{Z_0 I(-D - \Delta)} = j \tan \beta_g(D + \Delta) \qquad (4.52)$$

Hence a movable shorting plunger will present a variable reactive impedance, in complete analogy with the shorted stub of transmission-line theory. Dependence of impedance on the assumed location of the input terminals is typical of the impedance behavior of general discontinuities in waveguides. A length of waveguide preceding an impedance element transforms its observed value of impedance, as we have seen, by the impedance transformation law of Eq. (1.51), causing the transformed impedance to appear at the new input plane.

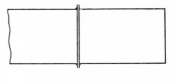

The incorporation of both lossless and loss-producing structural components into a general one-port impedance can produce, as might be supposed, devices which present impedances of essentially any complex value. Therefore, the circuit representation of a one-port

Fig. 4.4. Impedance representation of a one-port device.

device will be a general complex impedance, as indicated in Fig. 4.4.

Two-terminal-pair Impedances. In addition to one-port terminations, microwave impedance elements also comprise multiport devices with two or more input and output terminal pairs. A length of waveguide furnishes an elementary example of a two-port device, since it possesses one input and one output port. Typical examples of two-port devices are a length of waveguide containing a lossless discontinuity or obstacle of a general form representing a pure reactance;

loss-producing variable or fixed attenuators; and transitions from one type of wave-guiding system to another, as for example, a waveguide to coaxial line transition (Fig. 4.5).

In order to bring a two-port microwave device into the scheme of equivalent circuit representations, it is necessary to replace it with a suitable four-terminal electronic circuit. This circuit, when driven

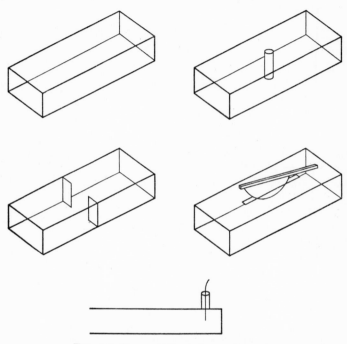

FIG. 4.5. Two-port impedance elements.

by voltages equal to the waveguide voltages of the microwave system, will carry terminal currents equal to the waveguide currents of the actual system.

There are two different, although related, ways in which we can describe the behavior of the four-terminal equivalent circuit which replaces an arbitrary microwave device. The first is by the mathematical expression of the fact that for a passive circuit there exists a set of linear relations between the voltages and currents at its external terminals:

$$V_1 = I_1 Z_{11} + I_2 Z_{12} \qquad (4.53)$$
$$V_2 = I_1 Z_{21} + I_2 Z_{22} \qquad (4.54)$$

The voltages and currents of Eqs. (4.53) and (4.54) are defined as indicated in Fig. 4.6a, and the complex constants Z_{11}, Z_{12}, Z_{21}, Z_{22} are the impedance coefficients of the linear relations between the terminal voltages and the terminal currents. These coefficients may be written compactly as the impedance matrix of the corresponding two-port device

$$[Z_{ij}] = \begin{bmatrix} Z_{11} & Z_{12} \\ Z_{21} & Z_{22} \end{bmatrix} \qquad (4.55)$$

We may also represent a two-port microwave device by means of a specific electronic circuit which responds to applied voltages in the same way as does the microwave device. There are many possible ways in which such an equivalent circuit may be constructed in any given case. The impedances used in the circuit will not in general be the same as the impedance coefficients of Eqs. (4.53) and (4.54). (The equivalent circuit of a one-port device is the exception to the latter statement, since its impedance equation is the Ohm's law expression for the simplest possible equivalent circuit.)

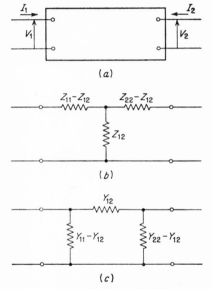

(a)

(b)

(c)

Fig. 4.6. Equivalent-circuit representation of four-terminal device.

The selection of an equivalent circuit for a two-port device is usually governed by criteria of simplicity and the utilization of physical symmetries of the construction of the device. For these reasons, a T or Π equivalent circuit is often chosen to represent a two-port device. For these relatively simple equivalent circuits, the values of the circuit parameters can be readily expressed in terms of the coefficients of the impedance matrix. These values are shown on the circuit elements of Fig. 4.6b and c. The T-circuit parameters may be verified by writing the Kirchhoff's law equations for the circuit. The Π-circuit parameters take their simplest form when expressed in terms of the admittance coefficients of admittance equations comparable to (4.53) and (4.54).

$$I_1 = Y_{11}V_1 + Y_{12}V_2 \qquad (4.56a)$$
$$I_2 = Y_{21}V_1 + Y_{22}V_2 \qquad (4.56b)$$

Numerical values of the circuit components of the equivalent circuit representing a given waveguide device may be obtained from solutions of the field equations subject to the boundary conditions of the specific discontinuities present and evaluation of the dominant mode terms, or by means of measurements.   Due to the complexity of the boundary-value problem in ordinary cases, the method of measurement is frequently more convenient for obtaining the circuit parameters.   For the determination of the three unknown impedance elements of a T or Π circuit, at least three external measurements are necessary.   These measurements may be made in close analogy with the corresponding problem of circuit theory: Measurements of impedance at one pair of terminals, with the second terminal pair open-circuited, short-circuited, and terminated with an intermediate value of impedance, can give sufficient information for the evaluation of the impedances of the equivalent circuit (see Appendix IV).

The equivalent circuit which is established for a given device is valid, in general, only at that frequency for which it has been established, since the impedances presented by microwave devices, whether of one, two, or n ports, do not exhibit the same dependence on frequency as do their respective equivalent circuits.   A simple example of this fact is easily seen in the case of the one-port shorted stub, which has a frequency dependence very dissimilar from that of the reactance which represents it at a single frequency:

$$Z_{\text{stub}} = jZ_0 \tan (\sqrt{\mu\epsilon\omega^2 - k_c^2}\, D)$$
$$Z_{\text{inductance}} = jL\omega$$

where D is the length of a shorted stub less than a quarter of a guide wavelength long and L is the inductance of the inductor which comprises the equivalent circuit of the stub at a given frequency.

Multi-terminal-pair Impedances.   The representation of multiport waveguide devices is accomplished by the extension of the methods just described for two-port devices, to the corresponding many-terminal-pair representations.   The n-terminal voltages and currents of an n-port device are linearly related by the set of n equations

$$
\begin{aligned}
V_1 &= I_1 Z_{11} + I_2 Z_{12} + I_3 Z_{13} + \cdots + I_n Z_{1n} \\
V_2 &= I_1 Z_{21} + I_2 Z_{22} + I_3 Z_{23} + \cdots + I_n Z_{2n} \\
&\;\cdots\cdots\cdots\cdots\cdots\cdots\cdots\cdots\cdots\cdots\cdots\cdots\cdots \\
V_n &= I_1 Z_{n1} + I_2 Z_{n2} + I_3 Z_{n3} + \cdots + I_n Z_{nn}
\end{aligned}
\tag{4.57}
$$

The complex coefficients of these equations comprise the $n \times n$

matrix of impedances:

$$[Z_{ij}] = \begin{bmatrix} Z_{11} & Z_{12} & Z_{13} & \cdots & Z_{1n} \\ Z_{21} & Z_{22} & Z_{23} & \cdots & Z_{2n} \\ \vdots & & & & \vdots \\ Z_{n1} & \cdots & \cdots & \cdots & Z_{nn} \end{bmatrix} \qquad (4.58)$$

The impedance matrices of linear passive devices are symmetrical about the principal diagonal; i.e., $Z_{ij} = Z_{ji}$. The matrix elements of a lossless device are pure-imaginary quantities. Inspection of Eqs. (4.57) shows that the value of the matrix element Z_{ij} is the ratio of the voltage at the ith port to the current at the jth port, when the currents at all other ports are zero.

The means whereby the equivalent circuit spanning the $2n$ terminals of an n-port device is to be determined are not as obvious as in the case of the two-port element. The same criteria of simplicity and utilization of structural symmetries of the device govern this choice also, however, and equivalent circuits have been established for many n-port devices.[†]

4.4. Scattering Coefficients of a Microwave Device

Two complementary modes of description of an n-port device, the impedance matrix and equivalent circuit representations, have been described in the preceding section. The purpose of both of these representations is to provide a means for relating the waveguide voltages observed at the terminals of the given device, with the waveguide currents flowing at the various other terminals. A third means of characterizing the electrical behavior of a microwave device is also available. The scattering coefficient representation of a microwave component relates the magnitudes and phases of the traveling waves of voltage entering and leaving the ports of the device.

We have seen in Eqs. (4.45) and (4.46) that the complete description of the waveguide voltage in the guide connected to any port of a junction or discontinuity region requires the use of incident and departing waves of voltage

$$V = V_a e^{-j\beta_o z} + V_b e^{+j\beta_o z} \qquad (4.59)$$

The coefficients of each traveling wave were normalized so that expressions of the form $V_a V_a^* / 2Z_0$ and $V_b V_b^* / 2Z_0$ represent the power carried by the traveling waves, where Z_0 is a constant characteristic of the guide. The terminal voltages at a given port are then obtained by

† Marcuvitz, *op. cit.*

setting the coordinate z in (4.59) equal to a constant characteristic of the configuration of the system.

In establishing the scattering coefficient description of a microwave device, we deal separately with the incident and departing traveling waves of voltage at the terminals of the device. The voltage waves are defined in essentially the same way as that used above, but normalized, by conventional usage, in a different way.

We write the complex voltages at the terminals of the device as a and b, representing the incident and departing waves, respectively, thus replacing Eq. (4.59) by

$$v_k = a_k + b_k \qquad (4.60)$$

where the subscript k refers to the kth terminal pair. These voltages may be normalized so that the power carried by a_k is $W_k = a_k a_k^*$. Scattering coefficients are then defined, such that the voltage wave b_i leaving the ith port owing to a voltage wave a_j incident upon the jth port when no waves enter any of the other ports of the device is given by

$$b_i = S_{ij} a_j \qquad (4.61)$$

In the general case, when a voltage is incident upon all of the n ports of the device, each incident voltage will make a contribution to the total resultant voltage wave departing from the ith port:

$$b_i = S_{i1} a_1 + S_{i2} a_2 + \cdots + S_{in} a_n \qquad (4.62)$$

Equation (4.62) is an expression of the linearity of response of a passive microwave system component which results from the linearity of Maxwell's equations. We similarly express the scattered waves departing from all of the ports by means of the set of scattering equations

$$
\begin{aligned}
b_1 &= S_{11} a_1 + S_{12} a_2 + \cdots + S_{1n} a_n \\
b_2 &= S_{21} a_1 + S_{22} a_2 + \cdots + S_{2n} a_n \\
&\cdots \cdots \cdots \cdots \cdots \cdots \cdots \cdots \cdots \cdots \\
b_n &= S_{n1} a_1 + S_{n2} a_2 + \cdots + S_{nn} a_n
\end{aligned} \qquad (4.63)
$$

The array of complex coefficients appearing in Eqs. (4.63) comprises the scattering matrix of the device:

$$
S_{ij} = \begin{bmatrix}
S_{11} & S_{12} & \cdots & S_{1n} \\
S_{21} & S_{22} & \cdots & S_{2n} \\
\cdots & \cdots & \cdots & \cdots \\
S_{n1} & \cdots & \cdots & S_{nn}
\end{bmatrix} \qquad (4.64)
$$

The diagonal element S_{jj} of the scattering matrix is the reflection coefficient at the jth port and represents the reflected voltage wave which would be observed at this port with an incident voltage wave of unit magnitude and zero phase, when all other ports are terminated in matched impedances (and hence no waves are reflected back into the other ports). In the case of a one-port device, the scattering matrix is the quantity which we have called the reflection coefficient of a termination:

$$S_{11} = \rho \tag{4.65}$$

The scattering matrix representation of a given microwave component is not independent of the impedance matrix representation of that component, since both representations describe the electrical behavior of the same object. In order to demonstrate the connection between the impedance matrix $[Z_{ij}]$, which is defined in terms of waveguide voltages and currents V_i and I_j, and the scattering matrix S_{ij}, defined in terms of the voltagelike quantities a_j and b_i, we must find the connection between the V_i, I_j system of variables and the a_j, b_i system. The voltages a_j are normalized so that the traveling wave a_j at the jth port carries the energy

$$W_j = a_j a_j^*$$

By the use of Eqs. (4.32) and (4.43), we see that

$$a_j a_j^* = \frac{\beta_g}{2\omega\mu} |V_{aj}|^2 \tag{4.66}$$

where $|V_{aj}|$ is the amplitude of the waveguide voltage wave corresponding to a_j.

Thus

$$|a_j| = \sqrt{\frac{\beta_g}{2\omega\mu}} |V_{aj}| \tag{4.67}$$

Equation (4.67) shows that the scattering coefficients S_{ij} are ratios of traveling waves of waveguide voltages, since the latter are proportional to the a_j variables.

The amplitude of a traveling wave of current is

$$|I_a| = \frac{|V_a|}{Z_0} = \frac{\beta_g}{\omega\mu} |V_a| \tag{4.68}$$

where we have used Eqs. (4.38) and (4.44).

Hence, with (4.67),

$$I_{aj} = \sqrt{\frac{2\beta_g}{\omega\mu}} a_j \tag{4.69}$$

Therefore, we may define a currentlike variable i_k, to accompany the voltage variable $v_k = a_k + b_k$ defined in Eq. (4.60):

$$i_k = a_k - b_k \qquad (4.70)$$

From (4.69) and (4.67), the ratio v_k/i_k has the character of normalized impedance

$$Z = \frac{V_{aj} + V_{bj}}{I_{aj} - I_{bj}} = \frac{\sqrt{2\omega\mu/\beta_g}\,(a_j + b_j)}{\sqrt{2\beta_g/\omega\mu}\,(a_j - b_j)} = \frac{\omega\mu}{\beta_g}\frac{(a_j + b_j)}{(a_j - b_j)}$$

whence

$$Z = Z_0 \frac{v_k}{i_k} = Z_0 z_k$$

Then, solving (4.60) and (4.70), we find

$$a_k = \frac{v_k + i_k}{2} \qquad (4.71)$$

$$b_k = \frac{v_k - i_k}{2} \qquad (4.72)$$

We may substitute for v_k its expression in terms of normalized impedance coefficients, $v_k = \sum_m z_{km} i_m$, obtaining

$$a_k = \tfrac{1}{2} \left(\sum_m z_{km} i_m + i_k \right) \qquad (4.73)$$

$$b_k = \tfrac{1}{2} \left(\sum_m z_{km} i_m - i_k \right) \qquad (4.74)$$

In Eqs. (4.73) and (4.74), the impedance coefficients are normalized to the Z_0 of the waveguides at the respective ports. In the present work we shall assume, unless otherwise specified, that all of the waveguides have the same Z_0. Equation (4.73) stands for the set of n equations for an n-port device:

$$a_1 = \tfrac{1}{2}[(z_{11} + 1)i_1 + z_{12}i_2 + \cdots + z_{1n}i_n]$$
$$a_2 = \tfrac{1}{2}[z_{21}i_1 + (z_{22} + 1)i_2 + \cdots + z_{2n}i_n]$$
$$\cdots\cdots\cdots\cdots\cdots\cdots\cdots\cdots\cdots\cdots\cdots \qquad (4.75)$$
$$a_n = \tfrac{1}{2}[z_{n1}i_1 + z_{n2}i_2 + \cdots + (z_{nn} + 1)i_n]$$

The $n \times n$ array of coefficients of Eqs. (4.75) is the matrix

$$[z_{ij} + \delta_{ij}]$$

where $\delta_{ij} = 1$ if $i = j$; $\delta_{ij} = 0$ otherwise. With this definition, we may write Eqs. (4.75) in matrix notation:

$$[a_i] = \tfrac{1}{2}[z_{ij} + \delta_{ij}][i_j] \qquad (4.76)$$

where $[a_i]$ and $[i_j]$ are the column matrices

$$[a_i] = \begin{bmatrix} a_1 \\ a_2 \\ \cdot \\ \cdot \\ \cdot \\ a_n \end{bmatrix} \qquad [i_j] = \begin{bmatrix} i_1 \\ i_2 \\ \cdot \\ \cdot \\ \cdot \\ i_n \end{bmatrix}$$

Similarly, Eq. (4.74) represents

$$[b_k] = \tfrac{1}{2}[z_{kj} - \delta_{kj}] [i_j] \tag{4.77}$$

We may substitute for $[i_j]$ in Eq. (4.77) its value obtained from Eq. (4.76):

$$[b_k] = [z_{kj} - \delta_{kj}][z_{ij} + \delta_{ij}]^{-1}[a_i]$$

Since $[b_k] = [S_{ki}][a_i]$ is the matrix equation defining the scattering matrix, we deduce that

$$[S_{ki}] = [z_{kj} - \delta_{kj}][z_{ij} + \delta_{ij}]^{-1} \tag{4.78}$$

Equation (4.78) is a matrix equation, and the calculation of the scattering coefficients from the impedance coefficients may be carried out by the use of matrix algebra.† It is instructive to note the familiar simple form which Eq. (4.78) assumes when applied to a one-port component:

$$S_{11} = \rho = \frac{z_r - 1}{z_r + 1} \tag{4.79}$$

Equation (4.79) is identical with Eq. (1.48) of Chap. 1, for the reflection coefficient ρ of a terminating impedance z_r.

4.5. Section of Waveguide

A section of uniform waveguide is a simple two-port device by the use of which we may display in comparison the three modes of representation of a microwave component. We possess the transmission-line equations connecting the input and output currents and voltages and thus may approach the analysis of the waveguide through the impedance-coefficient representation. Consider a length L of waveguide with input voltage and current V_1 and I_1 and output voltage

† For a summary of matrix algebra, see a calculus text such as H. Margenau and G. M. Murphy, "The Mathematics of Physics and Chemistry," D. Van Nostrand Company, Inc., Princeton, N.J., 1943, and later editions.

and current V_2 and I_2 (Fig. 4.7). The impedance equations connecting the voltages with the currents are

$$V_1 = I_1 Z_{11} + I_2 Z_{12} \tag{4.80}$$
$$V_2 = I_1 Z_{21} + I_2 Z_{22} \tag{4.81}$$

The general transmission line equations for the waveguide section are

$$V = V_a e^{-j\beta_g z} + V_b e^{+j\beta_g z} \tag{4.82}$$

$$I = \frac{1}{Z_0}\left(V_a e^{-j\beta_g z} - V_b e^{+j\beta_g z}\right) \tag{4.83}$$

In (4.82) and (4.83), V_a is the complex magnitude of the forward-traveling wave and V_b that of the backward-traveling wave.

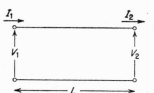

In Eq. (4.80), we observe that Z_{11} is given by

$$Z_{11} = \left.\frac{V_1}{I_1}\right|_{I_2=0} \tag{4.84}$$

FIG. 4.7. Section of waveguide.

We may define the input end of the guide section as the plane $z = 0$. Hence, V_1 and I_1 are obtained from the transmission-line equations (4.82) and (4.83) with coordinate z set equal to zero, with which (4.84) becomes

$$Z_{11} = Z_0 \left.\frac{V_a + V_b}{V_a - V_b}\right|_{I_2=0} \tag{4.85}$$

The restriction imposed by the condition $I_2 = 0$ may be obtained from (4.83) at $z = L$ and is found to be

$$V_b = V_a e^{-2j\beta_g L} \tag{4.86}$$

Using (4.86) in (4.85), we find that the normalized matrix element z_{11} is

$$z_{11} = -j \cot \beta_g L \tag{4.87}$$

Proceeding similarly to find Z_{21}, we start with

$$Z_{21} = \left.\frac{V_2}{I_1}\right|_{I_2=0} \tag{4.88}$$

Using $V_2 = V(L)$ and $I_1 = I(0)$, with the condition (4.86), the result for normalized z_{21} is

$$z_{21} = -j \csc \beta_g L \tag{4.89}$$

Because of the symmetry of the waveguide section, exchanging its input and output ends will not alter the values of the impedance coefficients found for it.   Hence the impedance matrix is symmetrical, and the complete matrix may be written, from Eqs. (4.87) and (4.89),

$$[z_{ij}] = \begin{bmatrix} -j \cot \beta_g L & -j \csc \beta_g L \\ -j \csc \beta_g L & -j \cot \beta_g L \end{bmatrix} \tag{4.90}$$

The equivalent T circuit for the waveguide section may now be formed as indicated in Fig. 4.6b, with the result shown in Fig. 4.8.

The scattering matrix of the waveguide section may be calculated from the normalized impedance matrix (4.90) by the use of Eq. (4.78), and the result obtained is

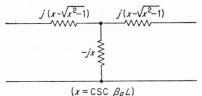

$$[S_{ij}] = \begin{bmatrix} 0 & e^{-j\beta_g L} \\ e^{-j\beta_g L} & 0 \end{bmatrix} \tag{4.91}$$

FIG. 4.8. Equivalent circuit of waveguide section.

The zeros on the diagonal of the scattering matrix indicate the known fact that there is no reflected wave from the input of a section of waveguide terminated in its own characteristic impedance.   The off-diagonal terms of the scattering matrix represent the phase retardation of a traveling wave in a guide section of length L.

4.6. Aperture in Conducting Plane Obstacle

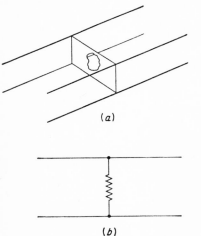

(a)

(b)

FIG. 4.9. (a) Generalized waveguide aperture; (b) equivalent circuit.

A waveguide impedance element consisting of a thin conducting plane extending transversely across a part of the waveguide cross section is useful in many applications (Fig. 4.9a).   The obstacle may consist merely of a fin or fins extending slightly into the waveguide, or it may be a nearly complete short circuit, pierced by a small coupling hole.   An element of this type is essentially a two-port device, since it includes input and output waveguide connections.   If the conducting plane forming the discontinuity is sufficiently thin, however, its equivalent circuit representation consists of a single transverse impedance or admittance (Fig. 4.9b).

The geometry of the aperture in a conducting plane is suitable for discussion in terms of the formula that we have developed from the modal expansion of fields in the neighborhood of a discontinuity [Eq. (4.21)]. Writing (4.21) for the dominant-mode term, with subscript 1 standing for the TE_{10} mode, we have

$$A_1 + B_1 = \frac{\iint F_{y0} E_{y1}\, dx\, dy}{\iint E_{y1}^2\, dx\, dy} \tag{4.92}$$

In Eq. (4.92), A_1 and B_1 are the amplitudes of the incident and departing waves of the dominant-mode field in rectangular waveguide, and E_{y1} is the transverse electric field $E_{y1} = E_0 \sin(\pi x/a)$. An expression is now required for F_{y0}, the distribution of y-component electric field over the plane of the aperture. One of the means available for obtaining an estimate of this distribution is the static field method. In this method, the field disturbances due to the aperture are assumed to be localized in a region which is small compared to a free-space wavelength. The wave equation for E_y is

$$\nabla^2 E_y + k^2 E_y = 0 \tag{4.93}$$

The "curvature" of the fields, represented by the term $\nabla^2 E_y$, is now assumed to be much larger than the term having coefficient

$$k^2 = \left(\frac{2\pi}{\lambda}\right)^2$$

The latter term is then neglected in comparison with the first, and the equation becomes

$$\nabla^2 E_y = 0 \tag{4.94}$$

Equation (4.94) implies that the field distribution is like that of the electrostatic field. This field can therefore be found as the solution of a related static problem for the geometry of the aperture. (We may note that the use of this method is equivalent to making the assumption that in the neighborhood of the irregularity, the fields rise and fall in time like quasi-static fields, for which the phase delay of waves is negligible over the region of consideration.)

When the distribution F_{y0} over a given aperture is known, and with the tangential field over the conducting part of the obstacle known to be zero, the integral of Eq. (4.92) can be evaluated over the cross section of the waveguide. We can see what the character of the solution of (4.92) will be by examining its behavior in the limiting cases of extremely large or extremely small aperture.

For an extremely large aperture, or vanishingly small extension of conducting fins, the function F_{y0} will differ negligibly from the undisturbed dominant-mode field E_{y1}, and the integral in the numerator on the right side of (4.92) will be nearly equal to the denominator, leaving a result that differs from unity by only a small amount, ξ. Then, for unit amplitude of the incident wave A_1, Eq. (4.92) becomes

$$1 + \frac{B_1}{A_1} = 1 - \xi \qquad (4.95)$$

However, B_1/A_1 is the reflection coefficient ρ for the dominant mode, and we have

$$\rho = -\xi \qquad (4.96)$$

In the limiting case of no obstacle, $\xi = 0$, and the reflection coefficient vanishes, which we know is true for open waveguide.

In the opposite case of an extremely small aperture, F_{y0} will make a very small contribution to the integral in the numerator of (4.92), and the resulting fraction has a very small value, say, η. Then, with unit incident-wave amplitude, (4.92) becomes

$$1 + \rho = \eta \qquad (4.97)$$

or

$$\rho = \eta - 1 \qquad (4.98)$$

Thus the reflection coefficient of a very small aperture is nearly equal to -1. In the limiting case of no opening in the conducting plane, $\eta = 0$, and the reflection coefficient is equal to -1, which is the correct result for a short-circuiting plate across the waveguide.

To carry this method further, we shall, of course, need to assume a definite form of aperture and obtain a distribution F_{y0} for it. In order to calculate the impedance of the aperture it will be necessary, as we have seen, to know the distribution of two of the components of field over the plane of the aperture (Sec. 4.1).

Mathematical procedures other than that we have described above are applicable to the problem of the calculation of the impedances of obstacles in waveguides. Impedances have been calculated by the use of variational methods, integral equation methods, and the method of Green's functions. Most of the solutions that have been thus found are approximational, since exact solutions of the field equations cannot be found for most boundary structures.

Impedance values for several plane apertures of special form are given in Table 4.1, in the approximations indicated.

TABLE 4.1. IMPEDANCES OF APERTURES IN RECTANGULAR WAVEGUIDE
Impedances referred to plane of the aperture

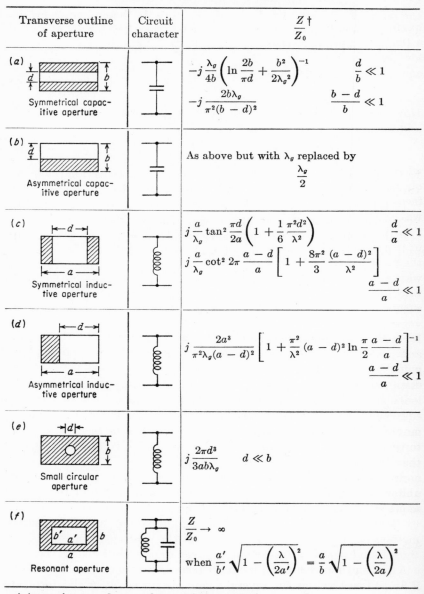

Transverse outline of aperture	Circuit character	$\dfrac{Z}{Z_0}$ †
(a) Symmetrical capacitive aperture		$-j\dfrac{\lambda_g}{4b}\left(\ln\dfrac{2b}{\pi d}+\dfrac{b^2}{2\lambda_g{}^2}\right)^{-1} \qquad \dfrac{d}{b}\ll 1$ $-j\dfrac{2b\lambda_g}{\pi^2(b-d)^2} \qquad \dfrac{b-d}{b}\ll 1$
(b) Asymmetrical capacitive aperture		As above but with λ_g replaced by $\dfrac{\lambda_g}{2}$
(c) Symmetrical inductive aperture		$j\dfrac{a}{\lambda_g}\tan^2\dfrac{\pi d}{2a}\left(1+\dfrac{1}{6}\dfrac{\pi^2 d^2}{\lambda^2}\right) \qquad \dfrac{d}{a}\ll 1$ $j\dfrac{a}{\lambda_g}\cot^2 2\pi\dfrac{a-d}{a}\left[1+\dfrac{8\pi^2}{3}\dfrac{(a-d)^2}{\lambda^2}\right] \qquad \dfrac{a-d}{a}\ll 1$
(d) Asymmetrical inductive aperture		$j\dfrac{2a^3}{\pi^2\lambda_g(a-d)^2}\left[1+\dfrac{\pi^2}{\lambda^2}(a-d)^2\ln\dfrac{\pi}{2}\dfrac{a-d}{a}\right]^{-1} \qquad \dfrac{a-d}{a}\ll 1$
(e) Small circular aperture		$j\dfrac{2\pi d^3}{3ab\lambda_g} \qquad d\ll b$
(f) Resonant aperture		$\dfrac{Z}{Z_0}\to\infty$ when $\dfrac{a'}{b'}\sqrt{1-\left(\dfrac{\lambda}{2a'}\right)^2}=\dfrac{a}{b}\sqrt{1-\left(\dfrac{\lambda}{2a}\right)^2}$

† Approximate values, under restrictions noted.

4.7. Transverse Ridge Obstacle

An obstacle similar to the asymmetrical capacitive aperture but having finite thickness in the direction of the waveguide axis (Fig. 4.10a) is of interest in that its electrical behavior is similar to that of a low-pass filter element. The admittances of the components of the equivalent II section shown in Fig. 4.10b are

$$\frac{B_a}{Y_0} = \frac{4b}{\lambda_g}\left[M + \left(\frac{2b}{\lambda_g}\right)^2 N \right] + \frac{b}{d}\tan\frac{2\pi l}{\lambda_g} \qquad (4.99)$$

$$\frac{B_b}{Y_0} = \frac{b}{d}\csc\frac{4\pi l}{\lambda_g} \qquad (d = b - h) \qquad (4.100)$$

where M and N are quantities depending on the geometry of the obstacle.† The admittances are referred to the plane of the vertical face of the obstacle upon which the waveguide waves are incident. A type of slow-wave structure, used in traveling-wave devices to reduce the phase velocity of the waveguide waves to a value less than the velocity of light, is constructed of a succession of closely spaced transverse ridges like those shown above. It should be observed that in this and similar cases, when two waveguide obstacles are separated by distances small enough so that their local higher-mode fields overlap, the equivalent circuit of each will be modified from the form pertaining to the isolated discontinuities, since the boundary conditions for the nonpropagating modes then are no longer the assumed continuation of uniform waveguide. The wave-propagation characteristics of periodic sequences of identical obstacles are discussed in Chap. 7.

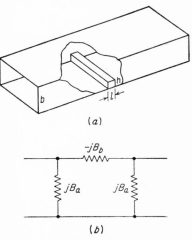

(a)

(b)

FIG. 4.10. Transverse ridge obstacle.

4.8. Tuning Post

A conducting post which extends into the waveguide parallel to the E field lines is an impedance element of much usefulness, because of its

† Marcuvitz, *op. cit.*, pp. 251–252.

simple construction and the ease with which it allows a wide range of admittances to be introduced in parallel with the waveguide as the length of the post is varied. The tuning post may take the form of a screw threaded into the broad face of the guide, or of a probe with a

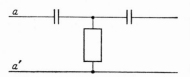

micrometer for depth adjustment and provision for change of location along the waveguide axis.

FIG. 4.11. Equivalent circuit of tuning post.

The equivalent-circuit behavior of the post may be represented by the T network shown in Fig. 4.11. The impedance character of the shunt arm of the network depends on the length of the post, or probe. At small probe lengths, the input impedance at the terminals aa' of the equivalent circuit is capacitive. As the probe length increases, the capacitive impedance becomes smaller, and when the probe length is approximately $\lambda/4$, where λ is the free-space wavelength, the tuning post resonates and presents a vanishing impedance, at the location of the post. With further increase of probe length, its impedance becomes inductive in character. Figure 4.12 shows the variation

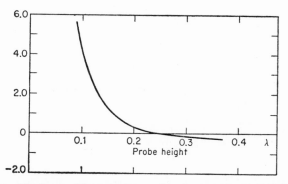

FIG. 4.12. Normalized capacitive reactance of tuning post versus height in units of free-space wavelength.

of the observed parallel impedance of a probe $\frac{1}{16}$ in. in diameter in X-band waveguide (of inside dimensions 0.4 by 0.9 in.) as a function of the probe height, measured in units of the free-space wavelength at the operating frequency of 11.0 kmc. The probe was located at the center of the broad face of the waveguide. The capacitive reactance is shown referred to the position of the probe on the guide axis. Resonance occurred with a probe length of 0.237λ, or approximately 5 per cent less than a quarter of the free-space wavelength.

The impedance of a tuning post in rectangular waveguide has been calculated by L. Lewin,[†] who solved for the dominant-mode fields corresponding to an assumed sinusoidal current distribution in the post. It was found that the impedance of a post at the center of the guide could not be expressed in closed form but required a series expansion for its expression. However, for the case of a post of length h and radius r, located at distance d ($d < a/2$), measured from the side of the guide, the reactance was found to be equal to

$$jx = j \frac{\sin (2kh) \ln (2d/r) - k(2d - r)(2 + \cos 2kh)}{(2\pi d^2 \lambda \lambda_g/a^3 b)(1 - \cos kh)^2} \quad (4.101)$$

where λ_g is the guide wavelength, λ is the free-space wavelength, $k = 2\pi/\lambda$, and the wavelength width and height are equal to a and b, respectively. Equation (4.101) shows that the reactance vanishes and resonance occurs for the condition

$$\sin (2kh) \ln \frac{2d}{r} = k(2d - r)(2 + \cos 2kh)$$

from which the resonant length of the post is, approximately,

$$h \approx \frac{\lambda}{4} - \frac{(d - r)/2}{\ln (2d/r)} \quad (4.102)$$

Equation (4.102) must be corrected for the effect of capacitance between the tip of the post and the opposite face of the waveguide, if the post approaches the opposite surface of the guide to within a distance of separation comparable with the radius of the post. The correction is negligible for greater separations, if post radius is not more than a few tenths of the guide width. A pair of tuning posts installed in a waveguide at a fixed interval along the guide axis can serve as an impedance-matching element similar in its operation to the double-stub tuner (Sec. 1.6).

4.9. Scattering Properties of Multiport Junctions

As examples of multiport waveguide elements, it will be instructive to consider the two symmetrical T junctions shown in Fig. 4.13. The T of Fig. 4.13a, in which the axis of the side arm which joins the main guide is parallel to the **E** field of the main guide, is called an E-plane T. Similarly, the junction of Fig. 4.13b is called an H-plane T, since the side arm is parallel to the transverse H field of the main guide. In order to discuss the scattering properties of these T's and other

[†] L. Lewin, "Advanced Theory of Waveguides," Iliffe and Sons, Ltd., London, 1951.

multiport devices, let us consider some useful general properties of the scattering matrices of linear, lossless microwave devices. The first property which we shall introduce is readily demonstrated by the use of the principle of the conservation of energy, as applied to transmission through a lossless junction.

Let it be assumed that a wave of unit voltage is incident upon arm 1 of an n-port device and that no voltage waves enter any of the other

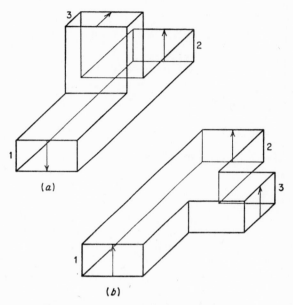

FIG. 4.13. (a) E-plane T; (b) H-plane T.

ports. Hence the power entering the device is $W_{in} = a_1 a_1^*$. Since the power leaving the jth port is equal to $b_j b_j^*$, the conservation expression is then

$$a_1 a_1^* = b_1 b_1^* + b_2 b_2^* + \cdots + b_n b_n^* \tag{4.103}$$

But $b_j = S_{j1} a_1$, where S_{j1} is the scattering coefficient connecting the jth port and the first port. Therefore,

$$a_1 a_1^* = (S_{11} a_1)(S_{11} a_1)^* + (S_{21} a_1)(S_{21} a_1)^* + \cdots \\ + (S_{n1} a_1)(S_{n1} a_1)^* \tag{4.104}$$

and hence

$$1 = S_{11} S_{11}^* + S_{12} S_{12}^* + \cdots + S_{1n} S_{1n}^* \tag{4.105}$$

In the same way, the sum of the squares of the amplitudes of any row or column of the scattering matrix add to unity.

$$1 = \sum_j S_{ij} S_{ij}^* = \sum_j |S_{ij}|^2 \tag{4.106}$$

A second important property of the scattering matrix may be derived from the conservation principle as expressed for general operation of the n-port device, with ingoing and outgoing waves at each of the ports. Then, the expression $W_{in} = W_{out}$ takes the form

$$\sum_j a_j a_j^* = \sum_k b_k b_k^* \tag{4.107}$$

If we now substitute $b_k = \sum_n S_{kn} a_n$, and the complex conjugate of this expression, into the right side of Eq. (4.107), the result turns out to be, after reassigning summation subscript notations for convenience,

$$\sum_j a_j a_j^* = \sum_j \left(\sum_k S_{jk} S_{jk}^* \right) a_j a_j^* + \left[\sum_m' \sum_n \left(\sum_j S_{jm} S_{jn}^* \right) a_m a_n^* \right]$$
$$+ \left[\sum_m' \sum_n \left(\sum_j S_{jm} S_{jn}^* \right) a_m a_n^* \right]^* \tag{4.108}$$

where the prime on the summation over m means that the term $m = n$ is not included in the sum. The first term on the right of (4.108) can be simplified by the use of (4.106). The last two terms on the right are of the form $F + F^*$, which is equal to $2 \operatorname{Re} F$, where Re means "real part of," so that (4.108) becomes

$$\sum_j a_j a_j^* = \sum_j a_j a_j^* + 2 \operatorname{Re} \sum_m' \sum_n \left(\sum_j S_{jm} S_{jn}^* \right) a_m a_n^* \tag{4.109}$$

or

$$0 = 2 \operatorname{Re} \sum_m' \sum_n \left(\sum_j S_{jm} S_{jn}^* \right) a_m a_n^* \tag{4.110}$$

The properties of the device under discussion remain the same irrespective of what combination of waves we send into it. Therefore, Eq. (4.110) must hold if waves enter two ports only. Thus, for example, we may transmit waves a_1 and a_2 into ports 1 and 2, with all other a_j set equal to zero. Equation (4.110) then becomes

$$0 = 2 \operatorname{Re} (S_{11} S_{12}^* + S_{21} S_{22}^* + S_{31} S_{32}^* + \cdots + S_{n1} S_{n2}^*) a_1 a_2^* \tag{4.111}$$

Since the phases of waves a_1 and a_2 are arbitrary, we conclude that the quantity in parentheses in Eq. (4.111) must be equal to zero.

$$0 = S_{11} S_{12}^* + S_{21} S_{22}^* + S_{31} S_{32}^* + \cdots + S_{n1} S_{n2}^* \tag{4.112}$$

Equation (4.112) consists of the sum of the members of the first column of the scattering matrix, multiplied by the complex conjugate of the corresponding members of the second column of the matrix, the result being equal to zero. In the same way as above we can prove the analogous condition concerning any pair of columns of the scattering matrix, and since the scattering matrix is symmetrical about the principal diagonal, any two rows combine similarly to yield a result of zero.

E- and H-plane T's, when constructed of empty waveguide, are poorly matched devices. By this is meant, that when two of the arms are terminated in matched impedances, the third arm does not present a matched impedance to the source. In terms of the language of scattering coefficients, this statement implies that S_{11}, S_{22}, and S_{33} are not equal to zero. With the arms of the T's numbered as in Fig. 4.13, a wave entering the side arm (arm 3) of the E-plane T yields outgoing waves at arms 1 and 2 which are relatively reversed in phase at equal electrical distances from the center of the T (Fig. 4.13a). This relative phase reversal of the waves leaving the main-guide arms does not occur in the H-plane T (Fig. 4.13b). The structural symmetry of the T's simplifies their scattering matrices. Thus, we conclude, from symmetry, that $|S_{13}| = |S_{23}|$ and $S_{11} = S_{22}$, in either T. Hence, the scattering matrix reduces to

$$[S_{ij}] = \begin{bmatrix} S_{11} & S_{12} & S_{13} \\ S_{12} & S_{11} & \pm S_{13} \\ S_{13} & \pm S_{13} & S_{33} \end{bmatrix} \tag{4.113}$$

where the positive sign refers to the H-plane T, and the negative sign to the E-plane T.

Two characteristic properties of the scattering matrix of a lossless junction were derived in Eqs. (4.105) and (4.112). We may illustrate the use of these properties by demonstrating that measurements of two reflection coefficients, S_{11} and S_{33}, are sufficient to completely determine the scattering matrix of a symmetrical T junction. The reflection coefficients are readily determined by means of conventional slotted-line impedance measurements made at each of the specified ports, with the remaining two ports terminated in matched loads during measurement. The complex reflection coefficient at each port is then available from the measured impedances by the use of the relation $S_{jj} = (z_{jj} - 1)/(z_{jj} + 1)$, from Eq. (4.79).

Considering the H-plane T, with positive signs in (4.113), we form, by the use of Eq. (4.105), the expressions

$$|S_{13}|^2 + |S_{13}|^2 + |S_{33}|^2 = 1 \tag{4.114}$$

and

$$|S_{11}|^2 + |S_{12}|^2 + |S_{13}|^2 = 1 \tag{4.115}$$

Applying Eq. (4.112) to columns 1 and 2 of the scattering matrix, we have

$$S_{11}S_{12}^* + S_{12}S_{11}^* + |S_{13}|^2 = 0 \tag{4.116}$$

and with columns 2 and 3,

$$S_{12}S_{13}^* + S_{11}S_{13}^* + S_{13}S_{33}^* = 0 \tag{4.117}$$

From Eq. (4.114), we obtain immediately

$$|S_{13}|^2 = \frac{1 - |S_{33}|^2}{2} \tag{4.118}$$

and from (4.115),

$$\begin{aligned} |S_{12}|^2 &= 1 - |S_{11}|^2 - |S_{13}|^2 \\ &= 1 - |S_{11}|^2 - \frac{1 - |S_{33}|^2}{2} \end{aligned} \tag{4.119}$$

Thus we have obtained the magnitudes of the remaining matrix elements in terms of $|S_{11}|$ and $|S_{33}|$. The calculation may be completed by finding expressions for the phase angles of S_{12} and S_{13}. From Eq. (4.116) we obtain

$$|S_{11}|\,|S_{12}|(e^{j(\theta_{11}-\theta_{12})} + e^{-j(\theta_{11}-\theta_{12})}) + |S_{13}|^2 = 0 \tag{4.120}$$

where θ_{11} and θ_{12} are the phase angles of S_{11} and S_{12}, respectively. Hence

$$\cos(\theta_{11} - \theta_{12}) = -\frac{|S_{13}|^2}{2|S_{11}|\,|S_{12}|} \tag{4.121}$$

Therefore, the phase angle of S_{12} is

$$\theta_{12} = \theta_{11} - \cos^{-1}\frac{-|S_{13}|^2}{2|S_{11}|\,|S_{12}|} \tag{4.122}$$

Equation (4.122) is evaluated by the use of the values of $|S_{13}|$ and $|S_{12}|$ already found in Eqs. (4.118) and (4.119). The remaining unknown is the phase angle of S_{13}. From Eq. (4.117) we have

$$(S_{12} + S_{11})|S_{13}|e^{-j\theta_{13}} = -|S_{13}|e^{j\theta_{13}}S_{33}^* \tag{4.123}$$

or

$$e^{2j\theta_{13}} = -\frac{S_{12} + S_{11}}{S_{33}^*} \tag{4.124}$$

where θ_{13} is the phase angle of S_{13}.

Therefore

$$\theta_{13} = \frac{\pi}{2} + \frac{1}{2j}\ln\frac{S_{12} + S_{11}}{S_{33}^*} \tag{4.125}$$

The complex matrix element S_{12}, available from Eqs. (4.119) and (4.122), is to be used in the evaluation of Eq. (4.125). With the phase of S_{13} determined by Eq. (4.125), the complete scattering matrix of the lossless symmetrical H-plane T is thus seen to be established by measurement of the two reflection coefficients S_{11} and S_{33}.

The procedure which has been developed above may be used for determining the scattering matrix of any device having the same symmetry as the H-plane T. The procedure has illustrated the mode of application of the properties of a lossless scattering matrix which are

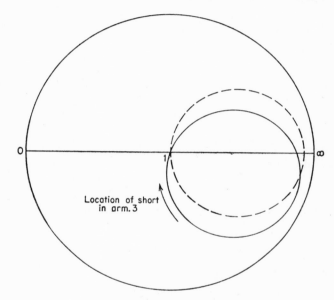

FIG. 4.14. H-plane T impedance.

stated in Eqs. (4.105) and (4.112). An alternative general method for the evaluation of scattering coefficients by measurement has been given by Deschamps.† In the Deschamps method, impedance measurements are made at one port of the device, with a variable termination at a second port, and scattering coefficients are determined by graphical construction in the Smith chart transmission-line diagram.

Theorems for Three-port Junctions. The E- and H-plane T's which have been discussed above are special cases of the general three-port junction of three waveguides. Three theorems of general applicability may be stated concerning the properties of three-port junctions.

† G. A. Deschamps, *J. Appl. Phys.*, vol. 24, p. 1046, August, 1953.

These theorems are derivable from the equivalent-circuit representation of the junctions.   Their statements are†

1. A short circuit may always be placed in one of the arms of a three-port junction in such a position that no power can be transferred through the other two arms.

2. If the junction is symmetrical about one of its arms, a short circuit can always be placed in that arm so that no reflections occur in power transmission between the other two arms (i.e., the arms present matched impedances).

3. It is impossible for a general three-port junction of arbitrary symmetry to present matched impedances at all three arms.

A practical example of the working of theorems 1 and 2 is shown in Fig. 4.14. The solid circle in the Smith chart is the locus of impedances observed at a main-guide arm (arm 1) of an X-band H-plane T as a shorting plunger is moved in the guide connecting to the side arm (arm 3). Arm 2 was terminated in a matched impedance. In Fig. 4.14, if the terminals at which impedances were measured had been located a small distance δl closer to the T junction, every impedance observed would have been rotated by an angle $2\beta_g \ \delta l$ along its own

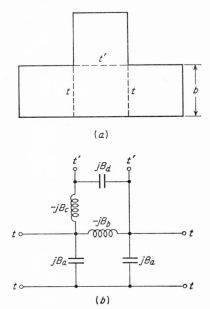

FIG. 4.15. (a) E-plane T; (b) Equivalent circuit.

standing wave circle.   The dashed-line circle represents the impedances appearing at new terminals $0.027\lambda_g$ closer to the T.   The new terminal plane has been so chosen that the input impedance reaches its maximum value, of approximately $30Z_0$.   Theorem 1 above was derived for the behavior of the three-terminal-pair equivalent circuit of the T junction.   The discrepancy of the observed maximum value of impedance from infinity is due to the departure of the waveguide T from exact correspondence with the behavior of its ideal equivalent circuit.   The position of the moving short in arm 3 at which the circle of input impedance passes through the center of the Smith chart is the

† C. G. Montgomery, R. H. Dicke, and E. M. Purcell (eds.), "Principles of Microwave Circuits," McGraw-Hill Book Company, Inc., New York, 1948.

case predicted by theorem 2.   At this point the T presents a matched impedance at the main-guide arms.

Equivalent Circuit for E-plane T.   A six-terminal equivalent circuit which may be used to represent the E-plane T is shown in Fig. 4.15b.†
The impedance presented at terminals tt and $t't'$ of the circuit correspond to those presented by the T at the transverse planes t and t' in Fig. 4.15a.   The normalized admittances of the circuit components are

$$\frac{B_a}{Y_0} \approx \frac{\pi b}{\lambda_g}\left(0.841 + 2.04\,\frac{b^2}{\lambda_g{}^2}\right)$$

$$\frac{B_b}{Y_0} \approx 0.859\,\frac{b}{\lambda_g}$$

$$\frac{B_c}{Y_0} \approx \frac{\lambda_g}{2\pi b}$$

$$\frac{B_d}{Y_0} \approx 1.56\,\frac{b}{\lambda_g}$$

4.10. Hybrid T

The symmetrical four-port junction of an H-plane arm and an E-plane arm with a section of waveguide is a microwave circuit device

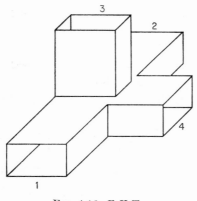

FIG. 4.16. *E-H* T.

having a number of useful applications.   This junction, called an *E-H* T, or hybrid T, has the properties, like those of the component junctions, that a wave entering arm 4 (Fig. 4.16) excites equal waves of like phase in arms 1 and 2 and a wave entering the E-plane arm (arm 3) excites equal waves of opposite phase in arms 1 and 2.   Due to the geometrical symmetry of the device, however, a wave in arm 3 excites no dominant-mode wave in arm 4, and reciprocally, there is no direct transmission from arm 4 to arm 3.   The properties of the hybrid T are most concisely expressed in terms of its scattering coefficients S_{ij}.   The reciprocity theorem provides that $S_{ij} = S_{ji}$.   The physical symmetry of the construction of the T is expressed in the properties $S_{13} = -S_{23}$ and $|S_{11}| = |S_{22}|$.   Moreover, as stated above, $S_{14} = S_{24}$ and $S_{34} = 0 = S_{43}$.   The scattering

† N. Marcuvitz, *op. cit.*

matrix of the hybrid T therefore has the form

$$[S_{ij}] = \begin{bmatrix} S_{11} & S_{12} & S_{13} & S_{14} \\ S_{12} & S_{22} & -S_{13} & S_{14} \\ S_{13} & -S_{13} & S_{33} & 0 \\ S_{14} & S_{14} & 0 & S_{44} \end{bmatrix} \qquad (4.126)$$

In Sec. 4.9, two important properties of the scattering matrices of lossless linear devices were derived. These properties are repeated here for reference:

$$\sum_j |S_{kj}|^2 = 1 \qquad (4.127)$$

$$\sum_k S_{kj}S_{ki}^* = 0 \qquad (4.128)$$

where (4.127) effectively states that if the members of the kth row (or column) of the scattering matrix are the components of a vector, the vector has unit magnitude, and (4.128) states that if the jth and ith rows (or columns) are vectors, the vectors are orthogonal. We may use these properties of the scattering matrix to show that if suitable matching devices are added to the E and H arms of a hybrid junction such as to make the reflection coefficients at these arms vanish, i.e., so that $S_{44} = 0$ and $S_{33} = 0$, the junction is matched at all ports, and ports 1 and 2 are decoupled. We shall see that these properties permit the matched hybrid T to perform a number of microwave circuit functions, such as that of impedance bridge, frequency discriminator, or duplexer.[†]

Consider now the application of the normalization condition (4.127) to columns 3 and 4 of the scattering matrix of the junction:

$$2|S_{13}|^2 + |S_{33}|^2 = 1 \qquad (4.129)$$
$$2|S_{14}|^2 + |S_{44}|^2 = 1 \qquad (4.130)$$

With the E and H arms matched, so that $S_{33} = 0 = S_{44}$, we have

$$|S_{13}| = |S_{14}| \qquad (4.131)$$

Thus, in the matched hybrid T, the power transfer between the E-plane arm and the main guide (1,2) is equal to that between the H-plane arm and the main guide, for equal incident voltages.

For the derivation of an additional property of the matched T, we apply Eq. (4.127) to columns 1 and 4 of the scattering matrix:

$$|S_{11}|^2 + |S_{12}|^2 + |S_{13}|^2 + |S_{14}|^2 = 1 \qquad (4.132)$$
$$2|S_{14}|^2 + |S_{44}|^2 = 1 \qquad (4.133)$$

[†] C. G. Montgomery (ed.), "Technique of Microwave Measurements," McGraw-Hill Book Company, Inc., New York, 1948.

Subtracting (4.133) from (4.132) with the use of Eq. (4.131) and the condition $S_{44} = 0$ yields

$$|S_{11}|^2 + |S_{12}|^2 = 0 \qquad (4.134)$$

Since both terms of (4.134) are positive, we conclude that

$$S_{11} = 0 \qquad (4.135)$$
$$S_{12} = 0 \qquad (4.136)$$

It was deduced from the symmetry of the hybrid junction that $|S_{11}| = |S_{22}|$. Therefore, we see that if the E- and H-plane arms of the junction are matched, the other two arms are matched also. There is, moreover, no transfer of power between the cross arms, 1 and 2, of the matched junction. The matching of the T at the E and H arms can be accomplished at a single frequency by the use of tuning screws or posts in these arms. Matching over a broader band of frequencies may be accomplished by the use of a post and aperture in the junction.† The matched hybrid T is often called a "magic T."

We can deduce the magnitude of the scattering matrix elements of the lossless magic T on the basis of the equal division of power between symmetrical arms 1 and 2 when energy is incident upon arm 3 or 4. This condition leads to the scattering matrix of the magic T:

$$[S_{ij}] = \frac{1}{\sqrt{2}} \begin{bmatrix} 0 & 0 & j & j \\ 0 & 0 & -j & j \\ j & -j & 0 & 0 \\ j & j & 0 & 0 \end{bmatrix} \qquad (4.137)$$

Equation (4.137) is the matrix of a T in which the input terminal planes have been chosen so as to yield a scattering matrix of simple form. The factors j are voltage phase factors, which could be altered, although not independently, by a shift of the assumed input planes along the waveguide leading to the T.

Impedance Representation of Magic T. The impedance matrix of the matched hybrid T may be derived from its scattering matrix by the use of Eq. (4.78). The result of this calculation shows that the impedance matrix is formally identical with the scattering matrix:

$$[z_{ij}] = \frac{1}{\sqrt{2}} \begin{bmatrix} 0 & 0 & j & j \\ 0 & 0 & -j & j \\ j & -j & 0 & 0 \\ j & j & 0 & 0 \end{bmatrix} \qquad (4.138)$$

† *Ibid.*

The zeros on the principal diagonal of the impedance matrix show that the waveguide voltage at any port of the magic T is independent of the current flowing at that port.   The voltage in port 1, for example, depends only on the current flowing in ports 3 and 4, the H- and E-plane ports, respectively.   If ports 3 and 4 are open-circuited,[†] so that no current flows in them, the voltage at port 1 is zero, irrespective of the current flowing at port 1.   The equivalent circuit of the magic T, shown in Fig. 4.17, gives insight into the origin of these properties of the T.   A series-resonant circuit appears at any of the input terminals of the device, when the remaining terminal pairs are open-circuited.   Thus the impedance behavior at any port of a magic

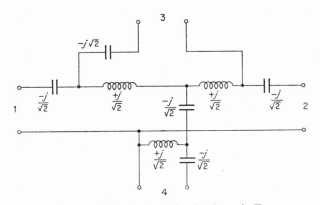

FIG. 4.17. Equivalent circuit of magic T.

T, when the other ports are open-circuited, is comparable with that of a shorted section of waveguide which is an integral number of half-wavelengths long.

The circuit properties of a hybrid T which is not matched are less simple than those of the matched T.   This is indicated by the character of the equivalent circuit shown in Fig. 4.18, which was derived from measurements made at 9.38 kmc on a hybrid T constructed of X-band waveguide.[‡]   The impedance character of the components of the equivalent circuit depends on the choice of input terminal planes at which the observed input impedances are defined to exist.   This

† An open circuit can be achieved by the connection of a quarter-wavelength section of shorted guide at these terminals.   If the waveguide is left unterminated, an open circuit is not obtained, however, because of the radiation resistance and discontinuity reactance which appear at an open-ended waveguide.

‡ Marcuvitz, *op. cit.*

statement is true in general of the impedance characterization of microwave devices.

Magic-T Impedance Bridge. The magic T is frequently employed as an impedance comparison device. A typical circuit connection

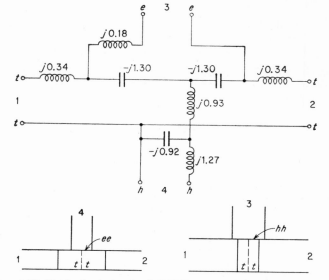

FIG. 4.18. Equivalent circuit of *E-H* T, referred to terminal planes shown.

for this application is shown in Fig. 4.19. Power is sent into the *H*-plane arm (4); a reference impedance and an "unknown" impedance

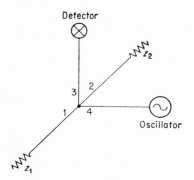

FIG. 4.19. Magic-T impedance bridge.

are connected to arms 1 and 2, respectively, and a detector receives the output from the *E*-plane arm (3). If the reference impedance is a matched load, it gives rise to no reflected wave, and hence no wave enters arm 1 of the T. If the unknown impedance is then not matched, it sends a reflected wave back into arm 2. The reflected wave divides at the junction, half of its energy going to the detector in arm 3 and half returning to the power source, since, as we have seen, $|S_{23}| = |S_{24}|$.

If the unknown impedance is brought to a condition of match, however, the disappearance of reflection will be signified by a null reading at the detector.

If the unknown impedance is fixed and a variable reference impedance is available, the unknown impedance may be measured in terms of the known reference impedance. For a wave of unit amplitude entering arm 4, waves of amplitude $1/\sqrt{2}$ in voltage are sent to arms 1 and 2. Here, ρ_1 and ρ_2 are the reflection coefficients of the reference and unknown impedances, respectively. Therefore the wave reaching the detector in arm 3 is equal to $\frac{1}{2}(\rho_1 - \rho_2)$, due to the sign difference between S_{13} and S_{23}. (It is here assumed that the unknown and reference impedances are located at equal distances from the junction. A difference of δl in the length of the connecting waveguides will add an additional phase delay of $2\beta_g\delta l$ to the wave from the longer guide.) Consequently, if the reference impedance is adjusted to give a null signal at the detector, then $\rho_1 = \rho_2$, and we have, using Eq. (4.79),

$$\frac{z_1 - 1}{z_1 + 1} = \frac{z_2 - 1}{z_2 + 1} \tag{4.139}$$

where z_1 and z_2 are the normalized impedances of the reference and unknown, respectively. Thus

$$z_1 z_2 + z_2 - z_1 - 1 = z_1 z_2 + z_1 - z_2 - 1 \tag{4.140}$$

or

$$z_1 = z_2 \tag{4.141}$$

Therefore, at balance,

$$|z_1| = |z_2| \tag{4.142}$$

or, equating real and imaginary parts,

$$r_1 = r_2 \tag{4.143}$$
$$x_1 = x_2 \tag{4.144}$$

Thus we see that the magic T may be used as a microwave bridge. When the bridge is balanced, the impedances being compared are equal in magnitude and phase when connected at equal distances from the T.

Another class of practical applications of the magic T is that which takes advantage of the isolation maintained between two circuits which it couples to the same final load. An example of this type of operation is the duplexing system shown in Fig. 4.20a. This arrangement permits the same antenna to be used by a microwave transmitter and receiver, while the transmitter power is kept out of the receiver. This system is inefficient and is restricted to low power operation, since only half of the power generated by the transmitter goes to the antenna, the other half being dissipated in the matched load. A waveguide switching system is used for duplexing at high transmitted power.

A second application of the magic T as an isolator is shown in Fig. 4.20b. In this example, a superheterodyne mixer stage receives signals from both the antenna and the local oscillator of the receiver, while local-oscillator power is prevented from reaching the antenna, by the

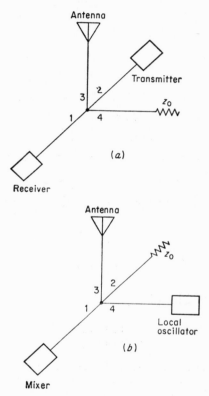

FIG. 4.20. Applications of magic T

separation between the E and H arms of a magic T. In this application the mixer stage must present a matched impedance at its input, to prevent reflection of oscillator power which would then be radiated from the antenna.

Another application of the magic T is made in the microwave discriminator, which is a device designed to produce a signal proportional to the departure of the frequency of its microwave input from a reference value. The reference frequency is determined by a cavity resonator, in the circuit arrangement shown in Fig. 4.21. The signal entering the H arm of magic T I is divided equally between a matched load and the H arm of magic T II. The crossarms, 1 and 2, of the second T are terminated in a cavity resonator and a short circuit. The arm terminated in the short circuit is $\lambda_g/8$ longer than the opposite crossarm. Thus, for unit voltage at the input to T I, equal voltages of magnitude $\frac{1}{2}$, but with a phase difference of $\pi/4$ radians, are incident upon the cavity resonator and shorted termination. The impedance

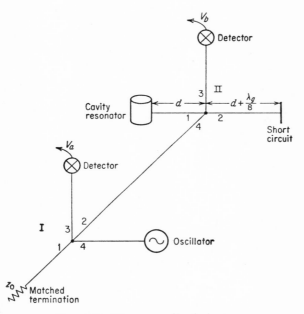

Fig. 4.21. Microwave discriminator.

of the short is $z_s = 0$, and its reflection coefficient is therefore $\rho_s = -1$. The impedance presented by the resonant cavity is like that of a short circuit at frequencies far from resonance, but in the neighborhood of resonance, the behavior of the cavity impedance is like that of a series-resonant circuit (Chap. 5). Thus, representing the cavity resonator as a series-resonant circuit, its impedance near resonance will be

$$z_c = j\frac{LC\omega^2 - 1}{C\omega} \tag{4.145}$$

Using $LC\omega_0^2 = 1$, where ω_0 is the angular frequency of resonance, and setting $\omega \approx \omega_0$ near resonance in the denominator of (4.145), we have

$$z_c = j\,\frac{\omega^2 - \omega_0{}^2}{C\omega_0{}^3} = jL\,\frac{(\omega + \omega_0)(\omega - \omega_0)}{\omega_0} \tag{4.146}$$

With the approximation $\omega + \omega_0 \approx 2\omega_0$ and the definition $\omega - \omega_0 = \delta\omega$, (4.146) becomes

$$z_c = j2L\,\delta\omega \tag{4.147}$$

The reflection coefficient of the cavity then is

$$\rho_c = \frac{j2L\,\delta\omega - 1}{j2L\,\delta\omega + 1} = -|\rho|e^{-j2\,\tan^{-1}2L\delta\omega} \tag{4.148}$$

Near resonance, $\delta\omega$ is small, and we write

$$\rho_c \approx -e^{-j4L\delta\omega} \tag{4.149}$$

Thus, neglecting phase factors which are common to both, the voltages of the waves entering the E and H arms of magic T II from the arms containing the short and the cavity resonator are, respectively,

$$\tfrac{1}{2}e^{-j\pi/2} \qquad -\tfrac{1}{2}e^{-j4L\delta\omega}$$

Hence the voltage reaching crystal detector b is

$$V_b = \frac{1}{2\sqrt{2}}\,(e^{-j\pi/2} + e^{-j4L\delta\omega}) \tag{4.150}$$

where the positive sign is used because of the difference of sign between S_{14} and S_{24} of the magic T.

The voltage reaching crystal detector a in the E arm of T I is

$$V_a = -\tfrac{1}{4}(e^{-j\pi/2} - e^{-j4L\delta\omega}) \tag{4.151}$$

The additional factor of $1/\sqrt{2}$ in (4.151) is due to the division of power at T I. The indication produced by the crystal detectors is proportional to the squares of the waveguide voltage wave amplitudes which are incident upon them. In the construction of the discriminator an attenuation factor of $\tfrac{1}{2}$ is introduced into the output of detector b, and the two detector outputs are combined in a circuit which forms the difference $U = |V_a|^2 - \tfrac{1}{2}|V_b|^2$:

$$U = \tfrac{1}{16}(|e^{-j\pi/2} + e^{-j4L\delta\omega}|^2 - |e^{-j\pi/2} - e^{-j4L\delta\omega}|^2) \tag{4.152}$$

Near resonance, $\delta\omega$ is small, and the exponential may be expanded:

$$U = \tfrac{1}{16}[|-j + (1 - j4L\,\delta\omega)|^2 - |-j - (1 - j4L\,\delta\omega)|^2] \tag{4.153}$$
$$U = \tfrac{1}{16}[1 + (1 + 4L\,\delta\omega)^2 - 1 - (1 - 4L\,\delta\omega)^2] \tag{4.154}$$
$$U = L\,\delta\omega \tag{4.155}$$

Thus, at resonance, the discriminator output is linear with the departure of frequency from the resonant value, being negative for frequencies below resonance and positive for frequencies above resonance, as shown in Fig. 4.22.† At large departures of frequency from resonance, the approximation of small $\delta\omega$ is no longer valid, and the discriminator output follows the dashed curve shown in Fig. 4.22. The frequency-proportional output voltage of the discriminator may be used to stabilize the frequency of a klystron oscillator at the cavity resonant

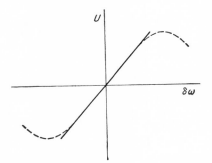

FIG. 4.22. Discriminator characteristic.

frequency,‡ since, as we shall see, the frequency of the klystron oscillator is dependent upon the voltage applied to the repeller electrode (Chap. 6).

PROBLEMS

4.1. By the use of Eq. (4.13), prove the orthogonality of E_{zm} and E_{zn}, axial components of electric field of two unlike TM modes.

4.2. With Eq. (4.11), prove the orthogonality of the transverse electric field components of two unlike TM modes.

4.3. Using the equivalent-circuit representation of a length D of waveguide,

(a) Verify Eq. (4.51) for the input impedance of a waveguide section with short-circuited termination.

(b) Prove that the input impedance of a waveguide section terminated in a matched load has a real normalized value of unity.

4.4. A vertical slit aperture of width d forms an impedance element in rectangular waveguide of width a and height b. A unit TE_{10}-mode wave of zero phase is incident upon the aperture. Assuming the trial solution for the field

† When the effect of losses in the cavity and coupled system is included, the slope of the discriminator curve at resonance is found to depend upon the losses, as well as upon the effective inductance L of the cavity. (Cf. R. V. Pound, in Montgomery, *op. cit.*, chap. 2.)

‡ *Ibid.*

component E_y at the plane of the slit

$$E_y = E_1 \left[1 - \frac{4}{d^2} \left(x - \frac{a}{2} \right)^2 \right] e^{j(\omega t + \theta)}$$

find the dominant-mode impedance of the slit.

4.5. Set up waveguide voltage and current definitions based upon transverse E and H components of the rectangular TM_{11} mode. Find a Z_0 for these functions such that $VI^*/2Z_0$ correctly gives the power transmitted by the mode.

4.6. Verify that the equivalent T and II circuits shown in Fig. 4.6 correspond to a two-port device having the impedance and admittance matrices, respectively, given in Eqs. (4.55) and (4.56).

4.7. A symmetrical two-port device has the normalized impedance matrix

$$\begin{bmatrix} 2 - 2j & 2 - j \\ 2 - j & 2 - 2j \end{bmatrix}$$

One port of the two-port device is terminated by an impedance z_r. It has been found that when z_r is connected to a slotted measuring guide, it causes a standing-wave ratio of $S = 5.8$ and a distance to first minimum of $d_{min} = 0.312\lambda_g$. What will be the normalized impedance looking into the other port of the two-port device?

4.8. A lossy section of waveguide of length L has a propagation characteristic for traveling waves that may be expressed as $\exp(-\gamma L) = \exp(-\alpha - j\beta)L = \exp(-0.1 - j)$. Assuming that the lossy section is terminated in a short circuit, show by the use of Eq. (4.90) or (4.91) what standing-wave ratio is produced when the lossy section is connected to a similar guide but having $\alpha = 0$.

4.9. A rectangular waveguide of width a and height b is terminated in an unmatched load having normalized impedance $z_r = 0.9 - j0.5$. Find the distance from load, and the aperture height, of a symmetrical capacitive aperture which will match this load to the waveguide. Assume that $b = a/2$, $\lambda_g = 2a$.

4.10. One crossarm (arm 1) of a magic T is terminated in a short circuit at a distance of one guide wavelength from the T. The opposite crossarm contains a movable short at distance d from the T, and power enters the H arm (arm 4) of the T. Show how the power leaving the E arm depends upon the distance d.

4.11. One milliwatt of power from a matched generator is incident upon the H-plane arm of a magic T. One of the cross-guide arms (arm 1) is terminated in a matched load, and the other (arm 2) in a short circuit.

(a) How much power reaches a matched detector in the E-plane arm?

(b) How much power reaches the matched load in arm 1?

(c) What accounts for the power not included in the total of (a) and (b) above?

4.12. Assuming that the short circuit in arm 2 of the magic T of Prob. 4.11 is located at a distance of $\lambda_g/2$ from the T, write the scattering matrix of the T when considered as a two-port device, with the E and H arms comprising the two ports. Refer the scattering matrix to ports located at transverse planes each $\lambda_g/2$ from the center of the T in these two arms.

CHAPTER 5

Microwave Resonators

Circuit resonance is a familiar phenomenon of conventional electronic circuit analysis; its most frequent application is in the design of circuits which will selectively amplify or transmit a single frequency or narrow band of frequencies. In sharply resonant circuits, the condition of resonance is often conveniently defined in terms of the appearance of a maximum or minimum value of impedance in the resonating branch of the circuit. A requirement for frequency-selective response may similarly be encountered in microwave system design, and since we have established an impedance description of microwave systems, it is reasonable to expect that the resonances of microwave system components will appear in the form of their impedance representations. This effect is in fact observed and is frequently employed in the treatment of resonating microwave components. The impedance point of view is not the only one we can adopt in analyzing the resonance of microwave components, however. The appearance of resonances in dynamical systems is of sufficiently general occurrence to make it worthwhile to consider here the nature of resonant behavior of physical systems.

5.1. Resonance in Dynamical Systems

Let us consider the example of a simple mechanical system consisting of a mass m moving in one dimension under the influence of an ideal spring restoring force kx, and impeded by a velocity-dependent frictional force $g\,dx/dt$, where k and g are constants. If the mass is also acted upon by the sinusoidal driving force $f_1e^{j\omega t}$, its equation of motion is

$$m\frac{d^2x}{dt^2} + g\frac{dx}{dt} + kx = f_1e^{j\omega t} \tag{5.1}$$

It may be readily verified that the displacement of the mass, under

133

these conditions, is given by

$$x = \frac{f_1 e^{j(\omega t + \phi)}}{[m^2(\omega_0^2 - \omega^2)^2 + g^2\omega^2]^{\frac{1}{2}}} \qquad (5.2)$$

where we have defined $\omega_0^2 = k/m$ and $\phi = -\tan^{-1}[g\omega/m(\omega_0^2 - \omega^2)]$. The elastic energy associated with this displacement is

$$V = \tfrac{1}{2}k \operatorname{Re} x^2 = \frac{1}{2}\frac{kf_1^2}{m^2(\omega_0^2 - \omega^2)^2 + g^2\omega^2} \cos^2(\omega t + \phi) \qquad (5.3)$$

The kinetic energy of the mass particle m is

$$T = \tfrac{1}{2}m\left(\frac{d}{dt}\operatorname{Re} x\right)^2 = \frac{1}{2}\frac{m\omega^2 f_1^2}{m^2(\omega_0^2 - \omega^2)^2 + g^2\omega^2}\sin^2(\omega t + \phi) \qquad (5.4)$$

The ratio of the time-average elastic energy to kinetic energy is, since $\langle\cos^2(\omega t + \phi)\rangle_{\mathrm{av}} = \langle\sin^2(\omega t + \phi)\rangle_{\mathrm{av}} = \tfrac{1}{2}$,

$$\frac{\langle V\rangle_{\mathrm{av}}}{\langle T\rangle_{\mathrm{av}}} = \frac{k}{m\omega^2} = \frac{\omega_0^2}{\omega^2} \qquad (5.5)$$

Therefore, at frequencies below resonance, when $\omega < \omega_0$, the average energy is predominantly elastic, stored in the spring, and above resonance the average energy is predominantly kinetic, residing in the particle velocity. At the frequency of resonance, $\omega = \omega_0$; the amplitudes of the two energies are equal and reach their greatest magnitude. The width of the resonance may be found by solving for the frequency $\omega_{\frac{1}{2}}$ at which the energy of oscillation has fallen to half its resonant value. This frequency may be defined by

$$\frac{x(\omega_{\frac{1}{2}})^2}{x(\omega_0)^2} = \frac{1}{2} \qquad (5.6)$$

Neglecting terms in $g^2/m^2\omega_0^2$, we find, from Eq. (5.2),

$$\frac{\omega_0 - \omega_{\frac{1}{2}}}{\omega_0} = \pm\frac{g}{2m\omega_0} \qquad (5.7)$$

The quantity $\omega_0 - \omega_{\frac{1}{2}}$ is the half-width of the resonant energy variation of the oscillator. If we define the full width of the resonance as the frequency interval $\Delta\omega$ between the half-energy points of the resonating oscillator, then we have $\Delta\omega = 2(\omega_0 - \omega_{\frac{1}{2}})$, as indicated in Fig. 5.1. We may now define the Q factor, or parameter measuring the sharpness of the resonance in its conventional form, as $Q = \omega_0/\Delta\omega$, with the result

$$Q = \frac{\omega_0}{\Delta\omega} = \frac{\omega_0}{2(\omega_0 - \omega_{\frac{1}{2}})} = \frac{m\omega_0}{g} \qquad (5.8)$$

An alternative and equivalent definition of the Q of a harmonic oscillator is that the Q is equal to 2π times the number of periods of the free transient oscillations required for the energy of the oscillator to fall to $1/e$ of its starting value.   Thus, $Q = 2\pi\tau_W/T_0$, where τ_W is the time constant of the transient in energy and T_0 is the natural period of

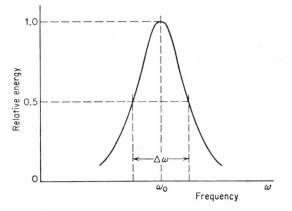

FIG. 5.1. Resonance curve.

the oscillator, equal to the period of the resonant frequency ω_0.   Hence, $Q = \omega_0\tau_W$.   Thus we have

$$|W| = W_0 e^{-\omega_0 t/Q}$$

We can then derive a useful expression for Q:

$$\frac{d|W|}{dt} = -\frac{\omega_0}{Q} W_0 e^{-\omega_0 t/Q}$$

or

$$Q = \omega_0 \frac{W}{P} \tag{5.9}$$

where W is the energy of the oscillator at resonance, and $P = -dW/dt$ is the rate of dissipation of energy due to losses.   Equation (5.9) for Q is valid in the general case.

We can verify Eq. (5.9) for the harmonic oscillator.   The rate of dissipation due to friction is equal to $dW/dt = F\,dx/dt = (g\,dx/dt)(dx/dt)$. Hence, the average rate of dissipation is

$$P = \frac{1}{T_0} \int_0^{T_0} \frac{dW}{dt}\,dt = \frac{1}{T_0} g \int_0^{T_0} \left(\frac{dx}{dt}\right)^2 dt$$

Substituting for x from Eq. (5.2) at the resonant frequency ω_0, we find

$$P = \frac{1}{T_0} \, g \, \frac{f_1^2}{2} \, \frac{T_0}{g^2} = \frac{f_1^2}{2g}$$

The use of the peak value of either V or T at resonance from Eq. (5.3) or (5.4) for the energy W in Eq. (5.9) yields

$$\omega_0 \frac{W}{P} = \omega_0 \frac{m}{g}$$

Thus we have verified Eq. (5.9), since the Q of the harmonic oscillator was found in Eq. (5.8) to be equal to $m\omega_0/g$.

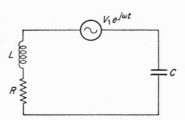

FIG. 5.2. Resonant circuit.

The natural oscillations of this mechanical system can be found by solving Eq. (5.1) with f_1 set equal to zero. When this is done, we find

$$x = x_1 e^{\Omega t} \tag{5.10}$$

where

$$\Omega = -\frac{g}{2m} \pm j \sqrt{\frac{k}{m} - \frac{g^2}{2m^2}} \tag{5.11}$$

If the losses of the system are assumed to be small, the term $g^2/2m^2$ in the radical may be neglected, with the result

$$x = x_1 e^{-(\omega_0/2Q)t} e^{j\omega_0 t} \tag{5.12}$$

where Eq. (5.8) has been used in the real exponent. Thus we see that the free oscillation of this mechanical oscillator with a small damping constant g has a natural frequency nearly equal to $\omega_0 = (k/m)^{\frac{1}{2}}$, and the oscillations decay with a time constant of $2Q/\omega_0$ sec.

The mechanical oscillator which has just been examined has a complete dynamical analog in the simple resonant electrical circuit shown in Fig. 5.2. With a driving force $V_1 e^{j\omega t}$, the equation for the displaced charge q in the circuit is

$$L \frac{d^2q}{dt^2} + R \frac{dq}{dt} + \frac{1}{C} q = V_1 e^{j\omega t} \tag{5.13}$$

This equation has the steady-state solution

$$q = \frac{V_1}{L[(\omega_0^2 - \omega^2) + R^2\omega^2/L^2]^{\frac{1}{2}}} \, e^{j(\omega t - \phi)} \tag{5.14}$$

where $\omega_0^2 = 1/LC$ and $\phi = \tan^{-1}[\omega R/L(\omega_0^2 - \omega^2)]$. The circuit current is $i = dq/dt = j\omega q$, and thus we may form the ratio of the average electric energy stored in the capacitor to the average magnetic energy stored in the inductor:

$$\frac{W_C}{W_L} = \frac{\langle q^2/2C \rangle}{\langle Li^2/2 \rangle} = \frac{1}{LC\omega^2} \tag{5.15}$$

$$\frac{W_C}{W_L} = \frac{\omega_0^2}{\omega^2} \tag{5.16}$$

Thus, at frequencies below resonance, $\omega < \omega_0$; the energy of the circuit is predominantly electric, and above resonance the energy is predominantly magnetic. At the resonant frequency the two energies are equal in amplitude and are out of phase by π radians of their time variation. Thus, neglecting the effect of losses, it may be considered that at resonance the energy in the circuit alternates in time from an entirely electric form to an entirely magnetic form.

The frequency $\omega_{\frac{1}{2}}$, at which the energy in the circuit has decreased to half its maximum value at resonance, is readily calculated to be given, with neglect of terms of the order of $R^2/L^2\omega_0^2$, by the expression

$$\frac{\omega_0 - \omega_{\frac{1}{2}}}{\omega_0} = \frac{R}{2L\omega_0} \tag{5.17}$$

from which the Q factor of the circuit is

$$Q = \frac{\omega_0}{2(\omega_0 - \omega_{\frac{1}{2}})} = \frac{L\omega_0}{R} \tag{5.18}$$

It is obvious from Eq. (5.18) that the Q of circuit has the alternative expression

$$Q = \omega_0 \frac{(Li^2/2)_{\omega_0}}{(Ri^2/2)_{\omega_0}} = \omega_0 \frac{W}{P} \tag{5.19}$$

where P is the average rate of dissipation of energy at the resonant frequency and W is the energy stored by the circuit at resonance, equal to the peak energy stored in the inductor.

Proceeding as in the case of the mechanical oscillator, we may find the free oscillation of the electrical circuit by setting V_1 equal to zero in Eq. (5.13). The oscillation of the circuit is then found to be

$$q = q_1 e^{\Omega t} \tag{5.20}$$

where

$$\Omega = -\frac{R}{2L} + j\omega_0 \sqrt{1 - \frac{R^2}{4L^2\omega_0^2}} \tag{5.21}$$

Thus, if the circuit losses are small, we may write

$$q = q_1 e^{-(\omega_0/2Q)t} e^{j\omega_0 t} \tag{5.22}$$

Equation (5.22), representing the free oscillation of the electrical resonator, is identical in form with Eq. (5.12) for the mechanical resonator. We may similarly observe the correspondences between Eqs. (5.14) and (5.2), for the driven oscillations of the two systems, and between Eqs. (5.16) and (5.5), for the properties of the energy distributions, as well as the identity in form of Eqs. (5.19) and (5.9), for the resonance widths of the electrical and mechanical oscillators.

We have thus shown that there are characteristics common to the behavior of dynamical systems to which energy of excitation has been added. The resonance of each system is distinguished by the values assumed by two parameters: the resonant frequency ω_0 and the sharpness of resonance Q. We have observed an additional distinctive characteristic of the energy in these systems. At the resonance frequency, the total energy oscillates periodically from the form analogous with potential energy to the form analogous with kinetic energy, with no excess of either form of energy present.

Resonance phenomena may occur in a number of types of structures which are used in microwave systems. Among these are included resonant cavities, resonant apertures combining the properties of the inductive and capacitive apertures which we have examined in Chap. 4, or, as we have seen, a tuning post in a waveguide, which may exhibit resonant behavior. The resonances of cavities, or conducting enclosures of general form, have properties in common with the elementary resonating systems which we have considered above. Cavity resonators differ from these elementary systems, however, in the fact that, instead of having a single resonance frequency, as does the one-mesh electric circuit, a hollow cavity can resonate at an infinite number of discrete frequencies. The resonant frequencies of the cavity resonator are in general not harmonically related, like the overtones of a vibrating string or column of air, but are given as the result of a characteristic-value equation of the wave equation. For each resonant frequency, a selectivity parameter Q can be defined as a measure of the width of the resonance.

The properties of resonant cavities arise fundamentally from the fact that, in order for the cavities to oscillate at all, there must exist electromagnetic fields which satisfy the boundary conditions presented by the cavity walls. The structure of the wave equation permits suitable fields to exist only at certain definite frequencies of oscillation, which may be called the eigenvalues of the problem. In dealing with the behavior of resonant cavities in microwave systems, the electromagnetic field problem may be solved to find the resonant frequencies and line widths of the cavity resonances. For each resonance an equivalent-circuit representation may be made.   The equivalent circuit summarizes the results of the field solutions and allows the resonator to be incorporated into the impedance representation of the remainder of the microwave system.

5.2. Rectangular-cavity Resonator

The task of obtaining solutions for the electromagnetic fields within a cavity resonator can often be simplified by taking advantage of the fact that many of the types of resonators in practical use can be considered to be sections of waveguide of standard form, with short-circuited terminations.   We are then able to use the known wave solutions for the waveguide in question, to produce a standing wave of field which will satisfy boundary conditions at the cavity walls.   Let

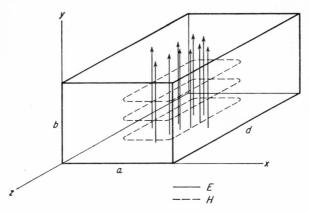

FIG. 5.3. Rectangular-cavity resonator.

us apply this procedure to a simple rectangular cavity of dimensions a, b, and d, with coordinates chosen as in Fig. 5.3.   Suitable solutions for the cavity electromagnetic fields can be based upon any of the propagating modes of rectangular waveguides.

An infinite number of possible cavity solutions corresponds to each waveguide mode, depending upon the number of cycles of variation of the standing waves of field present between the end walls of the cavity. For simplicity we may select, as an example, waves of the TE_{10} mode, with a single half-wavelength of standing wave in the cavity.   We write the z component of magnetic field as the superposition of two oppositely traveling waves:

$$H_z = H_1 \cos \frac{\pi x}{a} e^{-j\beta_g z} + H_2 \cos \frac{\pi x}{a} e^{j\beta_g z} \qquad (5.23)$$

The axial magnetic field must vanish at $z = 0$ and $z = d$, where it is normal to the conducting surfaces. This may be accomplished by taking $H_2 = -H_1$ and $\beta_g d = \pi$.

$$H_z = -2jH_1 \cos \frac{\pi x}{a} \sin \frac{\pi z}{d} \tag{5.24}$$

Application of Eq. (3.36) to each of the two waves in Eq. (5.23), with $k_c = \pi/a$ and $|\beta_g| = \pi/d$, yields

$$H_x = \frac{-j\pi/d}{(\pi/a)^2} \left(-\frac{\pi}{a} \right) H_1 \sin \frac{\pi x}{a} e^{-j\pi z/d}$$

$$- \frac{j\pi/d}{(\pi/a)^2} \left(-\frac{\pi}{a} \right) H_1 \sin \frac{\pi x}{a} e^{j\pi z/d} \tag{5.25}$$

$$H_x = 2j \frac{a}{d} H_1 \sin \frac{\pi x}{a} \cos \frac{\pi z}{d} \tag{5.26}$$

And, by the use of Eq. (3.35), we find

$$E_y = \frac{j\omega\mu}{(\pi/a)^2} \left(-\frac{\pi}{a} \right) H_1 \sin \frac{\pi x}{a} e^{-j\pi z/d}$$

$$- \frac{j\omega\mu}{(\pi/a)^2} \left(-\frac{\pi}{a} \right) H_1 \sin \frac{\pi x}{a} e^{j\pi z/d} \tag{5.27}$$

$$E_y = -2 \frac{\omega\mu a}{\pi} H_1 \sin \frac{\pi x}{a} \sin \frac{\pi z}{d} \tag{5.28}$$

The electric field of this cavity mode is thus seen to have its maximum value at the centers of the xz-plane faces of area ad, extending perpendicularly to these faces, and the magnetic field lines form closed loops parallel to the xz plane, as indicated in Fig. 5.3. This mode of resonance is designated as the TE_{101} mode, the third subscript indicating the number of variations of standing wave along the axial direction of the component traveling waves. The frequency of resonance may be determined by substituting any of the components of field into the wave equation. Using E_y, for example,

$$\nabla^2 E_y = -\mu\epsilon\omega^2 E_y \tag{5.29}$$

which is equivalent to

$$k_c{}^2 + \beta_g{}^2 = \mu\epsilon\omega^2 \tag{5.30}$$

from which we find the resonant frequency

$$\omega_{101} = \frac{1}{\sqrt{\mu\epsilon}} \sqrt{\frac{\pi^2}{a^2} + \frac{\pi^2}{d^2}} \tag{5.31}$$

If the standing-wave pattern in the axial direction had been required to comprise p half-wavelengths instead of the one half-wavelength of our example, the resonant frequency of the TE_{10p} mode would then be

$$\omega_{10p} = \frac{1}{\sqrt{\mu\epsilon}} \sqrt{\frac{\pi^2}{a^2} + \frac{p^2\pi^2}{d^2}} \tag{5.32}$$

Alternatively, if an arbitrary TE_{mn} or TM_{mn} mode wave is chosen for the construction of the fields in the cavity, the frequency of resonance is

$$\omega_{mnp} = \frac{1}{\sqrt{\mu\epsilon}} \sqrt{\frac{m^2\pi^2}{a^2} + \frac{n^2\pi^2}{b^2} + \frac{p^2\pi^2}{d^2}} \tag{5.33}$$

The resonant frequencies given by Eq. (5.33) pertain to a completely closed cavity, having walls of infinite conductivity. The presence of a coupling aperture or loop for the excitation of resonance will perturb the boundaries of the cavity and hence shift the resonant frequency, by an amount that depends in general upon the tightness of coupling. In many practical cases this perturbation is small, and Eq. (5.33) is applicable.

A closed cavity with infinitely conducting walls would oscillate indefinitely in one or several of its normal modes, depending upon the manner in which the oscillation is started. The energy of the electric field in a rectangular cavity oscillating in the TE_{101} mode is given by

$$W_E = \frac{\epsilon}{2} \iiint E_y^2 \, dx \, dy \, dz \tag{5.34}$$

Upon substituting E_y from Eq. (5.28), we find the peak value

$$W_E = \frac{\mu^2 \epsilon \omega^2 H_1^2 a^3 b d}{2\pi^2} = \mu H_1^2 \frac{ab(a^2 + d^2)}{2d} \tag{5.35}$$

where we have used Eq. (5.30) with $k_c^2 = \pi^2/a^2$ and $\beta_g^2 = \pi^2/d^2$. The energy of the oscillating magnetic field includes contributions from H_x and H_z and is equal to

$$W_M = \frac{\mu}{2} \iiint (H_x^2 + H_z^2) \, dx \, dy \, dz \tag{5.36}$$

By the use of Eqs. (5.24) and (5.26) for the two components of magnetic field, the magnetic energy is found to be

$$W_M = -\mu H_1^2 \frac{ab(a^2 + d^2)}{2d} \tag{5.37}$$

Thus at resonance, the electric and magnetic components of energy in the oscillating cavity are equal in magnitude, and out of phase by π radians.   Each individual resonance oscillation of the cavity resonator resembles in this respect the other oscillating systems which were discussed in Sec. 5.1.   We can treat each of the infinitely many resonances of the ideal cavity as a separate oscillator, each representable by an individual resonant circuit, and having an individual Q value.

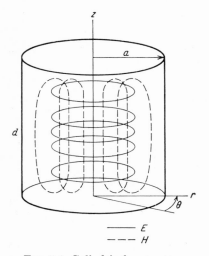

FIG. 5.4. Cylindrical resonator.

5.3. Cylindrical-cavity Resonator

As the fundamental form of cylindrical cavity resonator, we may select a right circular cylinder of radius a and length d, as in Fig. 5.4. The resonant fields of this cavity may be constructed from a suitable choice of the propagating modes of circular waveguide.   The resonator modes which exist in an actual case will depend upon the manner of exciting the cavity, and are chosen according to the use to which the cavity is to be put.   Let us consider as an example the TE$_{011}$ mode, which is frequently used in resonant cavity wavemeters.   As a starting component of field, a standing wave of axial magnetic field, H_z, is formed from the traveling waves.

$$H_z = H_1 J_0(k_c r)e^{j\beta_g z} + H_2 J_0(k_c r)e^{-j\beta_g z} \qquad (5.38)$$

The boundary conditions which must be satisfied by H_z are

At $z = 0$ and $z = d$:

$$H_z = 0$$

At $r = a$:

$$\frac{\partial H_z}{\partial r} = 0$$

We may satisfy the first condition by choosing $H_2 = -H_1$ and $\beta_g = \pi/d$. The condition at $r = a$ is satisfied by taking, from Table 3.4, $k_c a = p'_{01} = 3.832$.   The axial field thus is

$$H_z = 2jH_1 J_0\left(3.832\,\frac{r}{a}\right)\sin\frac{\pi z}{d} \qquad (5.39)$$

The transverse components of field are obtained from (5.38) by the use of Eqs. (3.72) and (3.71) and have the values

$$H_r = -2j \frac{\pi}{d} \frac{aH_1}{3.832} J_1\left(3.832 \frac{r}{a}\right) \cos \frac{\pi z}{d} \tag{5.40}$$

$$E_\theta = 2\omega\mu \frac{aH_1}{3.832} J_1\left(3.832 \frac{r}{a}\right) \sin \frac{\pi z}{d} \tag{5.41}$$

The electric field lines of the TE_{011} mode form closed circular loops centered on, and in planes perpendicular to, the cylinder axis. The **E** lines are threaded by closed loops of magnetic field lines in radial planes (Fig. 5.4). No free charge concentrations appear on the cavity walls in this mode, since the normal **E** field is everywhere zero at the walls. The surface currents **K = n × H** are

Curved surface:

$$K_\theta = 2jH_1J_0(3.832) \sin \frac{\pi z}{d}$$

End faces:

$$K_\theta = \pm 2j \frac{\pi}{d} \frac{aH_1}{3.832} J_1\left(3.832 \frac{r}{a}\right)$$

Thus the surface currents are entirely circumferential. No surface current tends to flow across the joint between the circular end faces and the curved walls of the cylinder. Hence the TE_{011} mode is well suited for use in the construction of cavity wavemeters, since one of the end faces can be mounted on a microme- ter screw and rotated to change the length of the cavity, thus ad- justing its resonant frequency. The TE_{011} fields can be excited by aperture coupling from the domi- nant-mode fields of rectangular waveguide, as illustrated in Fig. 5.5. Inspection of Tables 3.4 and 3.6 shows that in a given cylin- drical cavity, the TM_{111} mode is

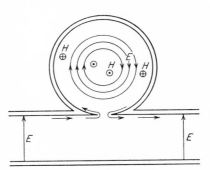

FIG. 5.5. Excitation of TE_{011} wave- meter by surface currents of rectangu- lar-waveguide dominant mode.

simultaneously resonant with the TE_{011} mode, since they both have the same cutoff constant k_c. The presence of TM_{111} mode oscillations in the cavity is undesirable, since the Q of this mode is lower than that of the TE_{011} mode, and the resultant cavity Q is lowered by the transfer of energy to the low-Q mode. The TM_{111} mode will be suppressed to a considerable extent by wavemeter construction of the type described, since a break in the cavity walls at the end edges interrupts the surface currents of the TM_{111} mode, thus reducing its degree of excitation.

Excitation of the TE_{111} mode can be further avoided by minimizing structural asymmetries, such as nonperpendicularity of the tuning plate with respect to the cavity axis. Hence precise construction is necessary to achieve single-mode operation of a TE_{011} cavity.

5.4. Q of a Cavity Resonator

The properties of the cavity resonator have been seen to correspond in several respects to those of a simple prototype dynamical oscillator. The cavity possesses resonant frequencies at which the energy of the oscillator reaches a large value, and at which the energy is divided so that equal average values are taken up in the two forms of energy available to the oscillator. The Q parameter of the resonant system, which measures its frequency width, or selectivity, was calculated in the case of the simple harmonic oscillator in terms of the fundamental definition $Q = \omega_0/\Delta\omega$, where $\Delta\omega$ is the interval between the frequencies for which the energy of the oscillator is equal to half of its resonant value. The Q was also calculated by means of alternative definitions which are equivalent to the first, as $\omega_0/2$ times the time constant of the decay of free oscillations of the system, or as ω_0 times the ratio of energy stored to the rate of energy dissipation.

We should like to be able to apply these methods of calculation which have been successful for the simple resonator to the determination of the resonance parameters of the cavity resonator. We cannot use the first method for the calculation of Q, since our method for calculating the field energy of a resonant cavity, namely that of fitting solutions of the wave equation to the cavity boundaries, yields solutions in a given cavity only at discrete frequencies, the frequencies of resonance. This limitation arises from the fact that our solutions are correct for cavity walls which have infinite conductivity. At any frequency other than the resonant values, the boundary condition requiring zero tangential electric field at the cavity walls is violated.

The second method of obtaining Q, in terms of the decay of transient oscillations, is more convenient for use in the experimental determination of Q than in calculation of its value. We shall therefore calculate the resonance width of the cavity resonator by means of the definition which was given in Eq. (5.9).

$$Q = \omega_0 \frac{W}{P} \tag{5.42}$$

where Q is taken as positive, and ω_0 is the resonance frequency, W, the energy of the oscillator, and P, the average rate of dissipation of energy, at the resonant frequency ω_0. It was found in Sec. 5.2 that the field energy contained within a rectangular cavity at resonance is constant and alternates between electric field energy and magnetic field energy. This is a general property of cavity resonators, and we may use it to simplify the calculation of Eq. (5.42). Since W is constant at resonance, it will be equal to the energy of the magnetic fields at the instant when the cavity energy is entirely magnetic:

$$W = \frac{\mu}{2} \iiint H^2 \, d\tau$$

If the dielectric medium filling the cavity is lossless, the rate of dissipation of energy will be that due to wall losses only: $P = (R_s/2)\iint K^2 \, da$, where R_s is the surface resistivity of the walls, and K is the surface current. Since $K^2 = H_t^2$, where H_t is the tangential magnetic field at the walls, and $R_s = (\pi f \mu/\sigma)^{\frac{1}{2}}$, Eq. (5.42) may be written

$$Q = \frac{2 \iiint H^2 \, d\tau}{\delta \iint H_t^2 \, da} \tag{5.43}$$

where δ is the skin depth in the material of the cavity walls.

We may now calculate the Q value of a typical simple cavity resonator. We have obtained the energy of the rectangular resonator illustrated in Fig. 5.3 as the value W_M given by Eq. (5.37). Hence the numerator of the Q expression, Eq. (5.43), will be $(4/\mu)W_M$. For the denominator of (5.43), we calculate the surface integrals over six faces, using the fact that integrals over opposite faces are equal.

$$\iint H_t^2 \, da = 2 \int_0^a \int_0^d (H_x^2 + H_z^2) \, dx \, dz \Big|_{y=0} + 2 \int_0^b \int_0^d H_z^2 \, dy \, dz \Big|_{x=0}$$
$$+ 2 \int_0^a \int_0^b H_x^2 \, dx \, dy \Big|_{z=0} \tag{5.44}$$

By the use of Eqs. (5.24) and (5.26) for H_z and H_x, we find

$$\iint H_t^2 \, da = 8H_1^2 \left(\frac{a^3}{4d} + \frac{ad}{4} + \frac{bd}{2} + \frac{a^3b}{2d^2} \right) \tag{5.45}$$

from which we obtain

$$Q = \frac{abd(a^2 + d^2)}{\delta(a^3d + ad^3 + 2ad^3b + 2a^3b)} \tag{5.46}$$

From Eq. (5.46) we find, for the Q of a cubical resonator of side a in the TE_{101} mode,

$$Q = \frac{a}{3\delta} \tag{5.47}$$

For a resonator of cubic shape, $a = b = d$. In the TE_{101} mode, $\mu\epsilon\omega^2 = 2\pi^2/a^2$. Therefore the Q of the cubical resonator in this mode is

$$Q = \frac{1}{3}\sqrt{\frac{\pi\sigma}{2\epsilon f}} \tag{5.48}$$

Thus, a cubical resonator in the TE_{101} mode which is resonant at 10 kmc and has silver-plated inner surfaces ($\sigma = 6.14 \times 10^7$) will have a Q of approximately 11,000. Slightly higher Q values are possible in other resonators of simple shape, such as the sphere or elongated cylinder,† but the form of Eq. (5.43) shows that Q values in general will be of the order of magnitude of the volume-to-surface ratio of the resonator, divided by the skin depth in the conductor at the frequency of resonance.

5.5. Aperture-coupled Resonator

The cavity resonance parameters ω_0 and Q which were calculated in the preceding sections were obtained by assuming that the cavity walls were closed and unbroken by any opening. Thus no provision was assumed to exist for the exchange of energy with an external system. An external connection is, of course, necessary in order to supply the energy of the cavity oscillations and to compensate for the energy dissipated in the walls. The cavity parameters calculated with the simplifying assumption of cavity isolation provide a basis for our understanding of the characteristic behavior of cavities. These results will require modification, however, in order to correctly represent an actual cavity coupled to an external system.

Electromagnetic coupling between a waveguide and a cavity resonator is usually established via an aperture or window in a common wall between the cavity and waveguide. Coaxial lines are frequently coupled to a cavity resonator by means of a current probe, or small one-turn loop, projecting into the cavity. The coupling aperture or loop must be arranged so that the fields of the coupling element tend to excite the mode which it is desired to establish in the cavity.

When resonant oscillations occur in a cavity coupled to an external microwave system, the entire coupled system is effectively required to participate in the cavity oscillations. The effective alteration of the

† W. W. Hansen, *J. Appl. Phys.*, vol. 9, p. 654, October, 1938.

volume and shape of the cavity which is brought about by the connection of the coupled system will perturb the resonant frequency of
the cavity by an amount dependent upon the tightness of coupling of
the cavity to the system. The circulating currents which are caused
to flow in the coupled system at resonance will be accompanied by
dissipative losses which lower the effective Q of the combined cavity
and microwave system.

The effects of the coupling of a cavity resonator to an associated
system are difficult to treat, in general, from the standpoint of the
electromagnetic fields because of the geometrical complexity of most
microwave systems. The problem
of the connection of a cavity resonator may be conveniently treated
by means of an equivalent-circuit
representation of the cavity and
system.

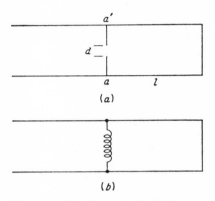

The construction of an equivalent
circuit to represent an aperture-
coupled cavity resonator may be
illustrated by means of the following simple example: We consider
the cavity resonator consisting of a
section of rectangular waveguide
terminated in a short circuit, preceded at distance l by a circular aperture of diameter d in a
transverse conducting plane. This

FIG. 5.6. (a) Aperture-coupled resonator; (b) transmission-line equivalent
circuit.

structure is illustrated schematically in Fig. 5.6a, and its transmission-
line equivalent circuit is shown in Fig. 5.6b. The circular aperture, at
plane aa', is equivalent to a parallel-connected inductor. Its normalized reactance is found from Table 4.1 to be

$$x_a = \frac{X_a}{Z_0} = \frac{d^3}{3ab} \beta_g \tag{5.49}$$

where subscript a refers to the aperture, and a and b are the width and
height of the waveguide, respectively. The normalized reactance
presented at plane aa' by the short-circuited section of waveguide
[cf. Eq. (4.51)] is equal to

$$x_1 = \tan \beta_g l \tag{5.50}$$

We now specify that the length of the short-circuited section of
waveguide has a length l of the order of one half-guide-wavelength.

For definiteness, we might specify that $|\pi - \beta_g l| < 0.1$. Then, we may use the fact that, for $\beta_g l$ nearly equal to π radians,

$$\tan \beta_g l = - \tan (\pi - \beta_g l) \approx \beta_g l - \pi \qquad (5.51)$$

The normalized input reactance of the cavity resonator then becomes

$$x_c = j \frac{x_a x_1}{x_a + x_1} \approx \frac{A\beta_g(\beta_g l - \pi)}{A\beta_g + \beta_g l - \pi} \qquad (5.52)$$

where we have defined $A = d^3/3ab$. Equation (5.52) shows that, in the present approximation, the input impedance of the resonator vanishes and resonance occurs, when $\beta_g l = \pi$. Hence, writing β_g' for resonant value of guide propagation constant, at resonance,

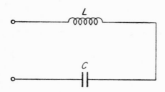

$$\beta_g' = \frac{\pi}{l} \qquad (5.53)$$

FIG. 5.7. Series-resonant circuit.

The vanishing of cavity input impedance at resonance is comparable with the impedance behavior of a lossless series-resonant circuit. Consequently, we may seek an equivalent series-resonant circuit representation of the cavity resonator of Fig. 5.6, valid in the neighborhood of resonance.

The reactance of a series-resonant circuit, as shown in Fig. 5.7, is

$$X_s = L\omega - \frac{1}{C\omega} \qquad (5.54)$$

$$X_s = \frac{(\omega + \omega_0)(\omega - \omega_0)}{C\omega \, \omega_0^2} \qquad (5.55)$$

In (5.55) we have defined $1/LC = \omega_0^2$, where ω_0 is the resonant frequency of the circuit. In the neighborhood of resonance we may write $\omega + \omega_0 \approx 2\omega_0$, and setting $\omega = \omega_0$ in the denominator of (5.55), we have

$$X_s \approx 2L(\omega - \omega_0) \qquad (5.56)$$

In Eq. (5.56) we have obtained a linear approximation for the reactance curve of the series circuit, in the neighborhood of resonance.

We may form a similar linear representation of the reactance X_c of the cavity resonator by forming the one-term Taylor expansion

$$X_c = Z_0 x_c \approx \frac{\partial x_c}{\partial \omega}\bigg|_{\omega_0} (\omega - \omega_0)Z_0 \qquad (5.57)$$

where Z_0 is the characteristic impedance of the waveguide. The reactances of the equivalent circuit and the cavity resonator may then

be brought into correspondence by equating the coefficients of
$\omega - \omega_0$ in Eqs. (5.56) and (5.57), with both x_s and x_c evaluated at the
same frequency ω_0. Using the fact that

$$\frac{\partial x_c}{\partial \omega} = \frac{\partial x_c}{\partial \beta_g} \frac{\partial \beta_g}{\partial \omega} \tag{5.58}$$

and since $\beta_g = (\omega^2/c^2 - \pi^2/a^2)^{\frac{1}{2}}$,

$$\frac{\partial x_c}{\partial \omega} = \frac{\partial x_c}{\partial \beta_g} \frac{\omega}{c^2 \beta_g} \tag{5.59}$$

With the value of x_c given by Eq. (5.52), Eq. (5.59) then becomes

$$\frac{\partial x_c}{\partial \omega} = \left[\frac{2 A \beta_g l - A \pi}{A \beta_g + \beta_g l - \pi} - \frac{A \beta_g (\beta_g l - \pi)(A + l)}{(A \beta_g + \beta_g l - \pi)^2} \right] \frac{\omega}{c^2 \beta_g} \tag{5.60}$$

Evaluated at the resonance value of β_g from Eq. (5.53),

$$\left. \frac{\partial x_c}{\partial \omega} \right|_{\omega_0} = \frac{\omega_0 l^2}{c^2 \pi} \tag{5.61}$$

Thus Eq. (5.57) becomes

$$X_c \approx \frac{\omega_0 l^2}{c^2 \pi} (\omega - \omega_0) Z_0 \tag{5.62}$$

When coefficients of $\omega - \omega_0$ in Eqs. (5.62) and (5.56) are equated

$$2L = \frac{\omega_0 l^2}{c^2 \pi} Z_0 \tag{5.63}$$

Thus the inductor of the equivalent series-resonant circuit has the
magnitude

$$L = \frac{\omega_0 l^2}{2 c^2 \pi} Z_0 \tag{5.64}$$

The corresponding equivalent-circuit capacitor is therefore

$$C = \frac{1}{L \omega_0^2} = \frac{2 c^2 \pi}{l^2 \omega_0^3} \frac{1}{Z_0} \tag{5.65}$$

The resonant angular frequency ω_0 in Eqs. (5.64) and (5.65) is defined
by the characteristic equation of the waveguide

$$\frac{\pi^2}{a^2} + \beta_g^2 = \frac{\omega^2}{c^2} \tag{5.66}$$

Hence, with the resonant value of β_g given by Eq. (5.53),

$$\omega_0 = c \sqrt{\frac{\pi^2}{a^2} + \frac{\pi^2}{l^2}} \tag{5.67}$$

The practical significance of the specific values of L and C which we have just obtained is that they compose a series-resonant circuit, of which the reactance varies at the same rate through the resonant frequency as does the reactance of the aperture-coupled resonator of our example. Our task has therefore been that of matching tuning rates at resonance. The equivalent circuit is thus a valid representation of the resonator only in the frequency range near the TE_{101} resonance defined by Eq. (5.53).

The general frequency response of the cavity resonator in this example is not represented by the simple single resonant circuit that has been found above, however. In its complete form, Eq. (5.52) for the resonator input impedance is

$$jx_c = j \, \frac{A\beta_g \tan \beta_g l}{A\beta_g + \tan \beta_g l} \tag{5.68}$$

The cavity impedance has a zero at $\beta_g l = \pi$, which is the case we have calculated. There are obviously also higher-order resonances at $\beta_g l = n\pi$, where n is an integer, and an equivalent series circuit may be found for each of these resonances. We note that the parameters of the aperture did not appear in our final expressions for the equivalent circuit elements L and C. This was due to our choice of definition for the impedance condition, in which the waveguide section placed a zero of impedance at the plane of the aperture. With this condition, the impedance of the aperture can have no influence on the resultant input impedance of the structure. A different situation is presented when, in Eq. (5.68), we have $A\beta_g = -\tan \beta_g l$. In this case, the input impedance becomes infinite and the natural representation for the cavity at this frequency is a lossless parallel-resonant circuit. The values of the parallel-circuit elements may also be found, by a procedure analogous to that we have used above. A linear expansion of the admittances of the resonant cavity and the parallel-resonant circuit may be formed, and the two brought into correspondence by equating coefficients of $\omega - \omega_0$, as we have done before.

An alternative method for finding resonator equivalent circuits is also available. This method consists of finding partial-fraction expansions in terms of the maxima of the admittance or impedance of the resonator, and identifying each maximum with the resonant admittance or impedance of a series or parallel electric circuit, respectively.[†]

In the present discussion we have, moreover, neglected losses in the waveguide and aperture. When the finite conductivity of the resonator surfaces is taken into account, a resistive element of correct value to

† S. A. Schelkunoff, *Proc. IRE*, vol. 32, p. 83, 1944.

account for the losses must be introduced into the equivalent circuit of the resonator.

5.6. Resonator Equivalent Circuits

The equivalent-circuit parameters of a cavity resonator may be established by means of measurement, and a considerable body of literature exists concerning the techniques of measurements which may be employed for this purpose.† An equivalent circuit for the cavity resonator may be constructed in a variety of forms. The form which is assigned to the equivalent circuit of the cavity will be governed by the specific requirements and the configuration of the problem involved.

The cavity resonator discussed in the preceding section was chosen so that the input impedance at the plane of the coupling aperture had a minimum value at resonance. If the input terminals had been placed a quarter-wavelength away from the plane of the aperture, the input impedance would then have been maximum at resonance, and the cavity equivalent circuit would then have been chosen as a parallel resonant circuit. Thus, either a series- or parallel-resonant circuit representation of the general resonator is possible.

In terms of the series-resonant representation of the resonator, the existence of cavity losses may be represented by the inclusion of a series resistance R. Figure 5.8a shows the equivalent circuit of a closed resonator, assumed to have no coupling to any outside circuit. The parameters of the intrinsic-cavity circuit are

$$\omega_0 = \frac{1}{\sqrt{LC}} \tag{5.69}$$

$$Q_0 = \frac{\omega_0 L}{R} \tag{5.70}$$

where Q_0 is the unloaded Q of the cavity. It is convenient to represent the coupling to an external guide or line by means of an ideal $n:1$ transformer and a series reactance element L_a, in order to account for the effect of the aperture impedance and the degree of coupling introduced by the aperture. Figure 5.8b shows the circuit assumed for the cavity and coupling system, connected to a generator having internal impedance Z_0. In most practical cases, the influence of the reactance

† M. Wind and H. Rapaport (eds.), "Handbook of Microwave Measurements," Polytechnic Institute of Booklyn, New York, 1954; D. D. King, "Measurements at Centimeter Wavelength," D. Van Nostrand Company, Inc., Princeton, N.J., 1952; E. L. Ginzton, "Microwave Measurements," McGraw-Hill Book Company Inc., New York, 1957.

L_a on the resonant frequency of the system is relatively slight, as was true of the TE_{101} cavity investigated in the preceding section.

The equivalent circuit of the coupled cavity, with the source and coupling impedance referred to the cavity side of the coupling transformer, is shown in Fig. 5.8c. The internal impedance of the source

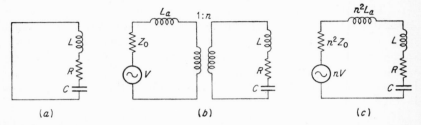

FIG. 5.8. Cavity equivalent circuits. (a) Intrinsic resonator; (b) cavity coupling to source; (c) source transformed to cavity-equivalent impedance loop.

as transformed to the effective resonant circuit is now seen to alter the Q of the coupled cavity. The new value of Q is defined as the loaded Q.

$$Q_L = \frac{L\omega_0}{R + n^2 Z_0} \tag{5.71}$$

A coupling coefficient β is now defined for the system in such a way that Eq. (5.71) takes the form

$$Q_L = \frac{L\omega_0}{R(1 + \beta)} \tag{5.72}$$

or

$$\beta = \frac{n^2 Z_0}{R} \tag{5.73}$$

Equation (5.72) is equivalent to

$$\frac{1}{Q_L} = \frac{1}{Q_0} + \frac{\beta R}{L\omega_0} \tag{5.74}$$

An additional parameter of the circuit is hence defined, as the external Q.

$$Q_{ext} = \frac{L\omega_0}{\beta R} = \frac{Q_0}{\beta} \tag{5.75}$$

Hence

$$\frac{1}{Q_L} = \frac{1}{Q_0} + \frac{1}{Q_{ext}} \tag{5.76}$$

Thus, when $\beta = 1$, $Q_0 = Q_{ext} = 2Q_L$. Since the coupling coefficient β is equal to $n^2 Z_0/R$, when $\beta = 1$ the coupled impedance of the source as seen in the cavity circuit is equal to the cavity resistance. Reciprocally, with $\beta = 1$, the coupled resistance of the cavity at resonance is equal to the resistance of the source, and the cavity is matched. This is the case of critical coupling. When $\beta < 1$, the cavity is under-coupled. If the cavity is undercoupled, its terminals will be located at a voltage maximum in the input line or waveguide at resonance. The normalized impedance at the terminals of the cavity is then equal to

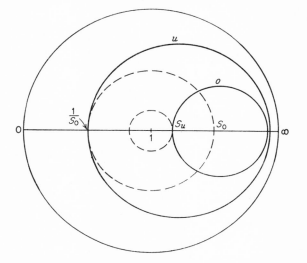

FIG. 5.9. Cavity input impedance loci: o, overcoupled; u, undercoupled. Dashed curves are standing-wave circles in input waveguide.

S_u (Fig. 5.9). In the opposite case of overcoupled cavity, the cavity terminals are at a voltage minimum, and the input terminal impedance is $1/S_0$, where S_0 is the standing-wave ratio of the overcoupled cavity.

PROBLEMS

5.1. Obtain the expression for the Q of a cylindrical cavity resonator of radius a and length d in the TE_{011} mode.

5.2. A cylindrical cavity resonator for use in a maser resonates at 9.22 kmc in the TE_{011} mode and at 24.2 kmc in the TE_{114} mode (cf. Sec. 8.2). Calculate the radius and length of a cylindrical cavity which has these properties (cf. Table 3.4).

5.3. Show that, at very high modal index numbers, the relative separation in frequency of the resonances of a rectangular cavity approaches $(\Delta\omega/\Delta n)/\omega \to 1/n$, where n is a modal index number.

5.4. An enclosure, shaped as indicated in Fig. 5.10, is to be used as a resonator (all dimensions are in centimeters).

(a) At what frequencies will this enclosure resonate?

(b) Calculate an approximate Q value for the resonator if the walls are copper.

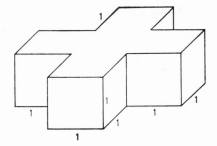

FIG. 5.10. Resonant enclosure.

5.5. A coaxial resonator is constructed of a section of coaxial line 5 cm in length, short-circuited at both ends, and having radius of inner conductor equal to 1 cm and radius of the outer conductor equal to 2.5 cm.

(a) What is the TEM_{001} resonant frequency of the cavity?

(b) Calculate the cavity Q.

5.6. (a) What is the TE_{011} resonant frequency of the coaxial cavity of Prob. 5.5?

(b) Calculate the Q of the cavity in the TE_{011} mode, and compare the ratio of this Q to the Q of the TEM_{001} mode with the similar ratio obtained from the method of approximate estimation described at the end of Sec. 5.4.

5.7. Calculate the normalized input impedance of a TE_{111}-mode resonator consisting of a section of circular waveguide of radius R, terminated in a short circuit, and coupled axially to the continuing waveguide by a centered circular aperture having diameter d. The aperture presents an inductive admittance in parallel with the guide, of magnitude

$$\frac{B}{Y_0} = \frac{\lambda_g}{4R}\left[0.714\left(\frac{2R}{d}\right)^3 - 2.344\right]$$

Assume that $R = 2.5$ cm, $d = 0.5$ cm, and cavity length is 3.2 cm. Plot the curve of impedance versus frequency in the neighborhood of resonance.

5.8. A TE_{10} rectangular resonator like that treated in Sec. 5.5 is found to have an unloaded Q value of $Q_0 = 2,500$. If the resonator is constructed of waveguide 0.9 in. wide and resonates at 10^{10} cps, what is the normalized value of R in the equivalent series circuit of the resonator?

5.9. Calculate the relative change in Q_0 of a rectangular TE_{101} cavity resonator caused by the introduction of a small volume V_s of material having conductivity σ into the region of maximum electric field. Assume that the dimensions of the sample of material are much smaller than the cavity dimensions, and that the waveguide field distributions may be considered to be unaffected by its presence. Cavity width, length, and height are a, d, and b, respectively.

5.10. With the use of the Smith chart impedance diagram, find the input admittance of a transmission cavity consisting of two symmetrical vertical apertures of width d, separated by a length l of rectangular waveguide operating in the dominant mode. Assume that the guide beyond the transmission cavity is matched, guide width $a = 0.9$ in., slit width $d = 0.25$ in., and $l = 1.575$ in. Use the narrow-slit aperture impedance approximation. Calculate input admittances at frequencies 9.0, 9.5, 10.0, and 10.5 kmc.

CHAPTER 6

Microwave Tubes I: Klystron and Magnetron

The transmission of energy in a microwave system is associated with the passage of traveling electromagnetic waves along a waveguide axis. The question of the generation of these waves can be resolved to one of energy conversion: if the source of energy is a battery or similar d-c supply, how is the static potential energy of the electrons in the battery to be converted to the energy of the electromagnetic fields in the waveguide? The related problem at lower radio frequencies is solved by the use of the familiar multielectrode vacuum tube. An alternating potential on the control grid of the vacuum tube permits an alternating current to flow in the plate circuit. A satisfactory simple picture can be constructed in which the tube is regarded as a valve controlling the flow of electrons in the anode conductor.

Electron flow in a wire can be converted to electromagnetic waves in a waveguide by means of probe or loop couplings, such as those which were discussed in Chap. 3. Conventional vacuum tubes are not efficient sources of currents at microwave frequencies, however. The assumption upon which their efficient design is based, namely that the electrons pass from cathode to anode in a time short compared with the period of the anode potential, no longer holds true at 10^9 to 10^{10} cps. The velocity acquired by an electron in moving from rest through a potential difference of V volts is approximately equal to $6 \times 10^7 V^{\frac{1}{2}}$ cm/sec. Hence a transit time of the order of magnitude of 10^{-8} sec may be required for an electron to travel from anode to cathode of a conventional vacuum tube. The anode and grid potentials may alternate from 10 to 100 times during the electron transit. The anode potential during the negative part of its cycle thus removes energy that was given to the electrons during the phase of positive anode potential. The over-all result of transit-time effects is that of a reduction in the operating efficiency of the vacuum tube, becoming more marked with

155

increasing frequency.   Efforts to reduce the transit time by decrease of cathode-to-anode spacing and increase of anode potential encounter limitations of excessive interelectrode capacitance and overheating of the anode.

Factors such as those which have been mentioned briefly above lead to the necessity for the design of tubes which are specifically suited for operation in the microwave-frequency range.   Although there are many differences in details of design among the various types of microwave amplifier or oscillator tubes, they may all be said to depend upon the same principles of operation: the potential energy of electrons at the battery terminals is converted into the kinetic energy of a beam or flux of rapidly moving electrons.   The electron beam then interacts with the time-varying fields of that part of the microwave system which is included within the tube.   If this interaction proceeds in such a way that the velocity of the electrons is lower after the interaction than before, the kinetic energy removed from the electrons can reappear as energy of the electromagnetic fields.   Thus, in the steady state, the tube may act as a source of wave energy.

The microwave tubes in practical use are different among themselves in the details of the mode of interaction between the electron beam and the rapidly varying fields.   Tubes may be classified into two groups: those in which the electron stream interacts with the alternating fields over only a relatively short interval in space and those in which the electron stream interacts with the microwave-frequency fields over most of its trajectory.   The only tube of importance now in the first category is the klystron.   The majority of the types of microwave tube of practical value are in the second group.   These include the magnetron and traveling-wave tubes of a number of types.

6.1. The Klystron

A klystron tube in its essential form is shown schematically in the diagram of Fig. 6.1.   The steady-current beam from electron gun KA passes through grids of resonator R_1.   The resonator may be considered to be a special form of coaxial-line section, short-circuited at the right end and terminated at the left end in the capacitor formed by the ends of the center conductor and outer conductor.   These opposing ends are covered by a grid mesh which is nearly transparent to the electron beam, and the spacing between grids is made as small as possible.   The integral of the resonator electric field between grids is the voltage $V_1 e^{j\omega t}$, by which the beam electrons are accelerated or decelerated in their traverse of the intergrid space.   The resonator voltage causes a periodic perturbation in the velocities of the electrons along the beam.   The effect of this velocity modulation upon the electrons of the beam as they drift in the field-free space between resonators R_1 and R_2 is to produce a bunching of the electrons into clusters along the beam.   This space-charge modulated beam then passes through the grids of cavity R_2.   The phase of the voltage $V_2e^{j\omega t}$ on these grids is maintained so that each cluster of electrons, as it passes between grids, encounters a retarding electric field.   The kinetic energy lost by each electron cluster owing to its reduction of velocity in this retarding field is converted to electromagnetic energy of the fields in the

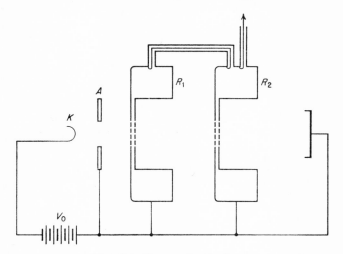

Fig. 6.1. Two-cavity klystron.

resonator.   Oscillator output energy is taken from cavity R_2.   The correctness of the phase of $V_2e^{j\omega t}$ with respect to electron bunch arrival is maintained by the use of a feedback line which drives cavity R_1 at the correct phase with respect to cavity R_2.   The necessity for beam bunching is, of course, due to the fact that a maximum amount of energy may be abstracted from the electron beam if most of the electrons pass through gap 2 at the phase instant at which its voltage impresses a maximum value of retarding field upon them.

The effectiveness of each pair of grids in changing the velocity (and hence the kinetic energy) of the electrons which pass it is greater, the shorter the transit time of the electrons across the gap between grids. This fact may be shown by a calculation of the change of energy of an electron as it passes through the cavity under electric force $F = qE$, where q is the electron charge and the electric field E is equal to gap voltage $V_1 e^{j\omega t}$ divided by gap spacing d.   The work done on or by the electron (depending upon whether it is being accelerated or retarded) is

$$W = \int F \, dz$$

$$= \int \frac{q V_1 e^{j\omega t}}{d} \frac{dz}{dt} \, dt \tag{6.1}$$

If the magnitude of the cavity potential V_1 is small compared with the anode potential V_0, the change of the velocity of the electrons while in

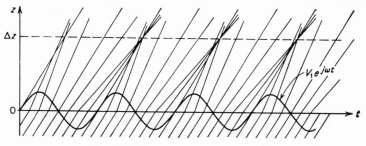

FIG. 6.2. Klystron velocity diagram.

the gap is small and their velocity dz/dt may be taken to be equal to $v_0 = (2qV_0/m)^{\frac{1}{2}}$.   Then

$$W = \frac{q V_1}{d} v_0 \int_{t_1}^{t_1 + \tau} e^{j\omega t} \, dt$$

where t_1 is the time at which the electrons enter the gap and τ is their transit time for crossing the gap.   Integration yields

$$W = \frac{\sin (\omega \tau/2)}{\omega \tau/2} q V_1 e^{j\omega(t_1 + \tau/2)} \tag{6.2}$$

Since $q V_1 e^{j\omega(t_1 + \tau/2)}$ is the energy change the electron would undergo if it had crossed the gap under constant field of the instant at which it actually passes the gap center, we see that a correction factor

$$k = \frac{\sin (\omega \tau/2)}{\omega \tau/2} \tag{6.3}$$

must be introduced for a finite transit time τ.

The effect of velocity modulation at gap 1 in producing bunching of the electron beam may be demonstrated by means of an electron-travel plot such as that in Fig. 6.2.   In this one-dimensional space-

time diagram, each line is taken to represent the path of a representative electron.   The slope of each line therefore represents the electron
velocity.   All electrons approach the resonator gap at $z = 0$ with the
same velocity v_0.   Electrons passing the gap at zeros of the gap voltage
$V_1 \exp(j\omega t)$ pass through with unchanged velocity; those passing
through during positive swings of gap voltage undergo an increase in
velocity (therefore, of slope).   The reverse is true of those electrons
which pass the gap during intervals of negative gap voltage.   It may
be seen in Fig. 6.2 that, at a distance Δz along the beam from the
resonator, the beam electrons have drifted into dense clusters.   In

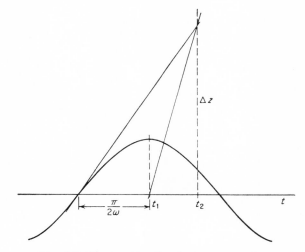

FIG. 6.3. Construction for electron encounter.

this representation the mutual electrostatic repulsion between electrons is neglected, but the qualitative results are similar to those
obtained when the effects of repulsion are included.
    The distance Δz from resonator 1 to the point where bunching occurs
may be calculated as that distance at which an electron receiving maximum acceleration overtakes an electron receiving zero acceleration.
Referring to Fig. 6.3, in which only the trajectories for maximum and
zero electron acceleration are plotted, it is seen by equating the two
expressions for Δz that the necessary condition is

$$v_0 \left(t_2 - t_1 + \frac{\pi}{2\omega} \right) = v_{\max}(t_2 - t_1) \tag{6.4}$$

Since $v_{\max} = [2q(V_0 + V_1)/m]^{\frac{1}{2}}$, where we assume the transit-time correction factor $k = 1$, and $v_0 = (2qV_0/m)^{\frac{1}{2}}$, Eq. (6.4) is

$$(t_2 - t_1)\left(\sqrt{1 + \frac{V_1}{V_0}} - 1\right) = \frac{\pi}{2\omega}$$

We assume small-signal operation, in which $V_1 \ll V_0$. Then

$$t_2 - t_1 \approx \frac{\pi}{\omega}\frac{V_0}{V_1}$$

The two electrons hence meet at

$$\Delta z = v_0(t_2 - t_1)$$
$$= \frac{\pi}{\omega}\frac{V_0}{V_1}\sqrt{\frac{2qV_0}{m}} \tag{6.5}$$

It is readily shown by a similar calculation, for an electron which passes the gap at zero gap voltage and one which passes at the nearest retarding minimum of voltage, that these electrons also form part of the dense electron cluster at the Δz of Eq. (6.5). This distance Δz marks the location of dense electron bunching which was shown graphically by the construction of Fig. 6.2. Thus a steady electron stream which is allowed to fall through the alternating potential drop $V_1e^{j\omega t}$ and then to drift in a field-free space becomes a bunched beam of electron clusters. The electron bunches can then impart kinetic energy efficiently to retarding fields of suitable phase, upon passage through resonator R_2.

We may also calculate the current flow represented by the bunched electron beam, as a function of time and distance along the beam, under the same assumptions as used above, namely, $V_1/V_0 \ll 1$ and neglect of mutual repulsion of electrons in the beam. (The neglect of electron mutual repulsion is in part justified by the existence of a column of positive ions along the beam, produced by the impact of the beam electrons on residual gas molecules in the tube. This positive-ion column reduces the forces which would tend to disperse a pure-electron beam.)

We consider that electrons pass gap R_1 at time t_1 and reach a point z along the beam at time t_2. Then

$$t_2 - t_1 = \frac{z}{v} = \frac{z}{\sqrt{2q(V_0 + kV_1e^{j\omega t_1})/m}}$$

or

$$t_2 = z\sqrt{\frac{m}{2qV_0}}\left(1 + k\frac{V_1}{V_0}e^{j\omega t_1}\right)^{-\frac{1}{2}} + t_1 \tag{6.6}$$

where the transit-time correction k has been included. The method of this analysis is to follow the course of a given small quantity of charge dq in its travel along the beam. Equating the expressions for this charge at the first gap (at $z = 0$, $t = t_1$) to the charge at a point at distance z along the beam and at later time t_2,

$$dq\ (0, t_1)\ =\ dq\ (z, t_2) \tag{6.7}$$

but since, in general, $dq = i\ dt$, where i is beam current,

$$i_1\ dt_1\ =\ i_2\ dt_2$$

Here, i_2 is the beam current at (z, t_2), and i_1 is the beam current at the first gap, equal to i_0, anode current. Therefore

$$i_2(z, t_2)\ =\ i_0\ \frac{dt_1}{dt_2} \tag{6.8}$$

Obtaining the expression for dt_1/dt_2 from Eq. (6.6), we have

$$i_2\ =\ i_0 \left(1\ -\ z\ \sqrt{\frac{m}{2qV_0}}\ j\omega\ \frac{kV_1}{2V_0}\ e^{j\omega t_1} \right)^{-1} \tag{6.9}$$

If the current i_2 contains contributions from electrons which have left the first gap at more than one value of t_1, expressions such as (6.9) must be summed over all values of t_1 contributing to the beam current:

$$i_2\ =\ i_0 \sum_n \left(1\ +\ z\ \sqrt{\frac{m}{8q}}\ \frac{\omega k V_1}{V_0^{\frac{3}{2}}}\ \sin\ \omega t_{1n} \right)^{-1} \tag{6.10}$$

where, in (6.10), the real part of the time variation has been written.

Graphical plots of the beam current, Eq. (6.10), for various values of the parameter M, defined as

$$M\ =\ \omega k z\ \sqrt{\frac{m}{8q}}\ \frac{V_1}{V_0^{\frac{3}{2}}} \tag{6.11}$$

show that the effect of velocity modulation upon the beam is to convert the steady direct current from the anode to a sequence of current pulses, representing the passage of electron bunches.

Typical bunched-beam current wave shapes are shown in Fig. 6.4. The fundamental component of the beam current wave, at the resonant frequency of resonator R_2, will have the principal effect in determining the power at frequency ω given to the resonator. Writing the beam current at the second resonator as a Fourier expansion at time t_2, we have

$$i_2\ =\ \sum_n a_n e^{jn\omega t_2} \tag{6.12}$$

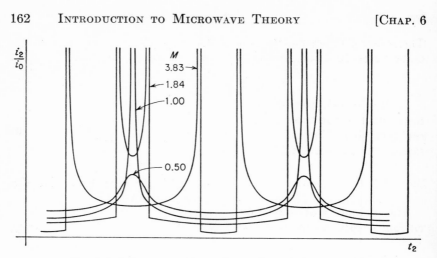

FIG. 6.4. i_2/i_0 versus t_2 for various values of parameter M.

We are interested in the magnitude of a_1, the coefficient of the fundamental term.   Solving for it, we obtain

$$\int_0^T i_2 e^{-j\omega t_2}\,dt_2 = \sum_n a_n \int_0^T e^{j(n-1)\omega t_2}\,dt_2 \tag{6.13}$$

where $T = 2\pi/\omega$.

The only term remaining on the right is the first, for which $n = 1$. On the left, for ωt_2, we may write, by the use of Eq. (6.6),

$$\omega t_2 = \omega t_1 + \frac{\omega z}{v_0}\left(1 + k\,\frac{V_1}{V_0}\,e^{j\omega t_1}\right)^{-\frac{1}{2}} \tag{6.14}$$

With the assumption of small signal strength, Eq. (6.14) may be written

$$\omega t_2 = \omega t_1 + \frac{\omega z}{v_0} - M e^{j\omega t_1} \tag{6.15}$$

where we have used Eq. (6.11), for the parameter M.   The real part of Eq. (6.15) is, if we write ϕ for ωt_1,

$$\omega t_2 = \phi + \frac{\omega z}{v_0} - M \cos \phi \tag{6.16}$$

Returning with this value of ωt_2 to Eq. (6.13) and using Eq. (6.8) to replace $i_2\,dt_2$ by $i_0\,dt_1$, we have

$$i_0 e^{-j\omega z/v_0} \int_0^{2\pi} e^{j(M\cos\phi-\phi)}\,\frac{d\phi}{\omega} = a_1 T \tag{6.17}$$

or

$$a_1 = \frac{i_0}{2\pi}\,e^{-j\omega z/v_0} \int_0^{2\pi} e^{j(M\cos\phi-\phi)}\,d\phi \tag{6.18}$$

The integral in the right yields $-4\pi j J_1(M)$, where $J_1(M)$ is the first-order Bessel function, of argument M.† Thus we have

$$a_1 = -2j i_0 e^{-j\omega z/v_0} J_1(M) \qquad (6.19)$$

In Eq. (6.19), the factor $\exp(-j\omega z/v_0)$ is the phase factor corresponding to the time delay for beam travel through distance z from resonator R_1. The fundamental component of beam current has its maximum amplitude at $M = 1.841$. Thus, using Eq. (6.11),

$$1.841 = \frac{\omega k z}{v_0} \frac{V_1}{2V_0} \qquad (6.20)$$

The distance z at which the maximum fundamental component of current occurs, assuming $k = 1$, is

$$z = \frac{3.682 v_0}{\omega} \frac{V_0}{V_1} \qquad (6.21)$$

It is interesting to compare this result with that obtained in Eq. (6.5), for the distance from the first resonator at which the electron trajectories converge,

$$z = \frac{\pi v_0}{\omega} \frac{V_0}{V_1} \qquad (6.22)$$

which is approximately 15 per cent less than the result of Eq. (6.21). The discrepancy is due in part to the approximations used in obtaining (6.5), and to the fact that the maximum of the fundamental component of current will not necessarily be observed at the location of maximum electron density along the beam, because of the presence of harmonic components of current in the beam.

The results which have been obtained above are subject to the restrictions of small-signal amplitude and neglect of mutual repulsion of the electrons in the beam. It can, however, be appreciated by observation of the current wave shapes shown in Fig. 6.4 that the klystron beam current has a high harmonic content. For this reason the klystron may be used as a frequency multiplier by using for R_2 a resonator which is resonant at the desired multiple of the frequency of the first resonator. In this application, separate excitation must be supplied to resonator R_1. A two-resonator klystron may also be used as an amplifier, with the input signal being applied to the first resonator and the output taken from the second resonator.

A form of klystron which is frequently used in low-power oscillator applications is the reflex klystron. This tube is shown schematically

† See Appendix III.

in Fig. 6.5. In the reflex klystron, the beam-bunching voltage is applied to the electron stream during its first traverse of the resonator grids. The beam emerges from the resonator into the retarding field due to the negative potential V_r of the repeller electrode. The repelling potential is adjusted so that the beam is reflected and passes back through the resonator grids after a drift time which is sufficient for

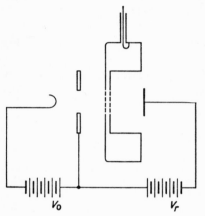

optimum beam-bunching to take place. The bunched beam supplies sufficient energy to the resonator at its second traverse to maintain oscillations and to furnish output power at a coupling loop or wave-guide output port. The mathematical analysis of the bunching process is closely similar to that of the two-resonator klystron, except that the time spent by the beam in the drift space is equal to

$$t_2 - t_1 = 2\,\frac{mv}{qE_r} \qquad (6.23)$$

FIG. 6.5. Reflex klystron.

where q and m are the charge and mass of the electron, respectively, and E_r is the field of the repeller electrode, here assumed to be effectively uniform. The electron velocity v is given by

$$v = \left[\frac{2q}{m}\,(V_0 + kV_1 e^{j\omega t_1})\right]^{\frac{1}{2}} \qquad (6.24)$$

where V_0 is the anode potential and V_1 the magnitude of the gap voltage. The current i_2 of the bunched beam upon return traverse of the resonator gaps may be calculated as before, by the use of the expression $i_2 = i_0\,dt_1/dt_2$. Using (6.23) and (6.24) and summing the contributions to i_2 due to electrons from various first-transit times t_1, we find the bunched-beam current of the reflex klystron to be

$$i_2 = i_0 \sum_n (1 - M_r \sin \omega t_{1n})^{-1} \qquad (6.25)$$

where M_r is the reflex klystron bunching parameter,

$$M_r = \frac{k\omega}{E_r}\frac{V_1}{V_0}\left(\frac{2mV_0}{q}\right)^{\frac{1}{2}} \qquad (6.26)$$

Comparison of Eq. (6.25) with Eq. (6.10), the comparable expression for beam current of the two-cavity klystron, shows that the character of the current waves is similar for the two tubes.   The difference in signs between the terms in parentheses in the two cases represents a time-phase shift of π radians and does not affect the form of the current wave, since the sine function itself changes sign periodically in time.   It should be noted that the direction of the field in the resonator gap is effectively reversed for the returning electrons, since a field that is accelerating for electrons making first transit is retarding for electrons traveling in the opposite direction, on return transit.

The effect upon the resonator of the passage of an electron bunch across the gap between grids has been described in terms of the transfer of the kinetic energy of the electrons to the electromagnetic energy of the resonator as the electrons move in the retarding field of the resonator.   We can look at this interaction in another way, however.   We may consider the current induced in the resonator by the passage of electron charge between the grids.   In order to examine the nature of this effect, let us consider an electron moving along the axis of a klystron resonator between two circular grids of radius r_1, separated by spacing d, as shown in Fig. 6.6. The potential at a point on grid

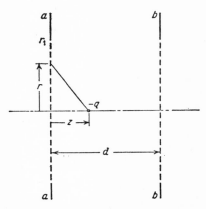

Fig. 6.6. Electron between grid planes.

plane aa at radius r from the axis may be calculated by the method of images† to be given by two terms of the form

$$V(r) \sim \frac{\pm q}{4\pi\epsilon_0 \sqrt{r^2 + z^2}} \qquad (6.27)$$

where q is the charge of the electron and z is the distance of the electron from the grid plane.   Then, the electric displacement vector normal to the plane of the grid at radius r is found to be

$$D_z(r) = \epsilon_0 \frac{\partial V}{\partial z} = \frac{qz}{2\pi(r^2 + z^2)^{\frac{3}{2}}} \qquad (6.28)$$

The density of surface charge induced on the grid plane is numerically equal to D_z.   The total charge induced on the grid, owing to the

† See, e.g., W. R. Smythe, "Static and Dynamic Electricity," 2d ed., McGraw-Hill Book Company, Inc., New York, 1950; R. G. Fowler, "Introduction to Electric Theory," Addison-Wesley Publishing Company, Reading, Mass., 1953.

presence of the electron, may be found by integrating (6.28) over the surface of radius r_1.

$$Q_{aa} = \int_0^{r_1} \frac{qz2\pi r \, dr}{2\pi(r^2 + z^2)^{\frac{3}{2}}}$$

$$Q_{aa} = q\left(1 - \frac{z}{\sqrt{r_1{}^2 + z^2}}\right)$$

Since d and z are both small compared to r_1, terms in z^2/r^2 are negligible with respect to unity, and the induced charge is approximately

$$Q_{aa} \approx q\left(1 - \frac{z}{r_1}\right) \tag{6.29}$$

Similarly, the charge induced on grid bb', at distance $d - z$ from q, is

$$Q_{bb} = q\left(1 - \frac{d - z}{r_1}\right) \tag{6.30}$$

The difference between these two induced charges is

$$Q_{aa} - Q_{bb} = q\frac{d - 2z}{r_1} \tag{6.31}$$

If the electron charge moves between grids at the speed $v = dz/dt$, a current i_{ab} equal to the time rate of change of $Q_{aa} - Q_{bb}$ flows in the resonator.

$$i_{ab} = -\frac{2qv}{r_1} \tag{6.32}$$

Thus, from the simple model which has been employed above, we may infer that the over-all effect of the passage of bunches of electron charge through the resonator grids will be the corresponding flow of an induced current over the interior surface of the resonator, proportional in magnitude to the velocity and quantity of charge in the bunches. The electromagnetic fields established by the induced current contribute to the total oscillatory energy in the cavity.

The phase of the cavity currents induced by the passage of the bunched electron beam will tend to influence the resultant phase of oscillation of the cavity. A change in the time of arrival of the bunches can be caused by changing the amount of time spent by the electrons in the drift space between repeller and cavity. This drift time is governed by the anode potential V_0 and the repeller potential V_r. If either of these potentials is changed so as to alter the phase of the induced current in the cavity away from that corresponding to the phase for the optimum retarding field, the resulting effect upon the oscillation of the resonator is equivalent to the introduction of a small susceptance in parallel with the resonator grids.† This effective susceptance appearing across the resonator increases or decreases the frequency of oscillation, according to its sign. In this way, the reflex klystron is voltage-tunable. Tuning is usually effected by changes of repeller voltage, since negligible power is required by the repeller electrode to which the anode current does not flow.

The change of frequency which can be produced by repeller voltage tuning is limited by the bandwidth and hence the Q, of the cavity. Reflex klystron tuning is accomplished at the expense of output power

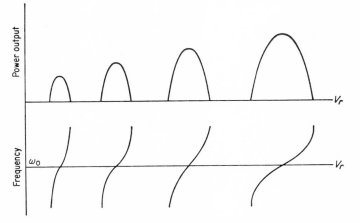

FIG. 6.7. Reflex klystron characteristics.

amplitude, since it necessitates a departure from the condition of optimum beam-energy transfer. Typical power and frequency characteristic curves for a reflex klystron are shown in Fig. 6.7. As shown in this diagram, operation in several klystron modes is possible, each new mode corresponding to a difference of one period of the fundamental oscillation, spent by the electron bunches in the drift space.

6.2. The Magnetron

In velocity modulation tubes of the type discussed in the preceding section, the electron beam interacts with the high-frequency fields only during the time interval in which the beam crosses the gap between resonator grids. A large class of microwave-frequency tubes exists in which the electron stream moves through extended regions

† This susceptance can be calculated by defining a suitable current-voltage ratio. See, e.g., J. J. Hamilton, "Reflex Klystrons," Chapman & Hall, Ltd., London, 1958.

occupied by the oscillating fields. This class of microwave tubes, called traveling-wave tubes, may be further divided into the subclasses of tubes in which the electrons move under the influence of crossed static electric and magnetic fields while interacting with the oscillating fields, and tubes in which there is no static magnetic field present other than a possible longitudinal beam-focusing field parallel to the direction of electron travel. These two types of traveling-wave tubes are designated as M- and O-type tubes, respectively.

M-type traveling-wave tubes may be either of the form in which the electron stream is a focused beam or of the form in which the electron

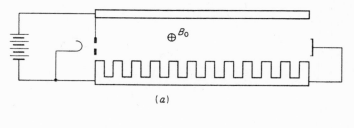

(a)

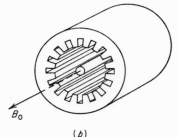

(b)

FIG. 6.8. Crossed-field magnetrons. (a) Linear; (b) radial.

stream flows radially outward from a cylindrical cathode. These two structural forms are illustrated schematically in Fig. 6.8a and b, respectively. The cylindrical traveling-wave magnetron, shown in Fig. 6.8b, is the principal M-type tube having radial electron flow.

A static magnetic field B_0 extends parallel to the axis of the magnetron. Electrons leaving the cathode are drawn toward the concentric anode structure by the positive anode potential V_0. As soon as the electrons acquire a velocity, however, they are subjected to the transverse magnetic force $q\mathbf{v} \times \mathbf{B}_0$, where q and $\mathbf{v}$ are electron charge and velocity, respectively. The combination of electric and magnetic forces causes the electrons to follow cycloidal paths in the cathode-anode space, as illustrated in Fig. 6.9. The simplest cycloid is a circle centered on the magnetron axis.   Let us consider the circular electron orbit, in order to investigate some of the characteristics of the electron motion.

We assume that the electron is moving with speed v in a circular orbit of radius r.   If the radius of the orbit is for the moment not changing, the equilibrium of radial forces is represented by

$$qvB_0 = \frac{mv^2}{r} + qE_r \quad (6.33)$$

where E_r is the radial electric field, which may be taken to be

$$E_r = \frac{E_0}{r} \quad (6.34)$$

where E_0 is a constant.

We now note that the kinetic energy T of the electron may be written

$$T = \frac{mv^2}{2} \quad (6.35)$$

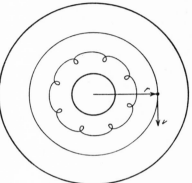

Fig. 6.9. Electron paths.

Using this expression in the force equation (6.33) and solving for radius r, we find

$$r = \frac{\sqrt{2m}}{qB_0} \left(T^{\frac{1}{2}} + \frac{qE_0}{2} T^{-\frac{1}{2}} \right) \quad (6.36)$$

Equation (6.36) shows that to each value of kinetic energy of the electron there corresponds a stable orbit of circular form.   Actually, the possibility of the infinitely many cycloidal motions which may be superposed upon this general circular drift motion loosens the relation between kinetic energy and radius by a considerable variance.   We know, however, that the static magnetic field B_0 cannot change the energy of an electron, since its force is always directed perpendicularly to the electron motion.

Therefore, when an electron has taken up a given cycloidal orbit, it will continue indefinitely in that orbit until some external agency acts to change its energy.   Such an agency is available in the oscillating electromagnetic fields which are set up within the anode structure of the magnetron.   If the fields act so as to remove energy from the electron, the electron will take up a new orbit at greater radius, at reduced electrostatic potential energy in the field of the cathode.   The reduction in electrostatic energy of the electron, corrected by the change of kinetic energy necessitated by the new orbit, represents the energy given to the oscillating fields. That is, we set $T(r) + V(r)$ equal to the total energy of the electron as a function of r, in which $V(r) = V_0(\ln r/a)/(\ln a/b)$, where a is the radius of the cathode, b is the radius of the anode surface, and $T(r)$ is the solution of Eq. (6.36) for T. Then the energy ΔW given by the electron to the retarding anode fields when the electron changes from an orbit of radius r_1 to an orbit of radius r_2 is

$$\Delta W = [T(r_1) + V(r_1)] - [T(r_2) + V(r_2)] \qquad (6.37)$$

The simple model of energy transfer which we have considered above is obviously an oversimplified one, since it neglects the effects of cycloidal motions, space charge in the cathode-anode region, and the time and space distribution of the anode fields. This model serves, however, to illustrate the nature of the mechanism whereby energy is transferred from the d-c source of anode potential to the oscillations in the magnetron cavity.

The electromagnetic field of the anode may be regarded as a traveling wave which moves around the interior surface of the segmented anode. Each anode slot behaves like an individual cavity resonator, with its aperture opening on the cathode-anode space. Although in principle each individual resonator has infinitely many modes, only the lowest, fundamental mode is of importance, because of the large cavity aperture which makes the excitation of higher modes difficult. Thus, if there are N slots in the anode structure, we have N resonators, each oscillating at the fundamental resonator frequency ω_0.

The anode resonators do not oscillate independently with random relative phase, however. Instead, they behave like many other systems of coupled identical oscillators observed in nature. (For example, in a block of solid matter, containing N atoms, each one of the single energy states of the electrons of the isolated atoms is replaced by a set of N energy states, or modes of motion of the electrons, when the atoms are joined in the solid.) In the present case of the magnetron anode, the fundamental cavity oscillation of the individual anode slot is now replaced by N modes of oscillation of the anode field as a whole. We may regard these N anode modes as a set of N ordered arrangements of the relative phases of adjacent oscillating slots. In the nth mode of oscillation, the phase angle between two adjacent slots is ϕ_n radians. Obviously, $N\phi_n$ must be an integral multiple of 2π, and we take

$$\phi_n = \frac{2\pi n}{N} \qquad (6.38)$$

where n is an integer.

We now consider the electron motions that correspond to useful magnetron operation.   The successive rise and fall of adjacent anode-slot fields may be regarded as a wave of field which travels along the anode surface.   In order for a transfer of energy to occur from the moving electron to the anode field, the electron must pass each anode slot at an instant when the slot field acts to decelerate the electron. Figure 6.10 represents schematically an instantaneous snapshot of the fields in a mode for which $\phi_n = \pi/3$.   (In this diagram the anode surface has been drawn in a plane, for the purpose of illustration of the field lines.)   In order for a coherent force to act upon the electron, it must pass from one slot to the next in a time which is represented by $\phi_n + 2m\pi$ radians of the slot-field oscillation, where m is an integer.

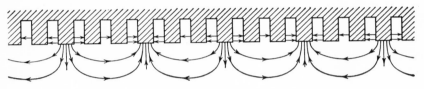

FIG. 6.10. Field of anode structure.

Therefore, the time required for an electron to make a complete revolution around the anode of N slots is

$$T_e = \frac{N(\phi_n + 2m\pi)}{\omega_0} \quad \text{sec} \tag{6.39}$$

This corresponds to an electron angular velocity of

$$\omega_e = \frac{2\pi\omega_0}{N(\phi_n + 2m\pi)} \quad \text{radians/sec} \tag{6.40}$$

If the cavities operate in a higher natural resonant mode, having frequency ω', the factor ω_0 above is replaced by ω'.

The anode mode in which magnetrons are ordinarily operated is the "π mode," in which $\phi_n = \pi$.   In magnetrons with symmetrical resonator systems, the integer m ordinarily takes the value 0.   Thus for π-mode operation with $m = 0$, the electron angular velocity is $2\omega_0/N$ radians/sec.   A technique called "strapping" is usually employed to insure stable π-mode operation of practical magnetrons. Strapping involves tie lines between alternate anode segments, attached to the anode ends.†

The qualitative description of the traveling wave of field at the anode surface which we have used above is verified when Maxwell's equations are solved subject to boundary conditions like those of the

† H. J. Reich, P. F. Ordung, H. L. Krauss, and J. G. Skalnik, "Microwave Theory and Techniques," p. 742, D. Van Nostrand Company, Inc., Princeton, N.J., 1953.

anode structure shown in Fig. 6.8b.   The solution for the θ component of electric field is found to consist of an infinite series of higher-mode terms, which are needed to represent the local field configurations in the neighborhood of the anode slots.   Of this series, the fundamental term, evaluated at the surface of the anode, corresponds to the traveling wave which we have discussed above, and is of the form[†]

$$E_{\theta 0} = jE_1 e^{j(\omega t - \beta_0 \theta)} \qquad (6.41)$$

where E_1 is a constant, and β_0 is given by

$$\beta_0 = \frac{2\pi n}{N\alpha} \qquad n = 1, 2, 3, \ldots \qquad (6.42)$$

in which α is the angular distance between anode slots.   Thus we see that $\beta_0 \alpha$ is equal to the ϕ_n of Eq. (6.38), and the fundamental-mode wave travels around the anode with angular velocity $d\theta/dt = \omega/\beta_0$. When the angular velocity of the field is made equal to the angular velocity of the electrons, as in Eq. (6.40), the electrons can give their kinetic energy to the field.

The analysis of the linear M-type traveling-wave tube of Fig. 6.8a is similar to that of the cylindrical magnetron, with the exception that the closure restriction of Eq. (6.38) is no longer necessary.

Traveling-wave tubes in general have the common requirement that they must possess a wave-guiding structure upon which there can exist a slow-wave component of field which travels at the speed of the electron beam and hence can exchange energy with it.   A wide variety of traveling-wave-tube structures is possible, and many types have been constructed and operated.[‡]

PROBLEMS

6.1. Calculate the distance Δz beyond a klystron first resonator at which an electron receiving maximum retardation is overtaken by an electron receiving no acceleration.   Compare the result with Eq. (6.5).

6.2. Considering the first term only in the summation for klystron bunched-beam current, find the peak gap voltage V_1 which would lead to the occurrence of a single infinitely high peak of current i_2 per cycle at 1 cm from the first resonator, if $V_0 = 10^3$ v, $\omega = 2\pi 10^9$/sec, and $k = 1$.

6.3. Consider klystron second-resonator grids upon which the cavity resonator places a voltage $V_2 \sin \omega t$.   An electron beam of fundamental velocity component $v_2 \sin (\omega t + \phi_2)$ is passed through the resonator.

[†] R. G. E. Hutter, "Beam and Wave Electronics in Microwave Tubes," D. Van Nostrand Company, Inc., Princeton, N.J., 1960.

[‡] International Convention on Microwave Valves, 1958.   *Proc. Inst. Elec. Engrs.*, vol. 105, Pt B, Suppls. 10–12, 1958, and E. J. Nalos, *Microwave J.*, vol. 2, no. 12, p. 31, December, 1959, and vol. 3, no. 1, p. 46, January, 1960.

(a) Regarding the grids as a capacitor of capacitance C, obtain an expression for the current to the grids with no beam present.

(b) Using Eq. (6.32), obtain an expression for the current to the grids due to the beam fundamental current.

(c) Combine the results of (a) and (b) above to show the manner in which the phase angle of the combined resonator current depends upon the phase angle ϕ_2 of the beam velocity.

6.4. If the maximum amount of fundamental-frequency power is to be extracted by the second resonator of a two-resonator klystron, the peak voltage V_2 of the second resonator must be nearly equal to the anode voltage V_0 (since it is assumed that $V_1 \ll V_0$). On the basis of this assumption, show that the maximum efficiency of the klystron for producing r-f energy at the resonator frequency from the d-c energy input is 58 per cent. What are some of the modifying factors in klystron performance which have been neglected in this assumption?

6.5. Show that, if the first pair of grids of a two-resonator klystron is driven with sawtooth voltage, in $2\pi n/\omega \leq t_1 \leq 2\pi(n+1)/\omega$, which has the value of $\omega V_1[t_1 - (2n+1)\pi/\omega]$, the distance from the first resonator at which the fundamental component of beam current has its maximum value is $z = 2v_0V_0/\omega V_1$.

6.6. By the use of a procedure like that followed for the two-resonator klystron, carry out the solution for the beam current of the reflex klystron [Eq. (6.25)].

6.7. Consider a model of a magnetron of linear form, in which an electron moves in a rectilinear path along the z axis in transverse static electric and magnetic fields. If $E_y = 10^4$ volts/m and $B_x = 0.1$ weber/m²,

(a) What is the velocity of the electron?

(b) If the electron passes through an abrupt retarding potential discontinuity of magnitude 100 volts, what new path would represent an equilibrium rectilinear motion for the electron? Describe qualitatively the actual motion of the electron after passing through the discontinuity.

6.8. In the anode-cathode space of an N-slot cylindrical magnetron with tube axis parallel to the z direction, there exists a wave field, the only magnetic field component of which is

$$H_z = \sum_n A_n[N_\mu'(ka)J_\mu(kr) - J_\mu'(ka)N_\mu(kr)]e^{j(\omega t - \mu\theta)}$$

where r and θ are cylindrical coordinates, a is the radius of the cathode, A_n is a constant, and $\mu = n + mN$, m an integer and $n = 0, 1, 2, \ldots$ and $k = (\mu_0\epsilon_0)^{\frac{1}{2}}\omega$. Calculate the electric field of the wave.

6.9. In a magnetron as described in Prob. 6.8 above, having $N = 10$ slots, calculate the energy being carried circumferentially around the cathode-anode space by the fundamental $(n = 0, m = 1)$ wave term. Assume that, at the frequency of operation, $a \ll \lambda$ and $b \ll \lambda$, where b is the radius of the anode surface. Then,

$$J_\mu(kr) \approx \frac{[(\frac{1}{2})kr]^\mu}{\mu!}$$

$$N_\mu(kr) \approx -\frac{(\mu-1)!}{\pi}\left(\frac{2}{kr}\right)^\mu$$

In the present case, assume that $ka = 0.10$, $kb = 0.15$.

6.10. In the magnetron of Prob. 6.9, calculate the ratio of current being carried by the fundamental wave to that being carried by the $(n = 2, m = 1)$ wave.

CHAPTER 7

Microwave Tubes II: Traveling-wave Tube

The microwave tube which is by convention called the traveling-wave tube is an O-type traveling-wave tube having a linear electron-beam path. The electron beam travels through a slow-wave-guiding structure subject to the electromagnetic field of the wave. A cumulative interaction takes place as the beam travels, whereby it is bunched into electron bunches which can effectively transfer kinetic energy to the field of the wave. As a result of this energy transfer, the traveling wave in the tube increases in amplitude as it progresses. Thus, the

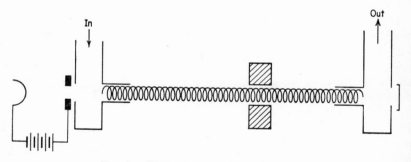

Fig. 7.1. Helix-type traveling-wave tube.

traveling-wave tube is an amplifier of microwave-frequency waves. It can serve as an oscillator as well, if a portion of the output is fed back into the input. The tube may oscillate if reflections due to impedance mismatch occur at the output coupling, causing a backward-traveling wave which carries energy back to the input. In practical tubes, these reflected waves may be suppressed by the insertion of lossy material at a point along the tube structure, as indicated in Fig. 7.1.

The slow-wave structure shown in Fig. 7.1 is a wire helix, upon which the axial velocity of the dominant wave is reduced below the

174

velocity of light by a fraction very nearly equal to the pitch of the helix. In many traveling-wave tubes, a magnetic field is applied parallel to the axis of the structure to prevent spreading of the electron beam as it travels. Electrostatic focusing methods have also been employed to maintain axial beam travel.†

The electron stream thus confined to move at a high average velocity v_0, along the axis of the traveling-wave tube, possesses intrinsic electrodynamic properties which result from interaction of the electrons in the beam. The mutual repulsion between electrons due to their negative charge, comparable with pressure in a gas, permits the beam to support waves of displacement and charge density which can travel along the electron beam of the traveling-wave tube. The electromagnetic behavior of the tube may thus be considered to consist of two aspects: the space-charge wave behavior of the beam and the propagation characteristics of the slow-wave-guiding structure. It is the interaction between these two aspects of the device which results in the characteristic behavior of the traveling-wave tube.

7.1. Dynamics of the Electron Beam

In order to investigate the electrodynamical behavior of an electron beam, we shall assume the simple model of a cylindrical beam, having well-defined boundaries, moving in the z direction within a slow-wave structure of cylindrical symmetry. The electrons at any cross section are all assumed to have the same velocity, parallel to the z axis. The electrons are assumed to have average velocity v_0, imparted to them by the electron gun of the tube. Superimposed on this average drift velocity, small fluctuations of axial velocity may occur. Any displacement of a transverse layer of electrons from its constant-velocity position in the beam will cause, by repulsion, a corresponding displacement of the electrons nearest it, thus causing progressive displacements along the beam. In this way, one-dimensional waves of displacement and velocity travel on the beam. By analogy with the travel of sound in a gas, the waves of velocity are accompanied by waves of perturbation in density of the medium, or in this case, of the space-charge density.

We assume a small-signal case and postulate that the amplitudes v_1 and ρ_1 of the waves of perturbation in velocity and charge, respectively, are small compared with the corresponding mean values v_0 and ρ_0. The displacements of charge in the beam give rise to local

† K. K. N. Chang, *Proc. IRE*, vol. 45, p. 1522, November, 1951; C. C. Johnson, *Proc. IRE*, vol. ED-5, no. 4, p. 233, October, 1958.

axial electric fields E_z and are also accompanied by waves of current density superimposed upon the steady beam-current density i_0. Thus we have

$$v = v_0 + v_1 e^{j(\omega t - \beta z)} \tag{7.1}$$

$$\rho = \rho_0 + \rho_1 e^{j(\omega t - \beta z)} \tag{7.2}$$

$$i_z = i_0 + i_1 e^{j(\omega t - \beta z)} \tag{7.3}$$

$$E_z = E_{z1} e^{j(\omega t - \beta z)} \tag{7.4}$$

where β is the propagation constant of the waves. In (7.1) to (7.3), we assume that v_1/v_0, ρ_1/ρ_0, and i_1/i_0 are all small compared with unity. Thus, since the beam-current density is $i = \rho v$, we write

$$i = \rho v \approx \rho_0 v_0 + (\rho_1 v_0 + \rho_0 v_1) e^{j(\omega t - \beta z)} \tag{7.5}$$

In Eq. (7.5), the term of magnitude $\rho_1 v_1$ has been omitted since it is the product of two small quantities and hence is neglected. Therefore

$$i_1 = \rho_1 v_0 + \rho_0 v_1 \tag{7.6}$$

We now write the equation of motion of the electrons under the force of the axial electric field E_z in the beam:

$$\frac{q}{m} E_z = \frac{dv}{dt} \tag{7.7}$$

where q and m are the charge and mass of the electron, respectively. The velocity v is a function of both position and time. Hence, (7.7) is

$$\frac{q}{m} E_z = \frac{\partial v}{\partial z} \frac{dz}{dt} + \frac{\partial v}{\partial t} \tag{7.8}$$

By the use of (7.1) to (7.4), we have

$$\frac{q}{m} E_{z1} = -j\beta v_1 v_0 + j\omega v_1$$

$$= j v_1 v_0 \left(\frac{\omega}{v_0} - \beta \right) \tag{7.9}$$

On the right in (7.9), v_0 has been used for dz/dt, since the term in v_1^2 is neglected.

We now require the expression for the conservation of charge in the beam:

$$\nabla \cdot i = -\frac{\partial \rho}{\partial t} \tag{7.10}$$

The one-dimensional divergence of the beam current is $\partial i_z/\partial z$. Hence, (7.10) becomes

$$j\beta i_1 = j\omega \rho_1 \tag{7.11}$$

By the use of Eq. (7.11) in Eq. (7.6), v_1 may be removed from Eq. (7.9), with the result

$$E_z = j \frac{m v_0^2}{q \rho_0 \omega} \left(\beta - \frac{\omega}{v_0} \right)^2 i_1 \qquad (7.12)$$

The z component of electric displacement is thus

$$D_z = j \frac{v_0^2}{\omega \, \omega_p^2} (\beta - \beta_0)^2 i_1 \qquad (7.13)$$

In Eq. (7.13), $\beta_0 = \omega/v_0$ by definition, and use has also been made of the definition

$$\omega_p{}^2 = \frac{q \rho_0}{m \epsilon_0} \qquad (7.14)$$

where ω_p is the plasma frequency† of a space charge of mean density ρ_0.

Let us now consider a small section of the electron beam enclosed within a cylindrical surface of length Δz and radius r_0, where $r_0 < \Delta z$,

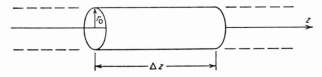

Fig. 7.2. Surface of integration surrounding beam.

as indicated in Fig. 7.2.   Consider the integral of the displacement and current density $i + \partial D/\partial t$ over this surface.   From the field equation for curl $\mathbf{H}$,

$$\nabla \times \mathbf{H} = \mathbf{i} + \frac{\partial \mathbf{D}}{\partial t}$$

$$\nabla \cdot \nabla \times \mathbf{H} = \nabla \cdot \left(\mathbf{i} + \frac{\partial \mathbf{D}}{\partial t} \right) = 0 \qquad (7.15)$$

since div curl of any vector is zero.   Thus, by Gauss' theorem,

$$\iint \left(\mathbf{i} + \frac{\partial \mathbf{D}}{\partial t} \right) \cdot d\mathbf{a} = 0 \qquad (7.16)$$

or

$$\iint i_z \, da + j\omega \iint D_z \, da + j\omega \iint D_r \, da = 0 \qquad (7.17)$$

In (7.17) the first two integrals are to be evaluated over the circular end faces of the volume element, and the third integral over the curved

† See J. A. Stratton, "Electromagnetic Theory," p. 327, McGraw-Hill Book Company, Inc., New York, 1941.

cylindrical surface.   We assume that the current density i_z is uniform over the cross section of the beam and that the length Δz of the cylinder is small, so that the difference between the total beam-current values at the two end faces is given by $(\partial i/\partial z)\,\Delta z$.   Similar assumptions are also made concerning the behavior of D_z, with the result that Eq. (7.17) becomes

$$\left(\frac{\partial i_z}{\partial z} + j\omega\,\frac{\partial D_z}{\partial z}\right)\Delta z\,\pi r_0{}^2 + j\omega D_r 2\pi r_0\,\Delta z = 0 \qquad (7.18)$$

where it has been assumed that D_r is uniform over the cylindrical surface of length Δz.

Replacing $\partial/\partial z$ with $-j\beta$ and using Eq. (7.13) for D_z, we find that Eq. (7.18) becomes

$$-j\beta i_1 + j\omega\beta\,\frac{v_0{}^2}{\omega\,\omega_p{}^2}\,(\beta - \beta_0)^2 i_1 + \frac{2j\omega}{r_0}\,D_r = 0$$

or

$$i_1 = -\frac{2\omega\beta_p{}^2}{\beta r_0}\,\frac{D_r}{(\beta - \beta_0)^2 - \beta_p{}^2} \qquad (7.19)$$

where we have defined $\beta_p{}^2 = \omega_p{}^2/v_0{}^2$.

From the structure of Eq. (7.19), we deduce that there is a singular value of the propagation constant β at which the current becomes large, since in general D_r remains finite.   Thus, an effective current resonance occurs, with propagation constant β given by

$$\beta - \beta_0 = \pm\beta_p \qquad (7.20)$$

Replacing β_0 and β_p with their equivalent quantities, we have

$$\beta = \frac{\omega \pm \omega_p}{v_0} \qquad (7.21)$$

For practical electron-beam charge densities, $\omega_p < \omega$ in the microwave region.†   Therefore Eq. (7.21) represents the propagation constants of two waves of current and space-charge density that may exist on the beam, irrespective of the presence of external excitation. They represent normal modes of electron behavior in a beam of given average charge density.   The waves, termed the slow wave and the fast wave, travel at velocities

$$v = \frac{\omega}{\omega \pm \omega_p}\,v_0 \qquad (7.22)$$

---

† The plasma frequency is equal to $f_p = \omega_p/2\pi = 9 \times 10^3 n_e{}^{\frac{1}{2}}$, where n_e is the electron density in reciprocal cubic centimeters.   In a low-powered traveling-wave tube, f_p may be of the order of 10^8 cps.

The existence of traveling waves of current and velocity, of which the rate of propagation, and hence the wavelength, depends on frequency, is reminiscent of the traveling waves of waveguide current and voltage in a waveguide. It turns out to be possible, in fact, to set up an extensive formal analogy between the electron-beam waves and transmission-line waves on a guiding system.[†] The effective characteristic impedance Z_0 of the electron beam is proportional to the average energy of the electrons and hence to the total d-c accelerating potential of the beam. An impedance mismatch for certain beam-wave frequencies may be introduced by a change of Z_0, caused by allowing the beam to pass through a voltage discontinuity between two electrodes. This fact may be made use of to prevent noise power, generated in the cathode of the tube, from traveling along the beam to the output, by the use of a suitable voltage jump at the input to the slow-wave section.[‡]

7.2. Coupling of Beam- and Slow-wave Structure

We are interested for our present purposes in the manner in which the electron-beam waves can interact with the traveling electromagnetic waves on an adjacent slow-wave-guiding structure in such a

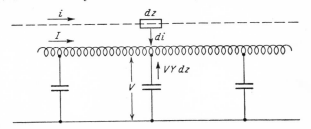

FIG. 7.3. Slow-wave structure and coupled beam.

fashion as to result in amplification of the waveguide waves. The occurrence of traveling-wave amplification may be shown by means of a relatively simple model, in which coupling is introduced between the wave system of the beam and the traveling waves on the slow-wave circuit. The assumed coupling is provided by the displacement current induced between the charge concentrations traveling on the beam, and the wave-guiding structure.

Figure 7.3 illustrates the assumed situation. The electron beam current i flows adjacent to a lossless transmission system, in which the

[†] W. J Kleen, "Electronics of Microwave Tubes," Academic Press, Inc., New York, 1958.

[‡] D. A. Watkins, *Proc. IRE*, vol. 40, p. 65, January, 1952.

waveguide current and voltage are I and V, respectively. The transmission system is represented by an equivalent distributed circuit, having impedance $Z = jX$ and admittance $Y = jB$ per unit length. If the beam were absent, the waveguide current and voltage would be related by the transmission-line equations

$$dV = -IZ\,dz \tag{7.23}$$
$$dI = -VY\,dz \tag{7.24}$$

Equations (7.23) and (7.24) represent a transmission line upon which waves travel with the propagation constant $j\beta_1 = (ZY)^{\frac{1}{2}}$.

The effect of the electron beam is now taken into account by the addition of an increment of current to dI in Eq. (7.24). This current increment is set equal to the beam current which flows into the element of beam length dz and therefore is $di = (\partial i / \partial z)\,dz$. Hence it is assumed that the current di flows as a Maxwellian displacement current, from the beam to the slow-wave circuit. The transmission-line equations with the electron beam present then are

$$dV = -IZ\,dz \tag{7.25}$$
$$dI = -VY\,dz - di \tag{7.26}$$

In Eqs. (7.25) and (7.26), d/dz may be replaced by $-j\beta$, with the result

$$-j\beta V = -IZ \tag{7.27}$$
$$-j\beta I = -VY + j\beta i \tag{7.28}$$

Combining (7.27) and (7.28) and replacing ZY by $-\beta_1{}^2$, we obtain

$$(\beta^2 - \beta_1{}^2)V = j\beta Zi \tag{7.29}$$

Equation (7.19) may be used for i, with the result

$$(\beta^2 - \beta_1{}^2)V = -\frac{2j\omega\beta_p{}^2 Z}{r_0} \frac{D_r \pi r_0{}^2}{(\beta - \beta_0)^2 - \beta_p{}^2} \tag{7.30}$$

The factor D_r on the right in (7.30) is ϵ_0 times the radial component of electric field E_r, at the surface of the beam. Since waveguide voltage V is defined to be proportional to the transverse electric field in a waveguide, we assume that D_r is related to V by a constant of proportionality. We therefore write Eq. (7.30) as

$$\beta^2 - \beta_1{}^2 = -\frac{A}{(\beta - \beta_0)^2 - \beta_p{}^2} \tag{7.31}$$

where

$$AV = -\frac{2\omega\beta_p{}^2 X\epsilon_0 E_r}{r_0}\pi r_0{}^2 \tag{7.32}$$

where the negative sign is introduced as an *ad hoc* assumption relating V and E_r, and we have used $Z = jX$.

We recall here for convenience the definitions of the various phase constants:

$$\beta_0 = \frac{\omega}{v_0} = \text{phase constant of average beam velocity}$$

$$\beta_p = \frac{\omega_p}{v_0} = \text{phase constant of plasma frequency}$$

$$\beta_1 = \sqrt{XB} = \text{propagation constant of slow waveguide alone}$$

Equation (7.31) may be written in the form

$$(\beta + \beta_1)(\beta - \beta_1)[(\beta - \beta_0)^2 - \beta_p^2] = -A \qquad (7.33)$$

Equation (7.33) is of fourth order in β and will therefore have four roots, corresponding to four traveling waves which may exist in our system. In the normal operation of a traveling-wave tube, the propagation constant of the traveling-wave disturbance will be approximately equal to the β_1 of the slow waveguide, and it will not differ greatly from the phase constant β_0 of the beam. Since β_p is smaller than β_0, we infer from the form of Eq. (7.33) that there are three forward-traveling solutions, and one backward-traveling wave which corresponds to the factor $\beta + \beta_1$. We are interested here in interactions between the forward-traveling waves and the space-charge waves on the beam, and the backward wave is therefore now of little interest.† In keeping with the properties of β discussed above, we replace $\beta + \beta_1$ by $2\beta_1$, and Eq. (7.33) may then be written

$$(\beta - \beta_1)(\beta^2 - 2\beta\beta_0 + \beta_0^2 - \beta_p^2) = -\frac{A}{2\beta_1} \qquad (7.34)$$

In order to determine the character of solutions of Eq. (7.34) for β, we may investigate the particular case in which the beam voltage is adjusted to a value such that $\beta_1^2 = \beta_0^2 - \beta_p^2$. We then may write Eq. (7.34) approximately as

$$(\beta - \beta_1)^3 = -\frac{A}{2\beta_1} \qquad (7.35)$$

since $\beta_0 \approx \beta_1$.

† Use is made of the backward-traveling wave in the backward-wave tube, or carcinotron. See, for example, D. A. Watkins, *Proc.* of Symposium on Advances in Microwave Techniques, Polytechnic Institute of Brooklyn, 1954, or R. G. E. Hutter, "Beam and Wave Electronics in Microwave Tubes," D. Van Nostrand Company, Inc., Princeton, N.J., 1960.

In solving Eq. (7.35), we recall that the propagation constant β may be complex, and we therefore include the complex roots of the right-hand side:

$$\beta - \beta_1 = \left(\frac{A}{2\beta_1}\right)^{\frac{1}{3}} (e^{j(2n+1)\pi})^{\frac{1}{3}} \tag{7.36}$$

where $(A/2\beta_1)^{\frac{1}{3}}$ is real. Using for brevity the substitution $b = (A/2\beta_1)^{\frac{1}{3}}$, we find that the three roots of (7.36) are

$$\beta = \beta_1 + b\left(\cos\frac{\pi}{3} + j\sin\frac{\pi}{3}\right) \tag{7.37}$$

$$\beta = \beta_1 + b(\cos\pi + j\sin\pi) \tag{7.38}$$

$$\beta = \beta_1 + b\left(\cos\frac{5\pi}{3} + j\sin\frac{5\pi}{3}\right) \tag{7.39}$$

Therefore the three forward-traveling wave solutions will have the wave functions

$$e^{-j(\beta_1+0.5b)z}e^{-0.866bz} \tag{7.40}$$

$$e^{-j(\beta_1-b)z} \tag{7.41}$$

$$e^{-j(\beta_1+0.5b)z}e^{+0.866bz} \tag{7.42}$$

The second wave, Eq. (7.41), is an unattenuated wave which travels slightly faster than the waves characteristic of the slow-wave structure. [We deduce that its propagation constant is somewhat smaller than β_1, as Eq. (7.35) shows that b is small in comparison with β.] The remaining two waves travel slightly more slowly than the waves of the guide alone, but of these, the first, Eq. (7.40), is attenuated exponentially as it travels, and the final wave, Eq. (7.42), grows exponentially as it travels.

Our result demonstrates the essential characteristics of traveling-wave tube operation. By coupling together the two wave systems, the slow waveguide, having two oppositely traveling waves at a given frequency, and the electron beam, with its pair of oppositely traveling space-charge waves, we have obtained a combined system having a total of four possible wave motions characteristic of the system as a whole. Of the forward-traveling waves, one is a growing wave, and under the restriction of conservation of energy within the device, it represents the transfer of the original kinetic energy of the beam to the electromagnetic fields in the tube, with resulting traveling-wave amplification.

7.3. Waves in Periodic Structures

In the discussion of the traveling-wave tube of the preceding section, a helix, or wire spiral, was introduced as a typical slow-wave

structure. The helix was employed in the construction of early
O-type traveling-wave tubes.† Although the helix still retains its
importance for low-power applications, the need for higher beam power
and greater frequency bandwidth than can be efficiently attained
with the helix has led to the development of a large variety of periodic
structures for use in traveling-wave tubes.‡

The fundamental requirement of a slow-wave structure, or delay
line, is that it must possess an axial component of electric field having
phase velocity less than the velocity of light.   Uniform hollow waveguides are obviously ruled out for this application since, as we have
seen in Chap. 3, the phase velocity of a uniform waveguide is always
greater than the velocity of light.

The wave traveling along the anode surface of the cylindrical traveling-wave magnetron discussed in the preceding chapter was regarded
as being due to the oscillating fields of the individual anode-slot resonators, which successively reached peak values in sequence.   In
π-mode operation, an electron traveling along the anode surface at a
speed which takes it from one slot center to the next in one half-cycle
of the slot frequency can always find itself in decelerating field over
each slot in turn.   We then consider that the electron is traveling at
the phase velocity of the fundamental component of the traveling
wave on the anode.   Alternatively, the electron may travel at a speed
which takes it between slot centers in a time equal to $(n + \frac{1}{2})$ cycles
of the slot frequency and still find itself in a decelerating field over the
slot centers.   We could then consider the electron to be traveling at
the phase velocity of a wave having the same frequency as the fundamental wave above, but having a wavelength $1/(2n + 1)$ times as
great.   A wave of the latter kind is called a Hartree component of the
anode field.   Figure 7.4 illustrates the travel of electrons with three
Hartree components of the field of a slow-wave structure operating in
the π mode.   The π mode of operation, in which successive anode segments oscillate with a phase difference of π radians, is a special case of
the more general mode of oscillation in which successive segments are
out of phase by an arbitrary phase angle $\phi = \beta_0 L$, where L is the distance between adjacent segments.§   In the general case, we may
consider that the point of maximum slot field moves along the guide

---

† R. Kompfner, *Proc. IRE*, vol. 35, p. 124, February, 1947.

‡ For a survey of slow-wave structures, see E. J. Nalos, *Microwave J.*, vol. 2,
no. 12, p. 31, December, 1959.

§ The phase factor β_0 should not be confused with the beam-velocity phase
factor employed in the preceding section.   Since the two factors will not be used
together here, no ambiguity should arise.

as a wave:

$$f_0 = e^{j(\omega t - \beta_0 z)} \tag{7.43}$$

This wave of phase does not, of course, represent the axial field, which in general will have a nonsinusoidal distribution in space. The field of the slow-wave structure must be distributed in accordance with

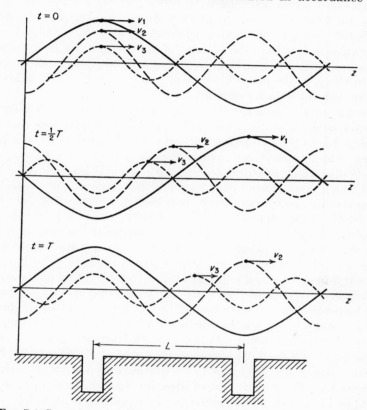

FIG. 7.4. Space-harmonic wave travel.   (Velocity vectors not to scale.)

Floquet's theorem for periodic boundaries. Floquet's theorem requires that the field solutions at corresponding points in the structure separated by a structure period L can differ in value only by a complex constant. This constant, for our purposes, is the phase constant $\exp(j\beta_0 L)$. Therefore, a satisfactory solution for the axial field will be of the form

$$E_z = e^{-j\beta_0 z} f(z) \tag{7.44}$$

where $f(z)$ is periodic in L. We may expand the field distribution function $f(z)$ in a Fourier series of fundamental period L:

$$E_z = e^{-j\beta_{0n}z} \sum_{n=-\infty}^{+\infty} a_n e^{-j(2\pi n/L)z} \tag{7.45}$$

where the a_n are the coefficients of expansion. Alternatively, we may write

$$E_z = \sum_{n=-\infty}^{+\infty} a_n e^{-j\beta_n z} \tag{7.46}$$

where

$$\beta_n = \beta_0 + \frac{2\pi n}{L} \tag{7.47}$$

The negative and positive values of n in the series (7.46) and (7.45) represent forward- and backward-traveling waves. These oppositely traveling waves may be considered to form the standing waves of field configuration in the periodic structure elements of the slow waveguide.

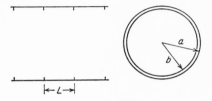

The individual terms of the Fourier series (7.46) are the Hartree components, or spatial harmonics, of the field, examples of which we have discussed above. All of the terms of the series vary harmoni-

FIG. 7.5. Circular guide with aperture discs.

cally in time with the same frequency, i.e., as exp $(j\omega t)$. Therefore the phase velocity of the nth harmonic is

$$v_{pn} = \frac{\omega}{\beta_0 + 2\pi n/L} \tag{7.48}$$

Hence the phase velocity is arbitrarily small for arbitrarily large n. The group velocity, however, given by $v_g = 1/(d\beta/d\omega)$, is

$$v_g = \left[\frac{d(\beta_0 + 2\pi n/L)}{d\omega} \right]^{-1} = \left(\frac{d\beta_0}{d\omega} \right)^{-1} \tag{7.49}$$

Thus we see that the group velocity is the same for all the spatial harmonics, and must depend on frequency ω only.

Let us here recall that we have used a plot of the relation between ω [or $k = (\mu\epsilon)^{\frac{1}{2}}\omega$] and propagation constant β to give a representation of the propagation characteristics of the hollow waveguide (Fig. 3.12). It will be instructive to investigate the form taken by the ω-β diagram of a periodic wave-guiding structure. We consider the example of a circular waveguide of radius a in which there is placed a small periodic structure-perturbation, such as loading apertures of radius b nearly equal to a, as shown in Fig. 7.5. At frequencies near the cutoff frequency ω_c of the unperturbed guide, the spacing L between apertures is small compared with the guide wavelength and the apertures will not affect the cutoff characteristics of the guide. Therefore the ω-β diagram will be much like that of the unperturbed guide, near cutoff, as indicated in Fig. 7.6a. As the frequency is increased until the propagation constant β approaches the value π/L, the waves reflected from the apertures begin to add in phase, until finally at $\beta = \pi/L$, all of the reflections add to equal the incident wave, and no energy can be propagated along the guide. The group velocity v_g is therefore zero at this value of β. Since $v_g = d\omega/d\beta$, the ω-β curve reaches a maximum, with zero slope, at $\beta = \pi/L$.

From the point of view of waveguide impedances, we can interpret the total reflection of energy when the spacing between apertures is equal to one half-guide wavelength in the following manner: We recall that an integral number of guide half-wavelengths acts as a $1:1$ impedance transformer. Therefore when $L = \lambda_g/2$, all the aperture impedances are transformed to the plane of any one of the apertures we may consider. An apparent short circuit thus appears at this plane, owing to the infinitely many impedances effectively in parallel, for an infinite length of guide. The reflection coefficient thus observed becomes unity, indicating total reflection.

We recall, however, from Eq. (7.49), that $v_g = (d\beta_n/d\omega)^{-1}$ has the same value for all of the spatial harmonics simultaneously. Therefore we convert our ω-β diagram to an ω-β_n diagram for the periodic structure and plot maxima of the ω-β curve at $\beta = 2\pi/L, 3\pi/L, \ldots$; $-\pi/L, -2\pi/L, -3\pi/L, \ldots$. This leads us to deduce that the ω-β_n curve is periodic in β_n and is an even function of β_n, as shown in Fig. 7.7a.

Moreover, if the frequency is increased above the value ω_1, at which propagation cutoff occurred, the guide wavelength of the unperturbed waveguide becomes less than the critical value for total reflection, and propagation is once more possible. Thus a new band of propagating frequencies exists above the ω-β_n propagation curve already constructed. This is represented by another ω-β_n curve which is also periodic in β_n and is an even function of β_n. An upper frequency limit for propagation is again reached when the reflected waves in this band interfere to produce a second total reflection of wave energy.

Thus the ω-β curves of a periodic structure consist in general of frequency bands in which propagation may occur, separated by forbidden bands of no propagation, as shown in Fig. 7.6a.

The width of the forbidden bands and the shape of the ω-β_n curves will depend, of course, on the configuration of the slow-wave structure.

This fact may be seen in our example: If the radius b of the apertures is reduced, the forbidden bands become wider and the slope of the ω-β_n curves decreases, until in the limit of zero aperture radius, the

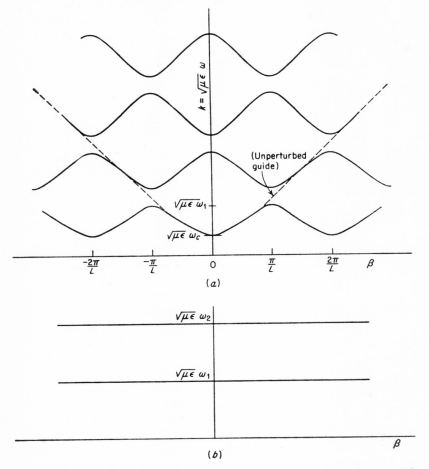

FIG. 7.6. ω-β diagrams of periodic structures.   (a) Aperture-loaded waveguide; (b) apertures of zero radius.

ω-β_n curves degenerate to straight lines at the resonant frequencies of the individual cavities, as shown schematically in Fig. 7.6b.

In the present example of the lightly loaded circular waveguide, we may obtain a representation of the ω-β curve, except near the band edges, from the corresponding curve of a circular waveguide operating in the TM$_{01}$ mode.   The lowest cutoff frequency will be nearly equal to

ω_c given by

$$\mu\epsilon\omega_c{}^2 = \left(\frac{2.405}{a}\right)^2 \tag{7.50}$$

where we have used the value of p_{01} from Table 3.6. If the aperture discs are thin, at ω_1, the distance L between apertures will be approximately equal to $\lambda_g/2$ of the TM$_{01}$ mode, and we will have

$$\left(\frac{2.405}{a}\right)^2 + \left(\frac{\pi}{L}\right)^2 = \mu\epsilon\omega_1{}^2 \tag{7.51}$$

or

$$\omega_1 = c\ \sqrt{\left(\frac{2.405}{a}\right)^2 + \left(\frac{\pi}{L}\right)^2} \tag{7.52}$$

where c is the velocity of light. The character of the electric field lines at the lower and upper cutoff frequencies is shown in Fig. 7.7a

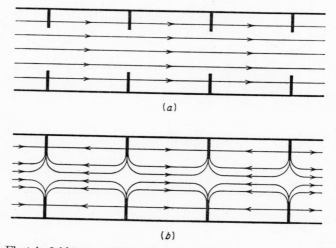

(a)

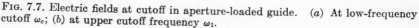

(b)

FIG. 7.7. Electric fields at cutoff in aperture-loaded guide.   (a) At low-frequency cutoff ω_c; (b) at upper cutoff frequency ω_1.

and b. At the upper cutoff frequency, Fig. 7.7b, we note the resemblance of the field distribution to the π mode of operation which was described in connection with the operation of the traveling-wave magnetron anode.

For higher-order Hartree harmonics, with propagation constant greater than π/L, distinction between β_0 and the β_n's of the space harmonics becomes less well-defined, and due to the periodicity of the ω-β curve, it makes little difference how we assign the zero of the integers n.

That is, for example, β_0 is equivalent to $(\beta_0 - n\pi/L) + n\pi/L$. Hence, changing β_0 by an integer multiple of π/L merely shifts the numbering of the β_n's, and any minimum of the lowest branch of the ω-β diagram provides a suitable origin for the scale of β_n.

In this simple example, we obtained our knowledge of the frequency dependence of β_0, and hence of the phase shift between successive sections of the periodic structure, from the wave solution for the unperturbed waveguide. This solution was originally obtained by requiring the axial field to satisfy the boundary condition $E_z = 0$ at the walls of the guide. In this way there arose the assignment of a characteristic value for the problem: $p = k_c a = 2.405$.

In order to solve the more general problem of finding the ω-β diagram and transmission characteristics of a periodic structure of arbitrary

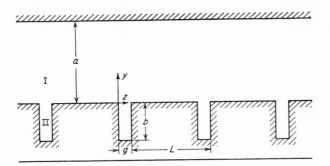

FIG. 7.8. Slotted slow waveguide.

form, it is necessary to begin anew and solve the boundary-value problem for the electromagnetic fields in the structure. It is often convenient in such cases to subdivide the region of electromagnetic field into parts, such as the regions labeled I and II in Fig. 7.8. Field solutions valid in the separate regions can then be written without great difficulty. The fields in the various regions are then required to match at the boundary surfaces between the regions. The equation resulting from the matching condition provides the ω-β relation and defines the passbands as the regions of real solutions for the propagation constants β_n.

7.4. Slotted Slow Waveguide

As an example of the method for determining the propagation characteristics of a periodic structure, let us consider the two-dimensional problem of a slotted wave-guiding structure such as that illustrated in

Fig. 7.8. We shall seek a solution for waves traveling in the z direction, under the assumption that the fields are uniform with respect to x.

At the outset, we must recall that we are seeking waves traveling at speeds less than the velocity of light. The propagation constants β_n of these waves will therefore be greater than the propagation constant k of waves in free space. In the case of the uniform hollow waveguide, the guide propagation constant was given by the expression

$$\beta_g = \pm \sqrt{k^2 - k_c^2} \tag{7.53}$$

in which k_c^2 is defined by

$$\frac{\nabla_{tr}^2 E_z}{E_z} = -k_c^2 \tag{7.54}$$

where ∇_{tr}^2 is the transverse Laplacian operator and k_c is real. Inspection of Eq. (7.53) shows that, in order to obtain slow-wave propagation constants such that $\beta_n > k$, we must employ solutions for which the operation represented by the left side of Eq. (7.54) yields a positive number. That is, we require

$$\frac{\nabla_{tr}^2 E_{zn}}{E_{zn}} = \kappa_n^2 \tag{7.55}$$

where E_{zn} is the nth space harmonic and κ_n is real.

Suitable solutions for the electric field in region I will be of the form

$$E_{zn} = E_{0n} \sinh \kappa_n(a - y)e^{-j\beta_n z} \tag{7.56}$$

The total field E_z is the sum of all the space-harmonic components:

$$E_z = \sum_{n = -\infty}^{+\infty} E_{0n} \sinh \kappa_n(a - y)e^{-j\beta_n z} \tag{7.57}$$

By the use of Eq. (3.50), we find the corresponding transverse magnetic field to be

$$H_x = j\omega\epsilon \sum_{n = -\infty}^{\infty} \frac{E_{0n}}{\kappa_n} \cosh \kappa_n(a - y)e^{-j\beta_n z} \tag{7.58}$$

In order to obtain solutions for the fields in region II, we assume that the slot width g is small in comparison with the depth b, so that the slots may be regarded as shorted sections of parallel-plane transmission line. The electric field will therefore be a standing wave in the y direction:

$$E_z = E_0 \sin k(y + b)e^{-j\beta_0 mL} \tag{7.59}$$

where $\exp(-j\beta_0 mL)$ is the phase factor for the fields in the slot at coordinate $z = mL$.   The magnetic field in the slot then is

$$H_x = j \frac{\omega\epsilon}{k} E_0 \cos k(y + b)e^{-j\beta_0 mL} \tag{7.60}$$

There now remains the task of joining the fields of regions I and II, over their surface of separation at $y = 0$.   At the plane $y = 0$, the region II field E_z has uniform amplitude over the slot gaps:

$$E_z = E_0 \sin kb \ e^{-j\beta_0 mL} \tag{7.61}$$

whereas, over the surface of the metal, E_z is zero.   Thus, by our assumption, the region II field at the interface between I and II has

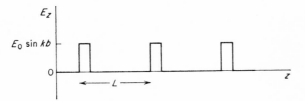

FIG. 7.9. Assumed field E_z at $y = 0$.

the discontinuous distribution illustrated in Fig. 7.9.   On the other hand, the region I field at the interface reduces to

$$E_z = \sum_n E_{0n} \sinh \kappa_n a \ e^{-j\beta_n z} \tag{7.62}$$

or, using the substitution $E_{0n} \sinh \kappa_n a = E'_{0n}$,

$$E_z = \sum_n E'_{0n} e^{-j\beta_n z} \tag{7.63}$$

Equation (7.63) may be regarded as a Fourier series expression for E_z.   The coefficients E'_{0n} must now be evaluated so that the series represents the distribution of Fig. 7.9.   Hence, we write

$$E_0 \sin kb \int_0^g e^{+j\beta_p z} \, dz = \sum_n E'_{0n} \int_0^L e^{-j(\beta_n - \beta_p)z} \, dz \tag{7.64}$$

where p is an integer.   Since both β_n and β_p are defined as in Eq. (7.47), all terms vanish on the right of (7.64) except the pth term, and we find

$$E_{0p} = \frac{gE_0 e^{j\beta_p g/2} \sin kb}{L \sinh \kappa_p a} \frac{\sin(\beta_p g/2)}{\beta_p g/2} \tag{7.65}$$

Equation (7.65) is thus the general coefficient of the spatial-harmonic terms in Eq. (7.57), when the index of summation p is replaced by n.

The coefficients (7.65) used in Eq. (7.58) do not, however, bring the region I and II expressions for magnetic field into equality at $y = 0$. We adopt the compromise measure, therefore, of requiring the magnetic fields (7.58) and (7.60) to match at the gap centers $z = mL + g/2$. When this is done, we find

$$\frac{g}{L} \sum_n \frac{1}{\kappa_n} \coth \kappa_n a \, \frac{\sin \, (\beta_n g/2)}{\beta_n g/2} = \frac{\cot kb}{k} \qquad (7.66)$$

Therefore, since $k = \omega(\mu\epsilon)^{\frac{1}{2}}$, Eq. (7.66) defines the ω-β diagram of the slow-wave structure. Since it is a transcendental equation, an analytic

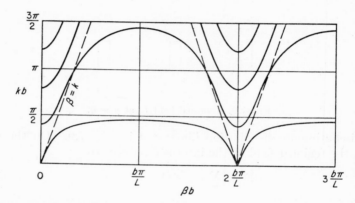

FIG. 7.10. k-β diagram for slotted structure ($a/L = 12.5$, $b/L = 5$, $g/L = 0.2$). (*Adapted with permission from D. A. Watkins, "Topics in Electromagnetic Theory," John Wiley & Sons, Inc., New York, 1958.*)

expression for the diagram cannot be obtained. Solutions can be found by specifying values for the dimensions g/L, b/L, and a/L, of the structure. Then, k may be calculated for assumed values of β_n, with the use of $\kappa_n^2 = \beta_n^2 - k^2$. When this is done, the ω-β curves of the slotted slow-wave structure are found to have the form indicated in Fig. 7.10.† The lowest passband is seen, in these characteristic curves, to extend to zero frequency. This is a consequence of the two-dimensional model we have used, in which there are two separated conductors, which can carry zero-frequency currents. It may be seen that the passbands overlap considerably in the neighborhood of

† D. A. Watkins, "Topics in Electromagnetic Theory," John Wiley & Sons, Inc., New York, 1958.

$\beta = n\pi/L$. As a consequence of this overlapping, there are no forbidden bands, and this structure will transmit at all frequencies. A
periodic waveguide structure which is part of a closed outer conductor
must, of course, have a lower cutoff frequency greater than zero. The
method of subdivision of field solutions which has been illustrated is
general, however, and may be used for the solution of waveguide
fields, or of arbitrary electromagnetic problems, in three dimensions.

PROBLEMS

7.1. A region of space contains n electrons/m³, through which a wave of electric
field $E_x = E_1 \exp [j(\omega t - \beta z)]$ is passing.

(a) Calculate the displacement x of the electrons.

(b) Define a polarization density $P = nqx = \rho x$, where q is the electronic charge,
and from it calculate the electric **D** vector in the medium. Show that the effective
relative dielectric constant of the medium is $\epsilon_r = 1 - \omega_p{}^2/\omega^2$, where ω_p is the plasma
frequency.

7.2. (a) Calculate the phase velocity of waves in a medium having $\mu = \mu_0$ and
the ϵ_r found in Prob. 7.1.

(b) Calculate the electron density n for which the phase velocity is 1 per cent
greater than the velocity of light, at $f = 10^8$ cps.

7.3. In a helix-type traveling-wave tube operating at 5×10^8 cps, the pitch
of the helix is $1:10$, and the beam density is such that the plasma frequency is
$\omega_p = 2\pi \times 10^8$ sec^{-1}. What accelerating anode voltage is required in order that
the condition $\beta_1{}^2 = \beta_0{}^2 - \beta_p{}^2$ shall be fulfilled?

7.4. Find the series for E_y in region I of the slotted slow-wave structure of
Sec. 7.4. What is the total flux of the Poynting vector in the z direction per unit
width of structure corresponding to the space-harmonic term for which $n = +1$?
Discuss the significance of this quantity.

7.5. Show by direct substitution that the individual spatial-harmonic terms
of the slotted-guide series, Eq. (7.57), satisfy the wave equation.

Would it be possible to excite a single one of the space-harmonic terms alone,
in the slow-wave structure? Explain.

CHAPTER 8

Magnetic Materials in Microwave Applications

The electromagnetic fields in the microwave components with which we have dealt thus far have been due to electrons in motion in electron beams and in the surface layers of the metals of which the components are made. The conducting metals have been the materials of importance since they permit electrons to move without interruption over distances large compared to the interatomic spacing. We have calculated the magnetic fields due to the motion of electronic charges in keeping with the law of Biot and Savart, $d\mathbf{H} = d\mathbf{i} \times \hat{\mathbf{r}}/4\pi r^2$. Quantum theory has shown, however, that it is necessary to consider another source of magnetic field in addition to the translational motion of electric charge. The electron itself has the property, in common with many other elementary particles, of possessing an intrinsic magnetic-dipole field and angular momentum. This combination of mechanical and magnetic properties of the electron leads to the appearance of characteristic magnetic properties in materials containing electron spins which may be employed in practical microwave devices.

8.1. Properties of the Electron Spin

A simple picture of the electron is that of a charged object spinning upon its own axis. The behavior of an individual electron is, however, subject to the rules of quantum mechanics. These rules specify that the angular-momentum vector of the electron can assume only the values $+h/4\pi$ or $-h/4\pi$ as observed with respect to any reference axis, where h is Planck's constant. Correspondingly, the magnetic moment can assume only the values $+q_e h/4\pi m$ or $-q_e h/4\pi m$ in any direction of reference, where q_e and m are the charge and mass of the electron, respectively. This element of magnetic moment associated with the electron is the Bohr magneton:

$$\mu_B = \frac{q_e h}{4\pi m} \qquad (8.1)$$

The axis of reference may be the direction of a magnetic field in which the electron is located.

Since the electron is a magnetic dipole, it will have different energies in the two possible states, with spin in the direction of the field and opposed to the direction of the field.   To show this fact we may use the analogy of a classical dipole having magnetic pole strength m and length L in a magnetic field of strength H_z.   Reversal of the dipole orientation by carrying one pole through a distance $2L$ in the z direction with respect to the other pole, against a force $F_z = mH_z$, requires an amount of work equal to $2mLH_z$, or $2H_z$ times the dipole strength mL (Fig. 8.1).   Thus the difference in energy between the two possible spin states of a single electron in field H_z is

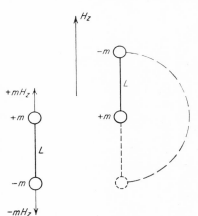

$$W = 2\mu_B H_z \qquad (8.2)$$

If the energy required to reverse the orientation of an electron in a steady magnetic field is supplied

FIG. 8.1. Reversal of classical dipole.

by an electromagnetic field, the quanta of the field must have the energy

$$hf = 2\mu_B H_z \qquad (8.3)$$

where f is the frequency of the radiation.   In a magnetic field of 3,500 gauss, the transition frequency is 9.8 kmc and is thus in the microwave region.

Electron-spin transitions having resonance frequencies close to the free-electron value given above are observed in atomic hydrogen, molecular fragments, and other atoms or molecules in which there is a single electron in an outer electron shell.   As atoms are built up in the periodic table starting from hydrogen, the electrons tend to fill up the quantum states corresponding to a given angular-momentum quantum number l, thus forming full shells before a new quantum shell is begun. The total angular momentum and magnetic moment of a full shell is zero.   Therefore, closed or full shells exhibit no magnetic properties aside from a diamagnetism of very small magnitude.   The electrons in a shell that is partially full tend to couple into groupings which behave magnetically like dipoles having magnetic moment greater than one Bohr magneton, and which can assume more values, or projections, with respect to a given axis, than the two possible states of a single electron.   The allowed spin-energy levels of such electron groupings in a magnetic field H_z are given by an expression of the form

$$W = m_s g \mu_B H_z \tag{8.4}$$

where m_s, the magnetic quantum number, can have integral or half-integral values, and g is the "g factor," or spectroscopic splitting factor of the level.   The g value of free electrons is 2.0023, but in solids, g may have other values, depending on the interaction of the electrons with their surroundings.   The circulations of electrons in their orbits constitute current loops which can contribute to the effective magnetic-dipole strength of free atoms, but in many solids this orbital motion is to some degree suppressed, or "quenched," by interactions with surrounding atoms.   Thus the magnetic properties of microwave interest are frequently due to the electron spins in solids.

There are classes of elements which do not adhere to the rule that electron shells are filled before the formation of a new shell is begun. These are the transition elements, examples of which are the iron group Sc, Ti, V, Cr, Mn, Fe, Co, Ni, and the rare earth elements from Ce to Lu.   In the transition elements, electron spins in the incomplete shells may combine so as to produce a large effective value of total dipole moment per atom.   Table 8.1 shows the effective numbers of Bohr magnetons in the total spin moment of ions of the iron group atoms.[†]

TABLE 8.1. EFFECTIVE NUMBER OF BOHR MAGNETONS PER ION

Ion.................	Ti^{3+}	V^{3+}	Cr^{3+}	Fe^{3+}	Fe^{++}	Co^{++}	Ni^{++}
Magnetons..........	1.8	2.8	3.8	5.9	5.4	4.8	3.2

The strongly magnetic materials are not necessarily those having large atomic spin moments, however, but are those in which the interaction between spins on neighboring atoms causes the spins over large regions, or domains, in the material to take up common orientations. This additive combination of spin moments is characteristic of the ferromagnetic and ferrimagnetic materials.   In the ferromagnetic

[†] C. Kittel, "Introduction to Solid State Physics," 2d ed , John Wiley & Sons, Inc., New York, 1956.

materials such as metallic iron, essentially all of the uncanceled spins are aligned mutually parallel, and the magnetization is strong. If there are N atoms per unit volume, each having an atomic moment equal to μ, the volume magnetization of the ferromagnet is $M = N\mu$.

In the ferrites, the effect of the coupling between spins is such as to divide the magnetic atoms into groups having oppositely oriented dipoles. If there are N_a atoms having moment μ_a all oriented in the same direction in group A, and N_b atoms of moment μ_b in group B, all oriented oppositely to group A, the resultant volume magnetization of the ferrimagnetic material is $M = N_a\mu_a - N_b\mu_b$.

In the naturally occurring ferrite Fe_3O_4, or magnetite, for example, we may write the composition as $(Fe^{++}O)(Fe_2^{3+}O_3)$. The two triply ionized iron atoms have oppositely oriented spins, and the magnetization of the material is effectively due to the Fe^{++}, as indi-

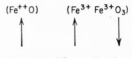

Fig. 8.2. Magnetization of magnetite.

cated schematically in Fig. 8.2. Other ferrites may be formed by the substitution of other magnetic ions for the Fe^{++}.

A third class of magnetic substances is that containing the paramagnetic materials. In paramagnetic substances the coupling between spins is relatively slight, so that the spins may be considered in first approximation to be a collection of independent dipoles. Consequently, the application of a constant magnetic field causes the spins to precess nearly independently about the direction of the applied field, thus yielding a relatively weak resultant volume magnetization. The energies of the precessing electronic dipoles are still given by an expression of the form of Eq. (8.4), for paramagnetic materials. The spin dipole of a given atom or ion may consist of the combination of several electron spins having a maximum value of m_s equal to an odd or even integer times $\frac{1}{2}$. We consider the case when the maximum m_s is equal to $\frac{3}{2}$, for example. The dipole may then assume energy

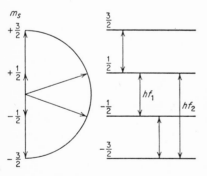

Fig. 8.3. System of spin levels.

levels of $+\frac{3}{2}$, $+\frac{1}{2}$, $-\frac{1}{2}$, or $-\frac{3}{2}$ times $g\mu_B H$, in a magnetic field H. (In some materials, the factor g may have different values at the different levels but is usually approximately constant and equal to about 2.) This typical energy level scheme is shown diagramatically in Fig. 8.3.

If energy corresponding to the difference between a pair of the energy levels is supplied or removed as electromagnetic radiation of frequency f, a spin in one of the levels may make a transition upward or downward, with the energy change

$$hf = \Delta m_s \, g \mu_B H \tag{8.5}$$

In free atoms the allowed transitions are those corresponding to a change in m_s of $\Delta m_s = \pm 1$ or 0 only, but in solids having sufficiently strong local fields due to neighboring atoms, this selection rule is relaxed, so that transitions of $\Delta m_s = \pm 2, \pm 3, \ldots$ are possible.†

8.2. Three-level Solid-state Maser

The maser is a microwave amplifier or oscillator which employs as its working substance a paramagnetic material having a suitable set of electron-spin energy levels separated by energy intervals $\Delta W = hf$ corresponding to frequencies in the microwave range. The physical effect upon which maser operation is based is that of the stimulated emission of radiation from atoms in a high-energy state. The presence of radiation having frequency corresponding to the energy difference between the high-energy state and a lower state of the atoms will cause stimulated transitions between the states. If there is a surplus of excited atoms, of high spin energy, over the normal equilibrium number at the working temperature of the paramagnetic material in a maser, the presence of radiation at the transition frequency causes a net surplus of transitions to the lower state. The resulting increase in density of radiant energy causes further stimulated emission from the excited atoms. If the excess radiant energy thus produced is conducted away, the paramagnetic material will finally fall to its equilibrium state of no excitation.

For continuous operation of the maser, it is clearly necessary to have always available a surplus of atoms in the higher-energy state. This supply of excited atoms may be obtained by the process of pumping between two energy levels. In the pumping process, a high density of radiation is supplied at the frequency corresponding to the level difference. The result of this process is that the number of atomic spins in the higher-energy state becomes greater than the thermal-equilibrium value. We may see how this occurs, in the following way.

In thermal equilibrium, the ratio of the numbers of atoms in two states of energy W_1 and W_2, where $W_2 > W_1$ (Fig. 8.4), is given by the

† W. Low, Paramagnetic Resonance in Solids, Suppl. 2 of "Solid State Physics," Academic Press Inc., New York, 1960.

Boltzmann factor:

$$\frac{N_2}{N_1} = e^{-(W_2 - W_1)/kT} \qquad (8.6)$$

where N_2 and N_1 are the numbers of atoms in the upper and lower states, respectively, k is Boltzmann's constant, and T is the absolute temperature. The probability that an atom in state 2 will fall spontaneously to state 1 in a time interval dt is proportional to dt. Writing $1/\tau$ as the constant of proportionality, we have

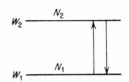

$$dP_{21} = \frac{1}{\tau} dt \qquad \text{spontaneous transition} \qquad (8.7)$$

FIG. 8.4. Two-level spin system.

where dP_{21} is the probability of transition in time dt. Therefore, for N_2 atoms in state 2, the rate of spontaneous emission from state 2 is

$$\frac{dN_2}{dt} = -\frac{N_2}{\tau} \qquad (8.8)$$

In thermal equilibrium, the number of atoms in each state must remain constant. Therefore, in thermal equilibrium with no radiation present, there must be a similar rate of upward transitions from state 1 to state 2:

$$\frac{dN_1}{dt} = -\frac{N_1}{\tau} \qquad (8.9)$$

If we now combine Eqs. (8.8) and (8.9) to examine the effect of these spontaneous processes on $N_2 - N_1$, the difference in occupation numbers of the two states, we have

$$\frac{d(N_2 - N_1)}{dt}\bigg|_{sp} = -\frac{N_2 - N_1}{\tau} \qquad (8.10)$$

where the subscript sp refers to spontaneous transitions. As it stands, Eq. (8.10) implies that $N_2 - N_1$ would eventually decay to zero in equilibrium. This is an incorrect conclusion, as shown by Eq. (8.6). The reason for this discrepancy is that we must include in Eq. (8.10) a term accounting for transitions due to interaction of the spins with the thermal vibrations of the surrounding lattice. Calling this term a and setting $N_2 - N_1$ equal to n, we have

$$\frac{dn}{dt}\bigg|_{sp} = -\frac{n}{\tau} + a \qquad (8.11)$$

At infinite time, dn/dt becomes zero and n reaches n_0, its equilibrium value with no radiation present. Hence, $a = n_0/\tau$, and we have for the spontaneous and thermal processes in the absence of radiation

$$\frac{dn}{dt}\Big|_{sp} = \frac{n_0 - n}{\tau} \tag{8.12}$$

If there is radiation present at the transition frequency

$$f_{12} = \frac{W_2 - W_1}{h}$$

the probability of stimulated transition in time dt is proportional to the radiation density U and to dt:

$$dP'_{21} = c_{21}U\, dt \qquad \text{stimulated transition} \tag{8.13}$$

where c_{21} is a constant of proportionality and dP'_{21} is the probability of stimulated transition from state 2 in time dt. Therefore, with N_2 atoms in state 2, the rate of stimulated transition is

$$\frac{dN_2}{dt} = -c_{21}UN_2 \tag{8.14}$$

It was first shown by Einstein[†] that the constant of proportionality for stimulated upward transitions from state 1 to state 2 is equal to that for stimulated downward transitions. Therefore we may write, for the stimulated upward transitions,

$$\frac{dN_1}{dt_1} = -c_{12}UN_1 = -cUN_1 \tag{8.15}$$

where we have taken $c_{12} = c_{21} = c$.

The rate of change of $n = N_2 - N_1$ due to transitions stimulated by the radiation is thus, using Eqs. (8.14) and (8.15),

$$\frac{dn}{dt}\Big|_{st} = -2cUn \tag{8.16}$$

where subscript st stands for stimulated transitions. The factor of 2 on the right accounts for the fact that, in this two-state system, a transition from either state changes n by 2.

With the combination of Eqs. (8.12) and (8.16), the total rate of change of the population difference n is found to be

$$\frac{dn}{dt} = \frac{n_0 - n}{\tau} - 2cUn \tag{8.17}$$

[†] A. Einstein, *Z. Physik*, vol. 18, p. 121, 1917.

which we may write as

$$-\frac{1}{\frac{1}{\tau} + 2cU}\frac{d}{dt}\left[\frac{n_0}{\tau} - \left(\frac{1}{\tau} + 2cU\right)n\right] = \frac{n_0}{\tau} - \left(\frac{1}{\tau} + 2cU\right)n$$

Equation (8.17) thus has the solution

$$n = \frac{n_0 - n_1 e^{-(1/\tau + 2cU)t}}{1 + 2\tau cU} \qquad (8.18)$$

where n_1 is a constant determined by the value of n at $t = 0$. Equation (8.18) shows that the pumping process will come to equilibrium more rapidly, as the pumping energy density U is made larger. In the state of final equilibrium under pumping, the exponential term vanishes, and the final equilibrium value of n is

$$n_\infty = \frac{n_0}{1 + 2\tau cU}$$

If the pumping power U is made very great, n_∞ approaches zero. In this condition the populations of states 1 and 2 are nearly equal. In paramagnetic materials, the relaxation time τ is extremely small at room temperature, and excessive pumping power would be required for room temperature maser operation. The maser material is usually cooled to low temperature to reduce the value of τ to a permissible value, in the neighborhood of 10^{-5} sec.

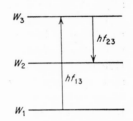

The Boltzmann relation [Eq. (8.6)] shows that the fully pumped condition $n_\infty \to 0$ is the situation that would exist at very high temperature. The pumping process is thus said to raise the spin temperature, and Eq. (8.6) may be used to define the spin temperature corresponding to a given value of N_2/N_1.

Fig. 8.5. Three-level maser.

Pumping would not be a convenient means for obtaining spin excitation for maser operation in a two-level spin system, since the pump and maser would have to be operated alternately, to avoid overloading the signal system with pump power. A more satisfactory procedure is the use of three levels of a multilevel spin system. It is then possible to pump between the lowest level and the highest, as illustrated in Fig. 8.5. By exciting the paramagnetic material with pump power at frequency f_{13}, the spin population of the level at W_3 is raised. Signal energy at frequency f_{32} may be introduced, causing stimulated downward transitions from level 3 to level 2 and the production of electromagnetic energy at this frequency, resulting in maser amplification. The pump power may be kept out of the signal system by making the pump and signal circuits sufficiently selective.   If the maser employs a resonant cavity for containing the paramagnetic material, the cavity must be simultaneously resonant at both f_{13} and f_{23}.

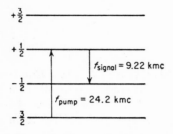

A typical three-level solid-state maser is of the type described by Makhov et al.,[†] employing synthetic ruby $(Al_2O_3:Cr^{3+})$ as the paramagnetic material.   The chromium ions, present in a concentration of 0.1 per cent, provided the paramagnetic dipoles, which in this crystal have a maximum m_s equal to $\frac{3}{2}$.   The level scheme is shown in Fig. 8.6.   A ruby crystal 0.2 cm³ in volume was placed at the center of

FIG. 8.6.   Maser operation in ruby (Cr^{3+}) at 4,230 gauss.

a cylindrical cavity, resonant at 9.22 and 24.2 kmc, in the TE_{011} and TE_{114} modes, respectively.   When pumping power is supplied from a klystron at 24.2 kmc, a small auxiliary klystron signal at 9.22 kmc applied to the cavity yields an amplified return signal at 9.22 kmc.

The noise introduced into an incoming signal by a maser amplifier can be very low, and its low noise factor is one of the distinguishing advantages of the maser.   The principal sources of noise are the effective resistances due to loss in the input waveguide and cavity walls, and spontaneous emission by the paramagnetic material.   These noise sources are small, largely because of the low operating temperature of the device.   It may be shown that a reflection-cavity maser is lower in noise factor than a transmission-cavity maser.[‡]

8.3. Magnetic Properties of Ferrites

We have observed that in ferrimagnetic materials the uncanceled electron spins are mutually parallel throughout domains of uniform magnetization.   Thus the macroscopic magnetization vector of a domain behaves effectively as a unit, under the influence of external magnetic fields.   For this reason, in investigating the response of ferrites to high-frequency fields, we may treat the electron-spin magnetization as a classical entity endowed with angular momentum and a magnetic moment.

[†] G. Makhov, C. Kikuchi, J. Lambe, and R. W. Terhune, *Phys. Rev.*, vol. 109, p. 1399, 1958.

[‡] J. P. Gordon and L. D. White, *Proc. IRE*, vol. 46, p. 1588, 1958.

We consider a spin angular-momentum vector **J** placed in a steady magnetic field **H**$_0$, as illustrated in Fig. 8.7. The magnetic field exerts a torque **T** on the magnetic moment **M** of the spin, tending to rotate it

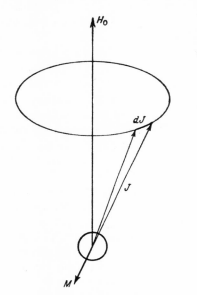

FIG. 8.7. Precessing dipole.

into alignment with the field, in keeping with the law of angular motion:

$$\mathbf{T} = \frac{d\mathbf{J}}{dt} \tag{8.19}$$

Since it has angular momentum, the spin does not change its angle with respect to the field, however, but precesses gyroscopically around H_0. It is this tendency toward precession in the presence of a polarizing field that endows magnetic materials, as we shall see, with characteristic behavior in high-frequency fields.

The magnetization **M** is related to the angular momentum **J** by a constant γ, the gyromagnetic ratio:

$$\mathbf{M} = \gamma \mathbf{J} \tag{8.20}$$

The torque **T** acting upon **M**, owing to a magnetic field **H**, is proportional to $\mu_0 \mathbf{H}$ and to the sine of the angle between **M** and **H**:

$$\mathbf{T} = \mu_0 \mathbf{M} \times \mathbf{H} \tag{8.21}$$

Therefore, with Eqs. (8.20) and (8.21), Eq. (8.19) becomes

$$\frac{1}{\gamma}\frac{d\mathbf{M}}{dt} = \mu_0 \mathbf{M} \times \mathbf{H} \tag{8.22}$$

We assume that the time variation of $\mathbf{M}$ is given by the factor exp $(j\omega t)$. Hence, Eq. (8.22) is

$$\mathbf{M} = \frac{\mu_0 \gamma}{j\omega} \mathbf{M} \times \mathbf{H} \tag{8.23}$$

Equation (8.23) is an equation connecting $\mathbf{H}$ and $\mathbf{M}$, which we may solve to obtain the magnetic susceptibility constants of the assembly of spins in our model. The assumptions under which (8.23) will be solved are that the magnetic $\mathbf{H}$ field consists of a small high-frequency vector field $\mathbf{H}_1$ superposed on a large constant polarizing field $\mathbf{H}_0$ in the $\hat{z}$ direction. The response of the medium to this $\mathbf{H}$ is assumed to be a large constant magnetization $\mathbf{M}_0$ in the $\hat{z}$ direction and a small time-varying component of magnetization, $\mathbf{M}_1$. Thus we assume

$$\mathbf{H} = (\hat{x}H_x + \hat{y}H_y)e^{j\omega t} + \hat{z}H_0 \tag{8.24}$$
$$\mathbf{M} = (\hat{x}M_x + \hat{y}M_y)e^{j\omega t} + \hat{z}M_0 \tag{8.25}$$

where the time-varying components in the z direction have been omitted since they are assumed to be negligible in magnitude compared with the steady components in that direction.

When Eqs. (8.24) and (8.25) are substituted into Eq. (8.23) and the result solved for M_x and M_y, these are found to be

$$M_x = \frac{\omega_0 \omega_M}{\omega_0^2 - \omega^2} H_x + j\frac{\omega\omega_M}{\omega_0^2 - \omega^2} H_y \tag{8.26}$$

$$M_y = -j\frac{\omega\omega_M}{\omega_0^2 - \omega^2} H_x + \frac{\omega_0 \omega_M}{\omega_0^2 - \omega^2} H_y \tag{8.27}$$

where

$$\omega_0 = -\mu_0 \gamma H_0 \tag{8.28}$$
$$\omega_M = -\mu_0 \gamma M_0 \tag{8.29}$$

Equations (8.26) and (8.27) define four components of the magnetic susceptibility matrix of the spins. These equations may be used to obtain the magnetic permeability of the medium for time-varying fields, by the use of the definition

$$\mathbf{B} = \mu\mathbf{H} = \mu_0(\mathbf{H} + \mathbf{M}) \tag{8.30}$$

or

$$B_x = \mu_0(H_x + M_x) \tag{8.31}$$
$$B_y = \mu_0(H_y + M_y) \tag{8.32}$$

where Eqs. (8.31) and (8.32) refer to time-varying components. Using

(8.26) and (8.27) in these expressions, we obtain

$$B_x = \mu H_x - j\kappa H_y \tag{8.33}$$
$$B_y = j\kappa H_x + \mu H_y \tag{8.34}$$

where†

$$\mu = \mu_0 \left(1 + \frac{\omega_0 \omega_M}{\omega_0^2 - \omega^2} \right)$$
$$\kappa = -\mu_0 \frac{\omega \omega_M}{\omega_0^2 - \omega^2} \tag{8.35}$$

The constant ω_0 is the gyromagnetic resonance frequency of the magnetic medium, and ω_M is a material constant which depends upon the strength of the saturation magnetization M_0 in the ferrimagnetic domains. The frequency $\omega_M/2\pi$ may have values of the order of 400 to 1000 mc.

With (8.33) and (8.34), we may write the matrix of permeability coefficients

$$\mathbf{\mu} = \begin{bmatrix} \mu & -j\kappa & 0 \\ j\kappa & \mu & 0 \\ 0 & 0 & \mu_0 \end{bmatrix} \tag{8.36}$$

The form of the permeability matrix, Eq. (8.36), reflects the physical fact that the magnetization of the ferrimagnetic medium is due to spin dipoles which precess about the polarizing magnetic field, assumed to be oriented along the z axis. The application of a small high-frequency field H_{1x} in the x direction, for example, perturbs the precession of the dipoles around the z axis. In the course of their perturbed precession, the projection of the magnetization vector normal to the z axis rotates through all directions in the xy plane, inducing a component of magnetic field B_{1y} in the y direction, in phase quadrature with the applied field H_{1x}, as given by

$$B_{1y} = j\kappa H_{1x} \tag{8.37}$$

This characteristic of a magnetically saturated ferrite, in which it couples the alternating magnetic field components in two orthogonal directions in the plane normal to the axis of the main polarizing field, is utilized in a practical waveguide device: the tetrahedral junction.

8.4. Tetrahedral Junction

The tetrahedral junction,‡ as illustrated in Fig. 8.8, is a coupling between two rectangular waveguides having common axes but having

---

† Although the sign chosen for κ in the definition (8.35) is arbitrary, the sign shown above has been adopted in customary usage.

‡ J. A. Weiss, *J. Appl. Phys.*, Suppl. to vol. 31, no. 5, p. 1688, May, 1960.

their E planes perpendicular. A rod or ellipsoid of a ferrite material is placed in the junction, on the axis of the guides, and magnetized by a constant field H_z parallel to the axis of the ferrite rod and guides.

With zero magnetic field H_z, the crossed waveguides are cut off with respect to each other, since there is no coupling between their perpendicular E field directions in the dominant mode. When the magnetic field is present, however, and waveguide power is supplied on one side of the junction, the microwave H-plane field penetrating into the cutoff region of the junction excites a disturbance in the precession of the spins in the ferrite. This disturbance in turn couples energy to the H-plane fields of the guide beyond the junction. The device may

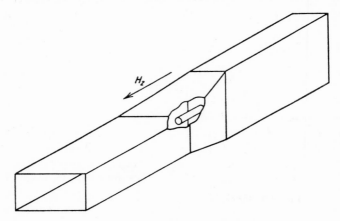

FIG. 8.8. Tetrahedral junction.

be constructed to have an insertion loss lower than 0.1 db, with polarizing field present, and as high as 60 db, with the polarizing field turned off.

8.5. Rotation of Wave Polarization in Ferrites

One of the first applications of ferrites to microwave system components was in the gyrator, a device which utilizes the rotation of the axis of polarization of a wave propagating in a magnetized ferrite. This phenomenon is called Faraday rotation in analogy with the comparable effect occurring in the passage of optical radiation through optically active substances.

Optical rotation is conveniently discussed in terms of the travel of circularly polarized waves. A conventional linearly polarized-wave vector of arbitrary orientation may be represented by the superposition of two oppositely rotating, circularly polarized waves of equal magnitude. Figure 8.9 illustrates examples of this superposition at several phase instants. It turns out, moreover, that circularly polarized waves constitute a natural mode of propagation in magnetized ferrites. By this is meant that the magnetic parameters of the medium assume a particularly simple form in relating the **B** and **H** vectors of a circularly polarized wave.

We recall that in circularly polarized-wave travel, the instantaneous **E** and **H** vectors rotate continuously in orientation, in the advancing wavefronts. Therefore, considering the **H** vector, we see that, for a clockwise (+) rotating vector traveling in the +z direction, H_y will be

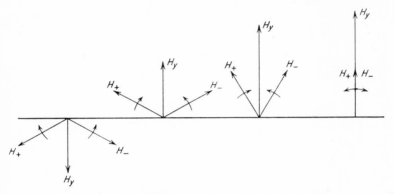

Fig. 8.9. Superposition of circularly polarized waves.

equal in magnitude to and $\pi/2$ radians delayed in phase with respect to H_x.

+ rotation:
$$H_x = e^{j\pi/2}H_y = jH_y \qquad (8.38)$$

Similarly, for a counterclockwise (−) rotating **H** vector,

− rotation:
$$H_x = e^{-j\pi/2}H_y = -jH_y \qquad (8.39)$$

The corresponding set of relations between the transverse components H_x and H_y of a wave traveling in the negative z direction is

+ rotation:
$$H_x = e^{-j\pi/2}H_y = -jH_y \qquad (8.40)$$

− rotation:
$$H_x = e^{j\pi/2}H_y = jH_y \qquad (8.41)$$

Let us now examine the effect of the magnetized ferrite medium upon the propagation of a clockwise circularly polarized wave, traveling in the direction of positive z.   This requires that we employ Eqs. (8.38) and (8.39) in the matrix permeability relations (8.33) and (8.34). We obtain

+ rotation:

$$B_x = (\mu + \kappa)H_x \tag{8.42}$$
$$B_y = (\mu + \kappa)H_y \tag{8.43}$$

− rotation:

$$B_x = (\mu - \kappa)H_x \tag{8.44}$$
$$B_y = (\mu - \kappa)H_y \tag{8.45}$$

Thus we see that, for circularly polarized waves, the matrix $\mathbf{u}$, which relates the components of the $\mathbf{B}$ vector with the components of the $\mathbf{H}$ vector in rectangular coordinates, is replaced by a single scalar effective permeability μ_{eff}.   The effective permeability for (+) rotating waves is different from that for (−) rotating waves.   Thus, for travel in the $+z$ direction,

+ rotation:

$$\mu_{\text{eff}} = \mu + \kappa$$

− rotation:

$$\mu_{\text{eff}} = \mu - \kappa$$

The wave-propagation constants of circularly polarized plane waves propagating parallel to the z axis, and hence parallel to the direction of magnetization, may now be found.   We write the two field curl equations, with the conditions $\partial/\partial x = 0 = \partial/\partial y$, $\partial/\partial z = k_z$, and $E_z = 0 = H_z$, for plane waves.   Using the determinantal form for the curl in rectangular coordinates, these are

$$\mathbf{\nabla} \times \mathbf{E} = \begin{vmatrix} \hat{\mathbf{x}} & \hat{\mathbf{y}} & \hat{\mathbf{z}} \\ 0 & 0 & k_z \\ E_x & E_y & 0 \end{vmatrix} = -j\omega(\hat{\mathbf{x}}B_x + \hat{\mathbf{y}}B_y)$$

$$\mathbf{\nabla} \times \mathbf{H} = \begin{vmatrix} \hat{\mathbf{x}} & \hat{\mathbf{y}} & \hat{\mathbf{z}} \\ 0 & 0 & k_z \\ H_x & H_y & 0 \end{vmatrix} = j\omega\epsilon(\hat{\mathbf{x}}E_x + \hat{\mathbf{y}}E_y)$$

Then, substituting from Eqs. (8.33) and (8.34) for B_x and B_y and writing the x- and y-component equations separately, we obtain

$$-k_z E_y = -j\omega\mu H_x - \omega\kappa H_y \tag{8.46a}$$
$$k_z E_x = \omega\kappa H_x - j\omega\mu H_y \tag{8.46b}$$
$$-k_z H_y = j\omega\epsilon E_x \tag{8.46c}$$
$$k_z H_x = j\omega\epsilon E_y \tag{8.46d}$$

Eliminating E_y from Eq. (8.46a) with the use of (8.46d),

$$\left(-\frac{k_z^2}{j\omega\epsilon} + j\omega\mu\right)H_x = -\omega\kappa H_y \tag{8.47}$$

For a forward-traveling clockwise (+) circularly polarized wave, $H_x = jH_y$. Therefore,

+ rotation:

$$k_z^{(+)} = \pm j\omega \sqrt{\epsilon(\mu - \kappa)} \qquad (8.48)$$

Similarly, for a counterclockwise (−) circularly polarized wave, with $H_x = -jH_y$, the propagation constant is

− rotation:

$$k_z^{(-)} = \pm j\omega \sqrt{\epsilon(\mu + \kappa)} \qquad (8.49)$$

The positively rotating wave is seen to have a larger phase velocity $\omega/k_z^{(+)}$ than the negatively rotating wave. In a vector representation, the tips of the field vectors of the two circularly polarized waves follow right- and left-handed helices, of different pitch. Figure 8.10 illustrates schematically the side view, or y projection, of these helices.

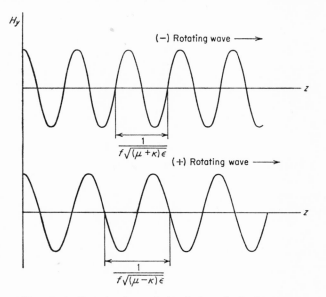

Fig. 8.10. Y projections of circularly polarized waves.

Let us consider the propagation of a linearly polarized wave of **H** field which is composed of two circularly polarized components. If axes are chosen such that the two circularly polarized waves reach maxima in the y direction simultaneously at $z = 0$, as shown schematically in Fig. 8.10, it may be seen that the y and x components of the resultant wave will be

$$H_y = e^{-j[(\mu-\kappa)\,\epsilon]^{\frac{1}{2}}\omega z} + e^{-j[(\mu+\kappa)\,\epsilon]^{\frac{1}{2}}\omega z} \tag{8.50}$$

and

$$jH_x = -e^{-j[(\mu-\kappa)\,\epsilon]^{\frac{1}{2}}\omega z} + e^{-j[(\mu+\kappa)\,\epsilon]^{\frac{1}{2}}\omega z} \tag{8.51}$$

where the magnitude of H has been chosen arbitrarily equal to 2.

We assume that at the frequency of operation, $\kappa \ll \mu$ [cf. Eqs. (8.35)]. Then the radicals in the exponents of (8.50) and (8.51) may be simplified, to yield

$$H_y = 2e^{-j(\mu\epsilon)^{\frac{1}{2}}\omega z} \cos\left(\frac{\omega\kappa}{2}\sqrt{\frac{\epsilon}{\mu}}\right) z \tag{8.52}$$

$$H_x = -2e^{-j(\mu\epsilon)^{\frac{1}{2}}\omega z} \sin\left(\frac{\omega\kappa}{2}\sqrt{\frac{\epsilon}{\mu}}\right) z \tag{8.53}$$

Equations (8.52) and (8.53) represent a rotation of the **H** vector of the wave during its travel. The direction of polarization of the wave has rotated by 90° in a distance of travel equal to

$$z = \frac{\pi}{\omega\kappa}\sqrt{\frac{\mu}{\epsilon}} \tag{8.54}$$

The result that we have obtained above was derived for circularly polarized waves traveling in the $+z$ direction. A distinctive characteristic of the ferrite medium is its nonreciprocity with respect to reversal of the direction of wave propagation. Therefore, we must investigate the effect of changing the direction of propagation in the medium. It was noted in Eqs. (8.40) and (8.41) that in wave travel in the $-z$ direction, the transverse components of **H** receive a reversal of relative sign. When (8.40) and (8.41) are used in the permeability matrix, the effective permeabilities in circular polarization for backward-traveling waves are found to be

$+$ rotation:

$$\mu_{\text{eff}} = \mu - \kappa \tag{8.55}$$

$-$ rotation:

$$\mu_{\text{eff}} = \mu + \kappa \tag{8.56}$$

Proceeding as before with the calculation of propagation constants; we find the relations expressing the rotation of the axis of polarization of the **H** vector of a backward-traveling wave to be

$$H_y = 2e^{+j(\mu\epsilon)^{\frac{1}{2}}\omega z} \cos\left(\frac{\omega\kappa}{2}\sqrt{\frac{\epsilon}{\mu}}\right) z \tag{8.57}$$

$$H_x = 2e^{+j(\mu\epsilon)^{\frac{1}{2}}\omega z} \sin\left(\frac{\omega\kappa}{2}\sqrt{\frac{\epsilon}{\mu}}\right) z \tag{8.58}$$

Comparing these results with Eqs. (8.52) and (8.53), the corresponding expressions for the rotation of polarization of a forward-traveling wave, we find that the space direction and magnitude of the rotation are the same for a given amount of wave travel along the z axis, whether in the forward or reverse direction. This represents nonreciprocal behavior, since an observer traveling with the wave would see opposite rotations of polarization, in the two directions of travel.

8.6. Gyrator and Faraday Rotation Isolator

The rotations of polarization discussed in the preceding section pertain to the propagation of plane waves in an unbounded medium. Similar rotations of polarization occur, however, during propagation in the TE_{11} mode in a ferrite-filled circular waveguide, when the ferrite is magnetized parallel to the axis of the guide.

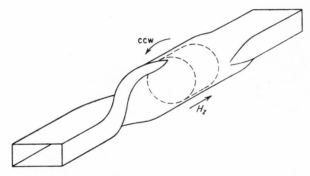

Fig. 8.11. Faraday rotation gyrator.

This phenomenon is utilized in the gyrator,[†] a device which induces a 180° relative reversal in phase of the waveguide wave propagating in one direction, as compared to zero relative reversal in the opposite direction. The gyrator is illustrated in Fig. 8.11 and its operation is as follows: A wave traveling from left to right undergoes a 90° counterclockwise rotation of polarization as it passes through the 90° waveguide twist. It then enters the circular-waveguide section and passes through the magnetized ferrite plug, in which it undergoes an additional counterclockwise rotation of 90°. Hence, in traveling from left to right, the wave effectively undergoes a 180° shift in phase. On the other hand, a wave entering at the right and traveling right to left undergoes a 90° rotation in the counterclockwise direction (as defined

† C. L. Hogan, *Revs. Modern Phys.*, vol. 25, p. 253, 1953.

by the direction arrow) in the ferrite, and then in passing through the waveguide twist, is rotated 90° clockwise, for a total of zero rotation. As a result of this nonreciprocal behavior, the electrical length of the transmission line between the two ports of the gyrator is one half-wavelength greater in one direction than in the other.

A related device using a ferrite element in circular waveguide is the Faraday rotation isolator. In this device, illustrated in Fig. 8.12, a wave traveling from left to right is rotated 45° counterclockwise in the 45° waveguide twist, and then is given a 45° clockwise rotation by the ferrite element, for a total of zero resultant rotation. A wave traveling from right to left, however, is rotated 45° clockwise by the

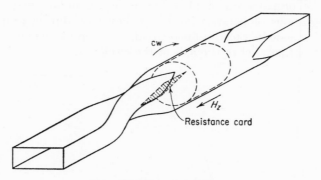

FIG. 8.12. Rotation isolator.

ferrite, as referred to the direction arrow, and then encounters incorrectly oriented rectangular waveguide beyond the twist, for which propagation is cut off. A resistive card is placed in the entrance to the twist, oriented so as to absorb energy from the **E** vector of the leftward-traveling wave. The isolator thus propagates effectively in the left-to-right direction only.

8.7. Ferrite Isolator in Rectangular Waveguide

In the Faraday rotation isolator described in the preceding section, the direction of wave propagation was parallel to the d-c magnetizing field in the ferrite. In the form of isolator normally used in rectangular waveguide, the magnetizing field is normal to the direction of wave propagation. Typical forms of rectangular-guide ferrite isolators are shown in Fig. 8.13. In these devices the ferrite material does not cover the cross section of the waveguide, since the transmission loss in forward propagation would be high in this case. Conventional isolators are constructed using a ferrite slab of a few inches in length in extension along the guide. Slabs of a wide variety of cross-sectional shapes and locations in the guide cross section may be used, depending upon the operating characteristics desired.

A representative isolator configuration is that shown in Fig. 8.13a, in which a ferrite slab of thickness δ extends the full height of the guide, in contact with one side wall. The d-c magnetizing field H_0 is directed

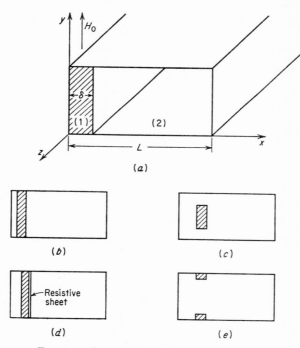

Fig. 8.13. Rectangular-guide ferrite isolators.

parallel to the short side of the guide, here chosen as the y direction. Wave propagation along the guide axis, taken as the z direction, is therefore normal to the magnetizing field.

The propagation characteristics of this isolator may be obtained from the solution of the boundary-value problem arising when the wave field is divided into regions 1 and 2, within the ferrite and the empty guide, respectively, and tangential fields are matched at the boundary. Suitable TE-mode solutions for the electric field in the two regions are†

† K. J. Button and B. Lax, *IRE Trans.*, vol. AP-4, p. 531, 1956.

Region 1:

$$E_y = E_1 \sin k_m x \, e^{-j\beta z} \tag{8.59}$$

Region 2:

$$E_y = E_0 \sin k_a(L - x) e^{-j\beta z} \tag{8.60}$$

The components of the magnetic field may be obtained from (8.59) and (8.60) by the use of Maxwell's equation:

$$\nabla \times \mathbf{E} = -j\omega\boldsymbol{\mu}\mathbf{H} \tag{8.61}$$

where the product $\boldsymbol{\mu}\mathbf{H}$, in the ferrite medium, is the matrix product of the permeability matrix $\boldsymbol{\mu}$ and the magnetic field $\mathbf{H}$.   With the permeability matrix written in the form appropriate to ferrite material with the polarizing magnetic field in the y direction, this product is

$$\boldsymbol{\mu}\mathbf{H} = \begin{bmatrix} \mu & 0 & -j\kappa \\ 0 & \mu_0 & 0 \\ j\kappa & 0 & \mu \end{bmatrix} \cdot \begin{bmatrix} H_x \\ H_y \\ H_z \end{bmatrix} \tag{8.62}$$

or

$$(\mu H)_x = \mu H_x - j\kappa H_z \tag{8.63}$$
$$(\mu H)_y = \mu_0 H_y \tag{8.64}$$
$$(\mu H)_z = j\kappa H_x + \mu H_z \tag{8.65}$$

In region 2, the free-space medium,

$$\mu\mathbf{H} = \mu_0\mathbf{H} \tag{8.66}$$

Using these expressions in Eq. (8.61), we have

Region 1:

$$j\beta E_1 \sin k_m x = -j\omega(\mu H_x - j\kappa H_z) \tag{8.67}$$
$$k_m E_1 \cos k_m x = -j\omega(j\kappa H_x + \mu H_z) \tag{8.68}$$

Region 2:

$$j\beta E_0 \sin k_a(L - x) = -j\omega\mu_0 H_x \tag{8.69}$$
$$-k_a E_0 \cos k_a(L - x) = -j\omega\mu_0 H_z \tag{8.70}$$

Solving (8.67) and (8.68) for H_z in Region 1, we find

Region 1:

$$H_z = j \frac{E_1}{\omega(\mu^2 - \kappa^2)} (\mu k_m \cos k_m x + \beta\kappa \sin k_m x) \tag{8.71}$$

and, from (8.70),

Region 2:

$$H_z = -j \frac{k_a E_0}{\omega\mu_0} \cos k_a(L - x) \tag{8.72}$$

The solutions in regions 1 and 2 are now joined at the boundary by equating the tangential components E_y and H_z at $x = \delta$.   The coefficients E_1 and E_0 are eliminated from these boundary equations, with the result

$$\frac{1}{\mu^2 - \kappa^2} (\mu k_m \cot k_m \delta - \beta \kappa) = -\frac{k_a}{\omega \mu_0} \cot k_a(L - \delta) \qquad (8.73)$$

The transcendental equation (8.73) determines the propagation constant β. The constants k_m and k_a depend upon β, according to

$$k_m{}^2 + \beta^2 = k_\perp{}^2 \qquad (8.74)$$
$$k_a{}^2 + \beta^2 = \mu_0 \epsilon \omega^2 \qquad (8.75)$$

Equations (8.74) and (8.75) are the result of substituting into the wave equation a component of the fields in regions 1 and 2, respectively. In Eq. (8.74) for the ferrite, $k_\perp$ is the propagation constant of the medium in the present orientation of the polarizing magnetic field H_0, with respect to the direction of wave travel. It may be shown that for propagation normal to the direction of H_0,[†]

$$k_\perp{}^2 = \frac{\mu^2 - \kappa^2}{\mu} \epsilon \qquad (8.76)$$

Equations (8.74) to (8.76) are used in Eq. (8.73), and numerical solutions may be found for β when particular values are assumed for ω, H_0, and the waveguide dimensions. This has been done for X-band waveguide at 9 kmc, with $H_0 = 3{,}000$ gauss and $\epsilon_r = 10$, by Lax and Button.[‡] The results of the calculation are shown plotted in Fig. 8.14. It may be seen that the solutions yield two modes of forward propagation, curves A and C, and two modes of reverse propagation, curves B and D, depending on the thickness of the ferrite slab. Modes A and B can propagate simultaneously, and having slightly different magnitudes of β, they represent possible operation of the device as a nonreciprocal phase shifter. Modes A and B are cut off, however, with ferrite slab thicknesses greater than about 4.5 mm. For a large range of slab thicknesses δ greater than this value, only the forward mode C propagates, and the waveguide then behaves as a unidirectional isolator. This mode is cut off at $\delta = 2.18$ cm, when the guide is nearly full of ferrite, and a mode D, of reverse propagation, appears.

The inserts in Fig. 8.14 show the distribution of the electric field in the various modes. These field plots suggest that in modes A and B, the normal TE_{10}-mode field distribution is being crowded into an effectively narrower waveguide. Mode C, because of its resemblance

[†] Hogan, *op. cit.* Equation (8.76) may also be derived by a procedure analogous to that which was used in obtaining Eq. (8.48).

[‡] Button and Lax; *op. cit.*

to the field of a wave traveling over a dielectric-coated surface, is called the "ferrite dielectric" mode.

Several modifications of this ferrite isolator are used in practice. The form of isolator in which the ferrite slab is moved away from the guide wall, as shown in Fig. 8.13b, has been given extensive theoretical treatment.† The ferrite slab may be coated with a resistive

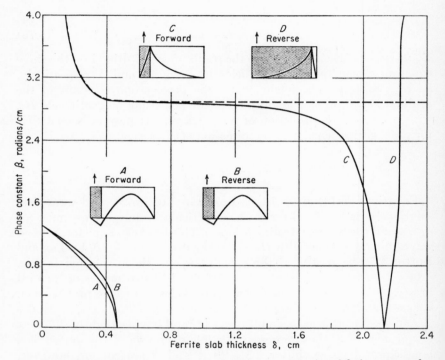

FIG. 8.14. Propagation constant versus thickness of ferrite slab in rectangular waveguide 0.9 by 0.4 in. at 9 kmc. Magnetic field = 3,000 gauss. (*By permission from B. Lax and K. J. Button, Theory of Ferrites in Rectangular Waveguides, Trans. IRE, vol. AP-4, p. 531, July, 1956.*)

sheet to increase the attenuation for reverse propagation. Isolators with partial-height slabs as in Fig. 8.13c may be used for increased bandwidth or uniform characteristics, and partial-height slabs may be fastened to the upper and lower surfaces of the waveguide as in Fig. 8.13e, to obtain improved heat dissipation at high-power levels.‡

† B. Lax, K. J. Button, and L. M. Roth, *J. Appl. Phys.*, vol. 25, p. 1413, 1954, and R. L. Comstock and C. E. Fay, *IRE Trans.*, vol. MTT-8, p. 605, 1960.

‡ M. T. Weiss, *IRE Trans.*, vol. MTT-4, p. 240, 1956.

Dielectric strips may be introduced in various forms, so as to modify the waveguide fields near the ferrite in order to achieve higher operating efficiency. In these various modifications, the electromagnetic behavior of the ferrite isolator is comparable in character with that of the isolator with the ferrite slab at the waveguide wall discussed above.

8.8. Magnetic Parametric Amplifier

Parametric amplification is a mode of signal amplification which may be effected in a large number of physical situations. The essential components of a parametric amplifier are a signal which is to be amplified, a power source in the form of an oscillator, the frequency of which in general may be different from that of the signal, and a time-varying circuit parameter which couples the signal and the power oscillator in such a way that power is transferred from the oscillator to the signal circuit, thus effecting amplification.

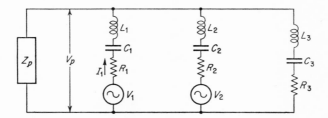

FIG. 8.15. Schematic representation of parametric amplifier.

A schematic representation of a parametric amplifier is shown in Fig. 8.15. Series-resonant circuits 1, 2, and 3, resonant at frequencies ω_1, ω_2, and ω_3, respectively, are coupled in parallel with a variable impedance Z_p. Voltage V_1 is the signal voltage, at the signal frequency ω_1, and V_2 is the voltage of the power oscillator, or pump, at frequency ω_2. The third circuit, the idler circuit, is resonant at $\omega_3 = \omega_2 - \omega_1$.

If the signal circuit is sharply resonant so that effectively only current at frequency ω_1 flows in the signal branch, we have

$$V_1 - I_1 R_1 = V_{p1} \tag{8.77}$$

where V_{p1} is the component of voltage at frequency ω_1 appearing across Z_p. Hence, the admittance presented to the signal voltage V_1 is

$$Y_1 = \frac{I_1}{V_1} = \frac{1 - V_{p1}/V_1}{R_1} \tag{8.78}$$

Thus, if the real part of V_{p1}/V_1 becomes larger than unity at frequency ω_1, the input conductance becomes negative, and the device may operate as an amplifier. In the microwave application of this characteristic, the input signal is separated from the returning signal by the use of a suitable device such as the magic T (Sec. 4.10). The circuit theory of parametric amplification has been treated in detail by a number of authors.[†] It is shown that a requirement for amplification is that the value of the reactance Z_p must be a function of V_p, i.e., that Z_p provides a nonlinear voltage-current relation.

For our present purposes, we observe that a microwave equivalent of the parametric amplifier circuit of Fig. 8.15 may be composed of a

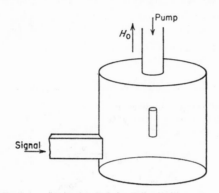

FIG. 8.16. Resonant-cavity parametric amplifier.

two-port cavity resonator system resonant at ω_1 and ω_2, containing a sample of ferrite to provide the coupling between the signal- and pump-frequency fields in the cavity. In a typical case,[‡] a ferrimagnetic parametric amplifier has been operated using a cylindrical-cavity resonator which was simultaneously resonant at pump frequency $\omega_2 = 8.64$ kmc in the TM_{120} mode and at signal frequency $\omega_1 = 5.93$ kmc in the TE_{011} mode. A ferrite slug was placed on the axis of the cylinder, as shown in Fig. 8.16, and the axial magnetic field H_0 adjusted so that the gyromagnetic resonance frequency of the ferrite [Eq. (8.28)] was equal to the idler frequency of 2.71 kmc. The maximum gain of the amplifier was of the order of 120 db at maximum pump-power input.

† J. M. Manley and H. E. Rowe, *Proc. IRE*, vol. 44, p. 904, 1956, and vol. 47, p. 2115, 1959; S. Bloom and K. K. N. Chang, *RCA Rev.*, vol. 18, p. 578, 1957; H. Heffner and G. Wade, *J. Appl. Phys.*, vol. 29, p. 1321, 1958; and S. Deutsch, *Proc. IRE*, vol. 48, p. 1505, 1960.

‡ W. L. Whirry and F. B. Wang, *J. Appl. Phys.*, vol. 30, p. 1505, 1959.

Resonant-cavity parametric amplification such as described above may be effected with a large number of possible circuit variations. Alternative operating conditions may involve different frequency relations in parametric amplification, as well as a variety of alternative modes of resonance in which the ferromagnetic sample may be operated.

A given ferrite compound may resonate at various frequencies in a given applied magnetic field, as a consequence of the presence of internal demagnetizing fields in individual samples, the magnitude of which depends upon the shape of the ferrite sample.† Moreover, the resonance frequencies of a given ferrite sample, and the losses occurring at resonance, may be governed also by the excitation of spin waves.‡ Spin waves may be considered to be departures from the uniform distribution of spin-moment vector density throughout the sample which was assumed to exist, in the calculation of the magnetic properties of ferrites which was made in Sec. 8.3.

PROBLEMS

8.1. The effects of energy losses from the spin system of a ferrite can be represented by the addition of an imaginary term to the denominator of Eqs. (8.35) for μ and κ so that they become

$$\mu_s = \mu_0 \left(1 + \frac{\omega_0 \omega_M}{\omega_0{}^2 - \omega^2 + 2j\alpha\omega_0} \right)$$

$$\kappa_s = -\mu_0 \frac{\omega \omega_M}{\omega_0{}^2 - \omega^2 + 2j\alpha\omega_0}$$

where $\alpha \ll \omega_0$.

Sketch curves of transmission coefficient and phase shift of a tetrahedral junction as in Sec. 8.4, as a function of frequency. Assume that the transmission characteristics are due to a ferrite having magnetic characteristics as above.

8.2. Show the effect of the loss term in μ and κ as given in Prob. 8-1 upon the propagation of a field component such as H_y [Eq. (8.50)] in a ferrite.

8.3. (a) Show that if $\omega\kappa(\epsilon/\mu)^{\frac{1}{2}}z/2 \ll 1$, the angle of rotation of polarization in a ferrite is proportional to the distance z of wave travel.

(b) Sketch the x and y projections of the magnetic field vector of a wave undergoing Faraday rotation as it travels in a ferrite, through a full cycle of rotation of the vector.

8.4. Write the form of the permeability matrix of a ferrite magnetized parallel to the x axis, and form the product $\mathbf{\mu} \cdot \mathbf{H}$ for this case.

8.5. Obtain transcendental equation (8.73) from Eqs. (8.59), (8.60), (8.71), and (8.72).

8.6. Discuss the use of visible-light energy for pumping in a maser.§

† Hogan, *op. cit.*

‡ L. R. Walker, *Phys. Rev.*, vol. 105, p. 390, 1957; P. E. Tannenwald, *Microwave J.*, vol. 2, no. 7, p. 25, 1959.

§ Cf. A. L. Schawlow and C. H. Townes, Infrared and Optical Masers, *Phys. Rev.*, vol. 112, no. 6, Dec. 15, 1958, and current literature.

CHAPTER 9

Millimeter Waves

The domain occupied by the microwave frequencies in the electromagnetic spectrum is of arbitrary extent, between approximately 10^9 and 10^{12} cps. This frequency interval thus adjoins the infrared band, which is usually considered to have a low-frequency limit of 10^{12} cps (Fig. 9.1). Considerable practical difficulty is met, however, in the effort to generate and transmit coherent radiation in the frequency decade from 10^{11} to 10^{12} cps. When equipment and techniques successful at free-space wavelengths of the order of 1 cm are scaled down for use in this range, the components become inconveniently minute in size and circuit and transmission losses become excessively high. For example, type RG-139/U waveguide, used for the frequency range 220 to 325 kmc, has inside dimensions of 0.034 by 0.017 in., and has attenuation of 5.12 to 3.48 db/ft in the dominant mode, from the lowest to the highest frequency in this range. This may be contrasted with attenuation of approximately 0.05 db/ft at 10 kmc in standard X-band guide (RG-52/U), having inside dimensions of 0.9 by 0.4 in.

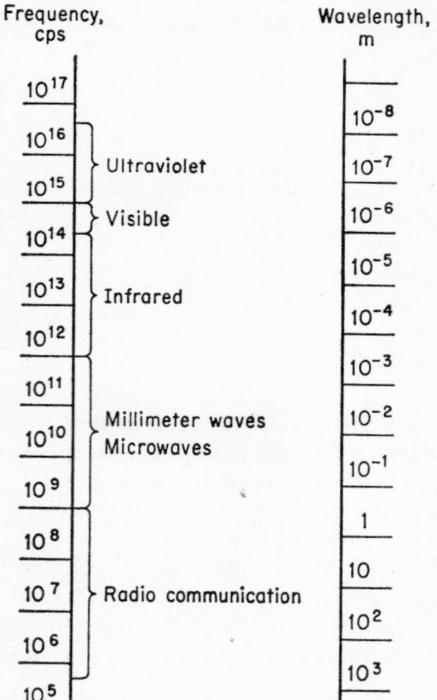

FIG. 9.1. Electromagnetic spectrum.

The millimeter-wave band difficulties of high attenuation and small component sizes are compounded by the fact that it has been found essentially impossible to generate appreciable amounts of fundamental-frequency energy above 10^{11} cps by means of small versions of klys-

trons, magnetrons, or traveling-wave tubes, such as are used at frequencies one-tenth as great. Obstacles preventing the use of these
sources are the difficulty of achieving the small dimensions required
for the resonant structures, which must be of the order of magnitude
of a wavelength in size, and the problem of prevention of thermal
damage due to dissipated energy. A typical reflex klystron oscillator
produced for operation at 70 kmc has a resonator 1.6 mm in diameter
and distance from electron gun to resonator of 0.3 mm, with other tube
dimensions proportionally small. The beam voltage and current are
2,500 volts and 15 ma, and output power is 0.1 to 0.2 watt.[†] A helix-
type traveling-wave tube reported by Christensen and Watkins for
operation at 50 to 60 kmc has a helix 1 in. in length, the operating temperature of which is 1300°C in continuous operation.[‡]

Millimeter-wave components such as those mentioned here are representative of the effort to extend established technical procedures to
frequencies above 10^{11} cps. The outcome of this effort has indicated
that this extension is not possible with the use of former materials and
methods. Radiation of submillimeter wavelength has many applications in the study of molecular structure, the properties of solids and
ionized gases, and in extraterrestrial communication. Considerable
attention has therefore been given to special methods of dealing with
this radiation.

9.1. Millimeter Waveguides

TE_{01}-mode Circular Guide. The frequency dependence of the
attenuation of various modes of propagation in hollow waveguides
(cf. Sec. 3.10) is shown in Fig. 9.2. All of the hollow-guide modes show
rising attenuation in the high-frequency limit, with the exception of
the TE_{01} mode in circular waveguide. In this mode the attenuation
decreases continuously with frequency. In practice, however, in
order to obtain the low attenuation of the TE_{01} circular mode, it is
necessary to employ waveguide of sufficiently large diameter. Typical
data for circular copper guides operating in the TE_{01} mode, in the range
52.6 to 57.6 kmc, is[§]

Inside diameter, in.	Measured attenuation, db/ft	Calculated attenuation, db/ft
$\frac{7}{16}$	0.0433	0.0370
$\frac{7}{8}$	0.0047	0.00365

[†] N. V. Philips Gloeilampenfabrieken, Type DX151, 1959.
[‡] W. V. Christensen and D. A. Watkins, *Proc. IRE*, vol. 43, p. 93, 1955.
[§] A. P. King, *Bell System Tech. J.*, vol. 35, p. 1115, 1956.

For pipes large enough to have desirably low attenuation in the TE_{01} mode at a given frequency, the pipe is above cutoff for many other modes of propagation. For example, in a 2-in.-diameter pipe at 55 kmc, 224 modes may propagate.

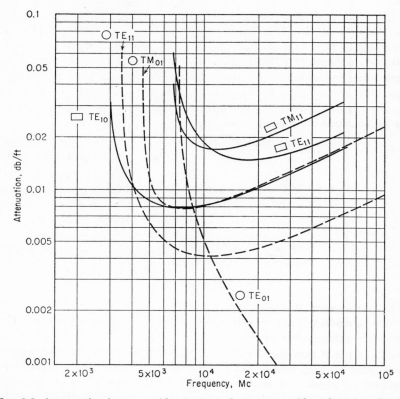

FIG. 9.2. Attenuation in waveguides (rectangular copper guide, 2 by 1 in.; circular copper guide, 2 in. diameter). (*Adapted with permission from T. A. Moreno, "Microwave Transmission Design Data," Dover Publications, Inc., New York, 1958.*)

The TE_{01} mode under these circumstances is unstable against mode conversion to unwanted modes having high attenuation. Mode conversion, particularly to the TE_{11} mode, occurs at slight bends in the guide or departures from circular cross section. Mode conversion may be suppressed by the use of a helically wound wire lining on the interior of the waveguide, which tends to suppress the wall currents of modes other than the TE_{01} mode.† Highly accurately wound

† W. D. Warters and H. E. Rowe, 1958 IRE WESCON Convention Record, pt. I.

helices, to tolerances of the order of 0.001 in. in 2-in. guide, are required for satisfactory low-loss operation of helical mode filters of this type, however. A dielectric coating on the interior of circular waveguide can suppress conversion to the TE_{11} mode by making the propagation constant of TE_{11} different from that of the TE_{01} mode.†

The combined use of helical lining and dielectric coating can improve the stability of the TE_{01} mode in the presence of guide bends. In plain copper pipe with 9-ft sections of helical mode filter installed every 200 feet, a bend of 8,000-ft radius of curvature increases the TE_{01}-mode loss per foot by 20 per cent over the theoretical value for straight pipe. In copper pipe with mode filter sections as above and dielectric coating on the interior, a bend of 2,000-ft curvature radius increases the attenuation by 20 per cent.

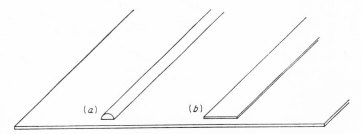

FIG. 9.3. Dielectric waveguides.

Dielectric-metal Waveguides.   Several types of wave-guiding systems involving dielectric material in conjunction with metal-guiding surfaces have low attenuation in the millimeter-wave domain. A representative example of this class of guides is the dielectric image line described by Wiltse.‡   This line consists of a dielectric strip extending along a conducting plane. A strip consisting of polystyrene-foam dielectric having a semicircular cross section of 0.07 in. radius (Fig. 9.3*a*) showed attenuation of only 0.015 db/m at 70 kmc on a copper image plane, but the attenuation rises rapidly above this frequency. Other dielectric shapes may also be used to guide a wave over the conducting plane at these frequencies. A polyethylene tape $\frac{3}{16}$ in. wide and 0.005 in. thick (Fig. 9.3*b*) guides a wave at 69.4 kmc with attenuation of 0.02 db/m. The electromagnetic field of the guided wave is closely localized around the dielectric strip in these guides. A qualitative test of field extension, made by noting the distance from the dielectric guide

† H. G. Unger, *Proc. Symposium on Millimeter Waves,* 1959, Polytechnic Press, Brooklyn, N.Y.

‡ J. C. Wiltse, *Proc. IRE,* vol. MTT-7, p. 65, 1959.

at which a conducting bar held near the guide first perturbs the transmission of energy, shows that the extent of the field around the semicircular strip described above is only 0.75 in. at 70 kmc.

It has been noted that conventional hollow waveguides are unsatisfactory at millimeter wavelengths because of their rapidly rising attenuation due to conductor losses in this range.   Transverse electric waves of type TE_{0n} guided between two infinite parallel plates show more favorable attenuation characteristics, however.   The conductor loss of these modes decreases with increasing frequency, as does the

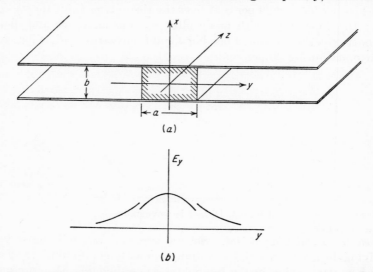

(a)

(b)

FIG. 9.4. (a) Parallel-plane dielectric guide, (b) distribution of E_y in transverse plane, $0 < y < b$.

TE_{01}-mode attenuation in circular guide.   The disadvantage of an unconfined wave field may be overcome by placing a dielectric strip between the parallel plates, as shown in Fig. 9.4a.   The dielectric strip guides a hybrid wave mode having TE and TM characteristics, which is closely localized about the strip.[†]   The nature of the field distribution in the lowest mode is indicated by the form of E_y, the transverse electric field component parallel to the plates.

Dielectric:

$$E_y = E_0' \cos \frac{\pi x}{b} \cos k_y y \, e^{-j\beta z} \qquad (9.1)$$

[†] J. W. E. Griemsmann and L. Birenbaum, *Proc. Symposium on Millimeter Waves*, 1959, Polytechnic Press, Brooklyn, N.Y.

Air:

$$E_y = E_0 \cos \frac{\pi x}{b} e^{-k_y(|y|-a/2)} e^{-j\beta z} \tag{9.2}$$

where

$$\left(\frac{\pi}{b}\right)^2 + k_{yd}^2 + \beta^2 = \mu\epsilon\omega^2$$

$$\left(\frac{\pi}{b}\right)^2 + k_y^2 + \beta^2 = \mu\epsilon\omega^2$$

The distribution of E_y is shown in Fig. 9.4b. There exist also field components H_x, E_x, E_z, and H_z, given by Griemsmann et al. The attenuation due to dissipation in the metal plates is proportional to $f^{-\frac{3}{2}}$, decreasing continuously with increasing frequency. The principal contribution to the attenuation of this guiding system in the limit of high frequencies will hence be due to losses in the dielectric. Consequently, a dielectric material with low loss tangent is required in its construction.

9.2. Resonant Structures

The decline in operating efficiency of microwave circuit components as they are reduced in size for use above 100 kmc may be avoided by the adoption of alternative structural forms to accomplish the functions required. For example, a hollow-cavity resonator, if operated in a dominant mode, becomes inconveniently small in size, and the accompanying drop in volume-to-surface ratio leads to low Q values. Resonators may be operated in higher-order modes to avoid smallness in size, but interfering modes relatively more densely distributed in frequency are encountered in the higher orders.

Dielectric-tube Resonator. Some improvement in resonator characteristics may be achieved by the use of a cylindrical tube of dielectric material mounted between parallel conducting plates (Fig. 9.5). The resonant frequencies of this structure are determined from the transcendental equation which arises when boundary conditions at the dielectric surface are satisfied.[†] A mode chart of the resulting resonances in TM_{0mn} modes for a typical resonator using dielectric material of $\epsilon_r = 2.08$ is shown in Fig. 9.6.

The field intensities decay rapidly in the radial direction away from the axis of the resonator, as indicated by the curves of Fig. 9.5. A pair of parallel plates of moderate extent is therefore sufficient to approximate the assumed infinite-plane boundaries, and a dielectric-tube

† R. H. Pantell, P. D. Coleman, and R. C. Becker, *IRE Trans.*, vol. ED-5, p. 167, 1958.

resonator may be used as a wavemeter in a structure of relatively small size. A wavemeter employing a dielectric tube of polytetrafluoroethylene has a calculated Q_0 of 4,200 in the $TE_{0,1,15}$ mode at 600 kmc. The subscript 15 implies that there are 15 half-wavelengths of field

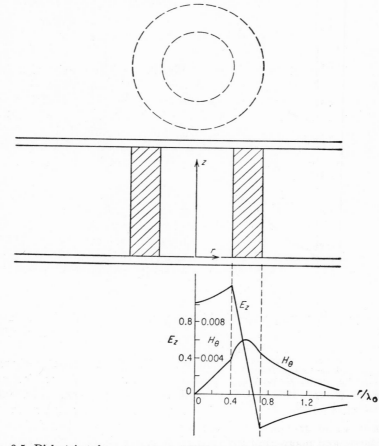

FIG. 9.5. Dielectric-tube resonator and TM_{01n}-mode field distribution. (*Adapted with permission from R. C. Becker and P. D. Coleman, "The Dielectric Tube Resonator: A Device for the Generation and Measurement of Millimeter and Submillimeter Waves," Proc. Symposium on Millimeter Waves, 1959, Polytechnic Institute of Brooklyn, Polytechnic Press, Brooklyn, N.Y., 1960.*)

along the axis of the tube. This Q_0 may be compared with the calculated Q_0 values of 1,620 and 3,880 of a hollow cylindrical copper resonator in the TE_{111} and the TE_{011} modes, respectively, at this frequency.

Fabry-Perot Resonator. A parallel-plate resonator resembling the Fabry-Perot interferometer of physical optics may be used for millimeter-wave radiation. Two perforated, flat, parallel conducting plates are placed between transmitting and receiving horn antennas, as shown in Fig. 9.7. If the wavefronts between plates are assumed to be plane, standing waves will be set up when the plate separation L is

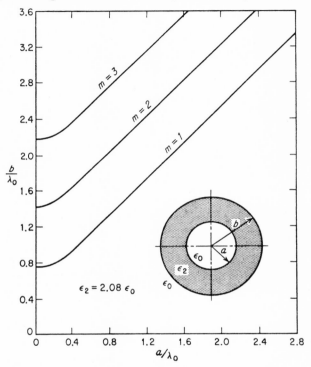

Fig. 9.6. Resonant dimensions of dielectric-tube resonator in TM_{0mn} modes. (*Adapted with permission from R. C. Becker and P. D. Coleman, "The Dielectric Tube Resonator: A Device for the Generation and Measurement of Millimeter and Sub-millimeter Waves," 1959, Polytechnic Institute of Brooklyn, Polytechnic Press, Brooklyn, N.Y., 1960.*)

equal to an integral number of half-wavelengths. The standing waves of electric and magnetic field then are

$$E_y = E_0 \sin \frac{n\pi z}{L} \tag{9.3}$$

$$H_x = -jE_0 \sqrt{\frac{\epsilon_0}{\mu_0}} \cos \frac{n\pi z}{L} \tag{9.4}$$

The Q_0 of this resonator may be calculated by the use of Eq. (5.43):

$$Q_0 = \frac{2}{\delta} \frac{\iiint H^2 \, d\tau}{\iint H^2 \, da}$$

where $\delta = (\pi f \mu \sigma)^{-\frac{1}{2}}$ is the skin depth in the material of the plates. Using Eq. (9.4) and neglecting the effect of the perforations in the plates, we find

$$Q_0 = \frac{L}{2\delta} \qquad (9.5)$$

With a skin depth of approximately 10^{-7} m in copper at 400 kmc, a resonator having plates separated by 0.01 m would have $Q_0 = 50,000$ at this frequency. Increasing the separation L of the plates increases Q_0 proportionally. Q values observed in practice will be somewhat lower than those calculated as above, owing to nonplanar wavefronts between the plates, loss of energy at the edges of the plates, and the

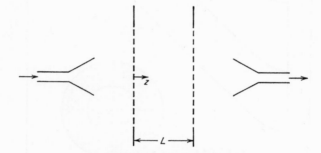

FIG. 9.7. Fabry-Perot resonator.

effect of the perforations which admit the radiation to the resonator. The Fabry-Perot resonator can yield higher Q values in general, however, than conventional microwave resonators.

9.3. Energy Sources

We have observed that practical difficulties have prevented the construction of satisfactory oscillators having fundamental frequencies much above 100 kmc. For this reason, much of the work in research and communications which has been done above 100 kmc has used energy obtained as higher harmonics of lower-frequency sources. Two approaches have been used in obtaining harmonic energy: one has been to apply filtration to the nonsinusoidal outputs of conventional or modified klystrons and magnetrons to select energy components at harmonics of the fundamental frequency of oscillation; a second approach has been to use the primary oscillator to drive a nonlinear circuit element such as a semiconductor crystal diode. Harmonic components of the response current of the diode are used to excite a millimeter waveguide current loop or probe with the higher-frequency energy.

As an example of the first method of power generation, a klystron constructed with a cavity resonant at both the fundamental frequency of 7.35 kmc and the 24th harmonic at 176 kmc has been used to generate a power output of the order of a few microwatts at 176 kmc.† Although the output of magnetrons tends to be relatively low in harmonic content, their larger total output power can yield appreciable harmonic components of power. A 2J31 magnetron, rated at pulsed output power of 20 kw at 24 kmc, has been found to have a tenth harmonic output of the order of 0.1 mw, at 240 kmc.‡

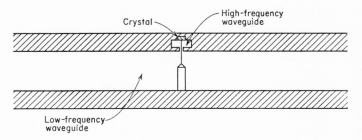

FIG. 9.8. Crystal frequency multiplier.

The crystal harmonic generator, having low output power, has been much used in laboratory applications, a typical crystal harmonic generator having the form shown schematically in Fig. 9.8.

The problem of the generation of millimeter- and submillimeter-wave power, which may be said to stem basically from the smallness of the wavelength of the radiation in comparison with the dimensions of objects that can be practically constructed and operated, has led to an extensive search for physical phenomena or events from which this nearly infrared radiation is given off coherently. Radiation of millimeter wavelengths is given off from every hot object, and from many noise sources, but such radiation is incoherent and represents, moreover, an infinitesimal part of the total energy produced by the source.

We may mention, as representative of the breadth of the range of physical effects or methods which have been proposed or tested as

† J. Bernier and H. Leboutet, *Compt. rend.*, vol. 239, p. 797, 1954.

‡ J. A. Klein, N. Lobser, A. H. Nethercott, and C. H. Townes, *Rev. Sci. Instr.*, vol. 23, p. 78, 1952.

sources for millimeter and submillimeter radiation,† the following:

1. Cerenkov radiation: the energy radiated by electrons traveling at speeds greater than the velocity of light in a material medium. (A bunched beam of electrons would be used in the microwave application.)

2. Purcell radiation: radiation emitted by an electron beam passing at a grazing path over the surface of a periodic structure such as a diffraction grating.

3. Plasma oscillations: radiation from an ionized gas which has the natural frequency of oscillation given by Eq. (7.14).

4. Cyclotron resonance: high-energy electrons traveling in cycloidal paths in a magnetic field may be caused to emit radiation upon interaction with a high-frequency field having a period related to their period of revolution.

The above list of radiation-producing effects is not complete but is representative of the physical character of the circumstances in which millimeter and submillimeter radiation arises. It is thus indicative of the practical concerns of electromagnetic theory in the submillimeter region of the frequency spectrum.

PROBLEMS

9.1. Summarize the transmission characteristics of a dielectric-coated single-wire transmission line, and compare them with those of the dielectric-metal waveguide referred to in Sec. 9.1.‡

9.2. Assume that energy is lost from the open edges of a Fabry-Perot resonator at a rate per unit area twice as great as the rate of dissipation of energy at the conducting surfaces. Show how the Q of the resonator then depends on L, the separation of the plates.

9.3. Obtain an estimate of the ratio of the power in the tenth harmonic of a klystron output wave to the fundamental frequency power [see the method of Eqs. (6.12) to (6.19)].

9.4. A cavity resonator in the form of a cube 1 mm on a side resonates in the TE_{101} mode. Assuming that the peak value of the electric field in the cavity is 1 volt/m and the Q of the cavity is 1,000,

(a) Calculate the energy contained in the cavity.

(b) Calculate the temperature of a hot enclosure in which the energy density in the frequency range $\Delta f = f/Q$ is equal to the average energy density of the cavity of (a) above. (Use the Rayleigh-Jeans law: $dE = 1.28 \times 10^{-47} f^2 T \, df$ joules/m³ at absolute temperature T in the frequency range df.)

† See also review articles by P. D. Coleman and R. C. Becker, Present State of the Millimeter Wave Technique and Art—1958, *IRE Trans.*, vol. MTT-7, p. 42, 1959, and I. Kaufman, The Band between Microwave and Infrared Regions, *Proc. IRE*, vol. 47, p. 381, 1959.

‡ See G. Goubau, Surface Waves and Their Application to Transmission Lines, *J. Appl. Phys.*, vol. 21, p. 1119, 1950, and Single Conductor Surface Wave Transmission Lines, *Proc. IRE*, vol. 39, p. 619, 1951.

APPENDIX I

Physical Constants

Velocity of light...... .... $c = 2.998 \times 10^8$ m/sec
Charge of the electron............. $q = 1.602 \times 10^{-19}$ coulomb
Mass of the electron................ $m = 9.108 \times 10^{-31}$ kg
Planck's constant................. $h = 6.625 \times 10^{-34}$ joule-sec
Permeability of free space........... $\mu_0 = 4\pi \times 10^{-7}$
Bohr magneton........ .... $\mu_B = 9.273 \times 10^{-24}$ amp m^2
Boltzmann constant................. $k = 1.380 \times 10^{-23}$ joule/°K

Dielectric constant of free space...... $\epsilon_0 = \dfrac{1}{c^2\mu_0} \approx \dfrac{1}{36\pi} \times 10^{-9}$

Vector Formulas

Vector identities

$$\mathbf{A} \cdot \mathbf{B} \times \mathbf{C} = \mathbf{B} \cdot \mathbf{C} \times \mathbf{A}$$

$$\mathbf{A} \times \mathbf{B} \times \mathbf{C} = \mathbf{B}(\mathbf{A} \cdot \mathbf{C}) - \mathbf{C}(\mathbf{A} \cdot \mathbf{B})$$

$$\boldsymbol{\nabla} \cdot \boldsymbol{\nabla} V = \nabla^2 V$$

$$\boldsymbol{\nabla} \times \boldsymbol{\nabla} V = 0$$

$$\boldsymbol{\nabla} \cdot \boldsymbol{\nabla} \times \mathbf{A} = 0$$

$$\boldsymbol{\nabla} \times (\boldsymbol{\nabla} \times \mathbf{A}) = \boldsymbol{\nabla}(\boldsymbol{\nabla} \cdot \mathbf{A}) - \nabla^2 \mathbf{A}$$

$$\boldsymbol{\nabla}(VV') = V'\boldsymbol{\nabla}V + V\boldsymbol{\nabla}V'$$

$$\boldsymbol{\nabla} \cdot (V\mathbf{A}) = V\boldsymbol{\nabla} \cdot \mathbf{A} + \mathbf{A} \cdot \boldsymbol{\nabla}V$$

$$\boldsymbol{\nabla} \times (V\mathbf{A}) = V\boldsymbol{\nabla} \times \mathbf{A} + \boldsymbol{\nabla}V \times \mathbf{A}$$

$$\boldsymbol{\nabla} \cdot (\mathbf{A} \times \mathbf{B}) = \mathbf{B} \cdot \boldsymbol{\nabla} \times \mathbf{A} - \mathbf{A} \cdot \boldsymbol{\nabla} \times \mathbf{B}$$

Vector operators in various coordinate systems, in the order rectangular, cylindrical, spherical

Gradient

$$\boldsymbol{\nabla}V = \hat{\mathbf{x}}\frac{\partial V}{\partial x} + \hat{\mathbf{y}}\frac{\partial V}{\partial y} + \hat{\mathbf{z}}\frac{\partial V}{\partial z}$$

$$\boldsymbol{\nabla}V = \hat{\mathbf{r}}\frac{\partial V}{\partial r} + \hat{\boldsymbol{\theta}}\frac{1}{r}\frac{\partial V}{\partial \theta} + \hat{\mathbf{z}}\frac{\partial V}{\partial z}$$

$$\boldsymbol{\nabla}V = \hat{\mathbf{r}}\frac{\partial V}{\partial r} + \hat{\boldsymbol{\theta}}\frac{1}{r}\frac{\partial V}{\partial \theta} + \hat{\boldsymbol{\phi}}\frac{1}{r \sin \theta}\frac{\partial V}{\partial \phi}$$

Divergence

$$\boldsymbol{\nabla} \cdot \mathbf{A} = \frac{\partial A_x}{\partial x} + \frac{\partial A_y}{\partial y} + \frac{\partial A_z}{\partial z}$$

$$\boldsymbol{\nabla} \cdot \mathbf{A} = \frac{1}{r}\frac{\partial(rA_r)}{\partial r} + \frac{1}{r}\frac{\partial A_\theta}{\partial \theta} + \frac{\partial A_z}{\partial z}$$

$$\boldsymbol{\nabla} \cdot \mathbf{A} = \frac{1}{r^2}\frac{\partial(r^2 A_r)}{\partial r} + \frac{1}{r \sin \theta}\frac{\partial(A_\theta \sin \theta)}{\partial \theta} + \frac{1}{r \sin \theta}\frac{\partial A_\phi}{\partial \phi}$$

Curl

$$\boldsymbol{\nabla} \times \mathbf{A} = \hat{\mathbf{x}}\left(\frac{\partial A_z}{\partial y} - \frac{\partial A_y}{\partial z}\right) + \hat{\mathbf{y}}\left(\frac{\partial A_x}{\partial z} - \frac{\partial A_z}{\partial x}\right) + \hat{\mathbf{z}}\left(\frac{\partial A_y}{\partial x} - \frac{\partial A_x}{\partial y}\right)$$

$$\nabla \times \mathbf{A} = \hat{\mathbf{r}} \frac{1}{r} \left[\frac{\partial A_z}{\partial \theta} - \frac{\partial (rA_\theta)}{\partial z} \right] + \hat{\boldsymbol{\theta}} \left(\frac{\partial A_r}{\partial z} - \frac{\partial A_z}{\partial r} \right)$$

$$+ \hat{\mathbf{z}} \frac{1}{r} \left[\frac{\partial (rA_\theta)}{\partial r} - \frac{\partial A_r}{\partial \theta} \right]$$

$$\nabla \times \mathbf{A} = \hat{\mathbf{r}} \frac{1}{r^2 \sin \theta} \left[\frac{\partial (r \sin \theta \, A_\phi)}{\partial \theta} - \frac{\partial (rA_\theta)}{\partial \phi} \right]$$

$$+ \hat{\boldsymbol{\theta}} \frac{1}{r \sin \theta} \left[\frac{\partial A_r}{\partial \phi} - \frac{\partial (r \sin \theta \, A_\phi)}{\partial r} \right] + \hat{\boldsymbol{\phi}} \frac{1}{r} \left[\frac{\partial (rA_\theta)}{\partial r} - \frac{\partial A_r}{\partial \theta} \right]$$

Scalar Laplacian

$$\nabla^2 V = \frac{\partial^2 V}{\partial x^2} + \frac{\partial^2 V}{\partial y^2} + \frac{\partial^2 V}{\partial z^2}$$

$$\nabla^2 V = \frac{\partial^2 V}{\partial r^2} + \frac{1}{r} \frac{\partial V}{\partial r} + \frac{1}{r^2} \frac{\partial^2 V}{\partial \theta^2} + \frac{\partial^2 V}{\partial z^2}$$

$$\nabla^2 V = \frac{\partial^2 V}{\partial r^2} + \frac{2}{r} \frac{\partial V}{\partial r} + \frac{1}{r^2} \frac{\partial^2 V}{\partial \theta^2} + \frac{\cot \theta}{r^2} \frac{\partial V}{\partial \theta} + \frac{1}{r^2 \sin^2 \theta} \frac{\partial^2 V}{\partial \phi^2}$$

APPENDIX III

Bessel Functions

The wave equation for a component of field, e.g., E_z, is

$$\nabla^2 E_z = -k^2 E_z$$

or

$$\frac{\partial^2 E_z}{\partial r^2} + \frac{1}{r}\frac{\partial E_z}{\partial r} + \frac{1}{r^2}\frac{\partial^2 E_z}{\partial \theta^2} + \frac{\partial^2 E_z}{\partial z^2} = -k^2 E_z$$

If

$$E_z = R(r)\cos n\theta\, e^{\pm j\beta_g z}$$

then

$$\frac{\partial^2 R}{\partial r^2} + \frac{1}{r}\frac{\partial R}{\partial r} + \left(k_c^2 - \frac{n^2}{r^2}\right) R = 0$$

where

$$k_c^2 = k^2 - \beta_g^2$$

This is Bessel's equation, of which the complete solution is

$$R = A_n J_n(k_c r) + B_n N_n(k_c r)$$

Let $U_n(kr)$ denote either $J_n(kr)$ or $N_n(kr)$. Then the following are properties of either Bessel function:

$$U_n(kr) = \frac{kr}{2n}\left[U_{n-1}(kr) + U_{n+1}(kr)\right]$$

$$\frac{\partial U_n(kr)}{\partial r} = k U_{n-1}(kr) - \frac{n}{r} U_n(kr)$$

$$\frac{\partial U_n(kr)}{\partial r} = \frac{n}{r} U_n(kr) - k U_{n+1}(kr)$$

$$\frac{\partial U_n(kr)}{\partial r} = \frac{k}{2}\left(U_{n-1} - U_{n+1}\right)$$

$$\frac{\partial U_0(kr)}{\partial r} = -k U_1(kr)$$

$$\frac{\partial U_1(kr)}{\partial r} = k U_0(kr) - \frac{1}{r} U_1(kr)$$

234

$$\int r^{n+1} U_n(kr)\ dr = \frac{r^{n+1}}{k}\ U_{n+1}(kr)$$

$$\int r U_0(kr)\ dr = \frac{r}{k}\ U_1(kr)$$

$$\int U_1(kr)\ dr = -\frac{1}{k}\ U_0(kr)$$

Bessel's integral is

$$J_n(kr) = \frac{j^{-n}}{2\pi} \int_0^{2\pi} e^{j(kr \cos \phi + n\phi)}\ d\phi$$

The integral may be carried out over any real interval of length 2π in ϕ.

Measurements for Equivalent T Circuit of a Two-port Element

The impedance elements of the equivalent T circuit of **Fig. IV**.1 may be determined by three measurements of impedance at port aa', made with three different impedances connected at port bb'. Suitable terminations at bb' are 0, ∞, and Z_0, which may be obtained by means of a half-wavelength shorted section, quarter-wavelength shorted section, and matched load, respectively.

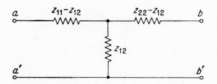

FIG. IV.1. Equivalent T circuit.

Then, assuming the connecting waveguides have equal values of Z_0, let z_{0c}, z_{sc}, z_m, respectively, be the normalized values of observed impedance at aa'. We have, from Fig. IV.1,

$$z_{0c} = z_{11} \tag{IV.1}$$

$$z_{sc} = z_{11} - z_{12} + \frac{z_{12}(z_{22} - z_{12})}{z_{22}}$$

$$z_{sc} = z_{11} - \frac{z_{12}^2}{z_{22}} \tag{IV.2}$$

$$z_m = z_{11} - z_{12} + \frac{z_{12}(z_{22} - z_{12} + 1)}{z_{22} + 1}$$

$$z_m = z_{11} - \frac{z_{12}^2}{z_{22} + 1} \tag{IV.3}$$

Combining Eqs. (IV.1), (IV.2), and (IV.3), the normalized elements of the equivalent T are

$$z_{11} = z_{0c} \tag{IV.4}$$

$$z_{22} = \frac{z_m - z_{0c}}{z_{sc} - z_m} \tag{IV.5}$$

$$z_{12} = \left[(z_{0c} - z_{sc}) \frac{z_m - z_{0c}}{z_{sc} - z_m} \right]^{\frac{1}{2}} \tag{IV.6}$$

Index

239